Treffpunkt Deutsch

ARBEITSBUCH/
HÖRVERSTÄNDNIS

FOURTH EDITION

Treffpunkt Deutsch

ARBEITSBUCH

E. Rosemarie Widmaier
McMaster University

Fritz T. Widmaier
McMaster University

HÖRVERSTÄNDNIS

CONTRIBUTING AUTHOR
Ruth Thomas-Renters
McMaster University

Upper Saddle River,
New Jersey 07458

Publisher: *Phil Miller*
Asst. Director of Production: *Mary Rottino*
Developmental Editor: *Karen Storz*
Project Manager: *Erin Connaughton*
Manufacturing Manager: *Mary Ann Gloriande*
Prepress and Manufacturing Buyer: *Camille Tesoriero*
Publishing Coordinator: *Claudia Fernandes*
Cover Design: *Adapted by Bruce Kensellaar*
Cover Photo: *Cupola of the* ***Reichstag*** *in Berlin. Per Eide/EdelPix*
Photos: *E. Rosemarie and Fritz T. Widmaier*
Illustrations: *Michael Widmaier*

This book was set in 11/13 New Baskerville by nSight, Inc. and was printed and bound by Bradford & Bigelow.
The cover was printed by Bradford & Bigelow.

Upper Saddle River, New Jersey 07458

Printed in the United States of America
10 9 8 7 6 5 4 3 2 1

ISBN 0-13-111099-3

Pearson Education Ltd., *London*
Pearson Education Australia Pte., *Sydney*
Pearson Education *Singapore,* Pte. Ltd.
Pearson Education North Asia Ltd., *Hong Kong*
Pearson Education Canada Ltd., *Toronto*
Pearson Educación de *Mexico,* S.A. de C.V.
Pearson Education—Japan, *Tokyo*
Pearson Education *Malaysia,* Pte. Ltd.
Pearson Education, Upper Saddle River, *New Jersey*

Table of Contents

PREFACE

The exercises and activities in the **Arbeitsbuch** have been designed to reinforce the vocabulary, structures, and themes in the corresponding chapters of **Treffpunkt Deutsch.** Each chapter of the **Arbeitsbuch** is divided into four sections.

Strukturen Each chapter is introduced by a succinct recapitulation of the grammar presented in the corresponding chapter of the textbook. This icon (☞) points you to the numbers of the exercises that practice a particular grammar point and the pages on which they are found. This icon (⚠) draws your attention to things that you particularly need to watch out for under a given grammar point.

Anwendung This section contains the practical application of the material presented in the **Strukturen** and is divided into three sub-sections:

Übungen. The **Übungen** feature a variety of exercises, including realia-based and picture-cued activities, sentence-building and sentence completion exercises, fill-ins, and matching exercises. This icon (☜) points you back to the pages where the structures practiced in the exercises are presented.

Zum Verstehen. This section features vocabulary-building exercises and reading comprehension activities that are based on short narratives and stories.

Zum Übersetzen. The translation exercises have been carefully designed so that you will be able to translate into idiomatic German, using the vocabulary and structures of a given chapter

Treffpunkt Deutsch

ARBEITSBUCH

ERSTE KONTAKTE

Strukturen

1. The numbers from 0 to 1000 (☞ Übungen E-1, E-2, E-3, pp. 3–4)

0 null			
1 ein**s**	11 elf	21 ei**nu**ndzwanzig	10 zehn
2 zwei	12 zwölf	22 zweiundzwanzig	20 zwanzig
3 drei	13 dreizehn	23 dreiundzwanzig	30 drei**ß**ig
4 vier	14 vierzehn	24 vierundzwanzig	40 vierzig
5 fünf	15 fünfzehn	25 fünfundzwanzig	50 fünfzig
6 sech**s**	16 se**chz**ehn	26 sech**s**undzwanzig	60 se**chz**ig
7 sieb**en**	17 sie**bz**ehn	27 sieb**en**undzwanzig	70 sie**bz**ig
8 acht	18 achtzehn	28 achtundzwanzig	80 achtzig
9 neun	19 neunzehn	29 neunundzwanzig	90 neunzig
10 zehn	20 zwanzig	30 drei**ß**ig	100 hundert

101 (ein)hunderteins	200 zweihundert	1000 (ein)tausend
102 (ein)hundertzwei	300 dreihundert	
usw.	usw.	

 All numbers up to 999,999 are written as **one word.**

2. The alphabet (☞ Übungen E-4, E-5, E-6, pp. 5–7)

a	ah	**g**	geh	**m**	emm	**s**	ess	**y**	üppsilon
b	beh	**h**	hah	**n**	enn	**t**	teh	**z**	tsett
c	tseh	**i**	ee	**o**	oh	**u**	oo		
d	deh	**j**	yott	**p**	peh	**v**	fow		
e	eh	**k**	kah	**q**	coo	**w**	veh		
f	eff	**l**	ell	**r**	airr	**x**	iks		

 Germans saying the alphabet do not include the three umlauted vowels **ä, ö, ü,** and the **Eszett (ß).**

NAME: ______________________________ DATE: ______________

Anwendung

Übungen

E-1 Rechenaufgaben. Solve the following arithmetic problems. Write full sentences, and write all numbers in words. (☞ Strukturen 1, p. 1)

1. Wie viel ist 12 plus 7?

   Zwölf plus sieben ist neunzehn.

2. Wie viel ist 16 plus 26?

   ____

3. Wie viel ist 70 minus 19?

   ____

4. Wie viel ist 56 plus 11?

   ____

5. Wie viel ist 89 minus 12?

   ____

6. Wie viel ist 101 plus 30?

   ____

7. Wie viel ist 1 000 minus elf?

   ____

E-2 Persönliches. Write all numbers in words. Use single digits except for your age and your house number. (☞ Strukturen 1, p. 1)

Ich bin ______________________ Jahre alt.

Meine Postleitzahl ist ______________________________

Meine Vorwahl ist ______________________________

Meine Telefonnummer ist ______________________________

Meine Hausnummer ist ______________________________

E-3 Auf dem Flohmarkt. In complete sentences, state what each item at this stand at the flea market costs. Write all numbers as words. The names of the objects are in the box below. (☞ Strukturen 1, p. 1)

die Jacke / das Sweatshirt / die Gitarre / der Fußball / das Telefon die Lampe / das Buch / das Weinglas / der Teddybär / die Vase

1. Die Gitarre kostet sechsunddreißig Euro.
2. ______________________________
3. ______________________________
4. ______________________________
5. ______________________________
6. ______________________________
7. ______________________________
8. ______________________________
9. ______________________________
10. ______________________________

NAME: ______________________ DATE: ______________

E-4 Ein Wortspiel. Write the letters represented by the following sounds. Say them aloud as you write. Always capitalize the first letter. (☞ Strukturen 2, p. 1)

geh - ell - ah - ess	Glas
oo - enn - ee - fow - eh - airr - ess - ee - teh - ah umlaut - teh	______
teh - eh - eh - kah - ah - enn - enn - eh	______
eh - enn - deh - eh	______
enn - ah - emm - eh	______
emm - ah - oo - ess	______
oh - airr - tseh - hah - eh - ess - teh - eh - airr	______
airr - eh - ess- teh - ah - oo - airr - ah - enn - teh	______
geh - ah - airr - teh - eh - enn	______
eh - oo - airr - oh - peh - ah	______
enn - oh - fow - eh - emm - beh - eh - airr	______

Now write the first letter of each word in the space below and read the German greeting.

______________________________!

E-5 Was passt zusammen? Read the following acronyms aloud and match them with the words they stand for by writing the appropriate acronym in the space provided. (☞ Strukturen 2, p. 1)

AEG / CDU / FAZ / DSF / SPD / BASF / WAZ
ZDF / USA / FDP / MAN / BRD / BZ / EU

1. WAZ Westdeutsche Allgemeine Zeitung
2. ____________ Zweites Deutsches Fernsehen
3. ____________ Bundesrepublik Deutschland
4. ____________ Christlich-Demokratische Union
5. ____________ Maschinenfabrik Augsburg-Nürnberg
6. ____________ Vereinigte Staaten von Amerika
7. ____________ Allgemeine Elektrizitäts-Gesellschaft
8. ____________ Badische Anilin- und Soda-Fabrik
9. ____________ Europäische Union
10. ____________ Berliner Zeitung
11. ____________ Sozialdemokratische Partei Deutschlands
12. ____________ Frankfurter Allgemeine Zeitung
13. ____________ Freie Demokratische Partei
14. ____________ Deutsches Sportfernsehen

NAME: ________________________ DATE: ____________

E-6 Fragen. Look at the previous exercise again and answer the following questions. (☞ Strukturen 2, p. 1)

1. Which three acronyms stand for political parties?

____

2. Which three acronyms stand for industries or companies?

____

3. Which acronym stands for a TV station dedicated to sports?

____

4. Which other acronym stands for a TV station?

____

5. Which three acronyms stand for daily newspapers (two from large German cities and one from a region in the west of Germany)?

____

6. Which three acronyms stand for countries or a group of countries?

____

Zum Übersetzen

E-7 Wir lernen einander kennen. Translate into German.

1. FLORIAN: Hi! I'm Florian and this is Tina.
   LORI: Where are you from?
   TINA: I'm from Hamburg and Florian is from Innsbruck.

2. FRAU STOLZ: Excuse me, are you Ms. Meyer?
   FRAU BERG: No, my name is Berg.

KAPITEL 1

Strukturen

Identifying people and things

1. Nouns: gender and definite articles (☞ Übungen 1-1, 1-2, 1-3, pp. 13–14)

Nouns referring to males are usually masculine.

der Mann *man; husband* **der** Vater *father*

Nouns referring to females are usually feminine.

die Frau *woman; wife* **die** Mutter *mother*

Nouns referring to things can be masculine, feminine, or neuter.

der Computer **die** Lampe **das** Telefon

 In German all nouns are capitalized.

2. Plural forms of nouns (☞ Übung 1-4, p. 14)

In vocabulary lists, the plural forms of nouns are usually abbreviated.

abbreviation of plural form	listing	plural form
-	der Amerikaner, -	die Amerikaner
¨	die Mutter, ¨	die Mütter
-e	der Freund, **-e**	die Freunde
¨e	die Maus, **¨e**	die Mäuse
-n	die Karte, **-n**	die Karten
-en	die Vorlesung, **-en**	die Vorlesungen
-er	das Kind, **-er**	die Kinder
¨er	das Buch, **¨er**	die Bücher
-s	das Auto, **-s**	die Autos
-nen	die Freundin, **-nen**	die Freundinnen

 All three definite articles have the same plural form: **die.**

3. The indefinite articles *ein* (a, an) and *kein* (not a, not (any), no) (☞ Übungen 1-5, 1-6, pp. 15–16)

	masculine		neuter		feminine		plural	
INDEFINITE ARTICLE NEG. INDEF. ARTICLE	**ein** **kein**	Ball	**ein** **kein**	Glas	**eine** **keine**	Rose	— **keine**	Rosen

Word order

4. Position of the verb (☞ Übung 1-7, p. 17)

sentence type	position of verb	
yes/no questions	first element	**Regnet** es heute? ***Is** it **raining** today?*
information questions	second element	Was **zeigt** das Thermometer? *What **does** the thermometer **read?***
statements	second element	Heute **ist** es kalt und es **regnet.** *Today it **is** cold and it **is raining.***

- Verb forms like *is raining* and *does read* do not exist in German.
- **Ja, nein,** and the conjunctions **und, oder, denn, aber,** and **sondern** do not count as elements in a sentence.

5. Question words (☞ Übung 1-8, p. 18)

wann?	*when?*	**wie viel?**	*how much?*
warum?	*why?*	**wie viele?**	*how many?*
was?	*what?*	**wo?**	*where? (in what place?)*
wer?	*who?*	**woher?**	*where . . . from? (from what place?)*
wie?	*how?*	**wohin?**	*where? (to what place?)*

Wo = *where;* **wer** = *who.*

6. Expressions of time and place (☞ Übung 1-9, p. 19)

german		
	TIME	PLACE
Gehst du	**heute Abend**	**ins Kino?**
english		
	PLACE	TIME
Are you going	***to the movies***	***tonight?***

7. Position of *nicht* (☞ Übung 1-10, p. 20)

Nicht precedes words or expressions that are specifically negated.

Peter kommt **nicht aus Hamburg.**
Es ist **nicht kalt.**
Es ist **nicht sehr** windig.
Ich gehe **nicht in die Disco.**
Ich gehe **nicht oft** in die Disco.
Ich gehe **nicht mit Bernd** in die Disco.
Claudia kommt **nicht heute Abend,** sondern morgen Abend.

If no word or expression is specifically negated, **nicht** stands at the end of the sentence.

Claudia kommt heute Abend **nicht.**
Martin kommt auch **nicht.**
Heute scheint die Sonne **nicht.**

Use **kein/keine** to negate

- a noun preceded by **ein/eine:**

Ist das ein Restaurant oder eine Kneipe?	Das ist **kein** Restaurant und auch **keine** Kneipe. Das ist ein Bistro.

- a noun without an article:

Sind das Österreicher?	Nein, das sind **keine** Österreicher, das sind Deutsche.

Talking about people and things without naming them

8. Personal pronouns: subject forms (☞ Übung 1-11, p. 21. See also Strukturen 9!)

	singular		plural	
1ST PERSON	**ich**	*I*	**wir**	*we*
2ND PERSON	**du**	*you (familiar)*	**ihr**	*you (familiar)*
	Sie	*you (formal)*	**Sie**	*you (formal)*
3RD PERSON	**er**	*he*		
	es	*it*	**sie**	*they*
	sie	*she*		

The pronouns in the 3rd person singular are chosen according to the principle of grammatical gender:

der Mann	→	**er**	**der** Ball	→	**er**
das Kind	→	**es**	**das** Haus	→	**es**
die Frau	→	**sie**	**die** Vase	→	**sie**

Expressing states and actions

9. The present tense of *sein* (☞ Übung 1-11, p. 21)

singular			plural		
ich	bin	*I am*	wir	sind	*we are*
du	bist	*you are*	ihr	seid	*you are*
er/es/sie	ist	*he/it/she is*	sie	sind	*they are*
		Sie sind *you are*			

10. The verb: infinitive and present tense (☞ Übungen 1-12, 1-13, pp. 22–23)

fragen		antworten		reisen		tun	
ich	frage	ich	antworte	ich	reise	ich	tue
du	frag**st**	du	antwort**est**[1]	du	reis**t**[2]	du	tu**st**
er/es/sie	frag**t**	er/es/sie	antwort**et**[1]	er/es/sie	reis**t**	er/es/sie	tu**t**
wir	frag**en**	wir	antwort**en**	wir	reis**en**	wir	tu**n**[3]
ihr	frag**t**	ihr	antwort**et**[1]	ihr	reis**t**	ihr	tu**t**
sie	frag**en**	sie	antwort**en**	sie	reis**en**	sie	tu**n**[3]
Sie	frag**en**	Sie	antwort**en**	Sie	reis**en**	Sie	tu**n**[3]

[1]If a verb stem ends in **-t** or **-d** or in certain consonant combinations like the **-gn** in **regnen,** an **-e-** is inserted before the personal endings **-st** and **-t.**
[2]If a verb stem ends in **-s, -ß,** or **-z,** the personal ending in the 2nd person singular is not an **-st** but only a **-t.**
[3]Verbs with the infinitive ending **-n** also have the ending **-n** in the 1st and 3rd person plural and in the **Sie**-form.

 German uses the present tense to express future time if the context shows clearly that one is referring to the future.

Nächstes Jahr **fliege** ich nach München.

*Next year **I'm flying** to Munich.*
*Next year **I'll be flying** to Munich.*
*Next year **I'm going to fly** to Munich.*

NAME: ______________________________ DATE: ______________

Anwendung

Übungen

1-1 Leicht zu verstehen. *(Easy to understand.)*

a. You can easily guess the meaning of the nouns below. Circle the noun in each group that does not fit the category. (Strukturen 1, p. 9)

1. die Klarinette die Lampe die Violine die Flöte	4. der Freund der Vater die Mutter der Sohn	7. das Bier der Wein die Butter die Milch	10. die Telefonnummer die Adresse der Fußball der Name
2. die Rose die Lilie die Tomate die Tulpe	5. die Bluse das Gras der Pullover die Jacke	8. der Arm der Finger die Lippe der Schuh	11. das Schwein das Lamm der Bulle der Fisch
3. die Banane die Orange der Apfel die Karotte	6. die Musik die Vase der Ton die Note	9. das Auto der Hammer das Boot der Bus	12. der Ring das Büfett die Couch das Bett

b. The ending of a noun sometimes signals its gender. Look at the nouns listed above and write the noun ending that is most frequently associated with the article **die.** ______

c. Find the two nouns in the list that have the ending **-e,** but not the article **die.**

der ____________________ der ____________________

1-2 Familie Ziegler. (Strukturen 1, p. 9)

1. Supply the definite articles.

______ Mutter heißt Brigitte, ______ Vater heißt Klaus, _____ Sohn heißt Robert und _____ Tochter heißt Nina.

2. Referring to the information above, supply the appropriate nouns with their definite articles.

Bruder / Schwester / Vater / Frau / Mann / Tochter / Sohn / Mutter

Brigitte ist ____________________ von *(of)* Nina und Robert und ____________________ von Klaus. Klaus ist ____________________ von Brigitte und ____________________ von Nina und Robert. Nina ist ____________________ von Robert und ____________________ von Brigitte und Klaus. Robert ist ____________________ von Klaus und Brigitte und ____________________ von Nina.

1-3 Was passt wo? Supply the appropriate nouns with or without the definite article as required. (☞ Strukturen 1, p. 9)

die Musik / die Telefonnummer / der Freund / der Pullover / die Adresse

1. Thomas ist mein ______________________.
2. ______________________ ist viel zu laut.
3. Ist ______________________ warm?
4. Peters ______________________ ist 53 41 21.
5. Peters ______________________ ist Zennerstraße 16, 81679 München.

der Name / der Computer / die Mutter / die Milch / das Barometer

6. ______________________ ist sauer!
7. Was zeigt ______________________?
8. Mein ______________________ ist Ziegler.
9. Meine ______________________ ist sehr intelligent.
10. ______________________ kostet 1 200 Euro.

1-4 Pluralformen. Write the plural forms of the following nouns, along with the definite article. (☞ Strukturen 2, p. 9)

1. die Klarinette, -n ______________________
2. der Hammer, ¨ ______________________
3. das Wort, ¨er ______________________
4. die Amerikanerin, -nen ______________________
5. das Hotel, -s ______________________
6. der Fußball, ¨e ______________________
7. die Million, -en ______________________
8. der Arm, -e ______________________
9. der Finger, - ______________________
10. das Haus, ¨er ______________________
11. die Knackwurst, ¨e ______________________

NAME: ________________________________ DATE: ______________

1-5 Was passt wo? Fill in the blanks with the correct forms of the indefinite article and with appropriate nouns from the lists below. (☞ Strukturen 2 & 3, p. 9)

das Jahr, -e / das Jahrhundert, -e / die Sekunde, -n der Tag, -e / die Woche, -n / der Monat, -e

1. Eine Minute hat sechzig ______________.
2. ________ Woche hat sieben ______________.
3. Dreihundertfünfundsechzig Tage sind ________ ______________.
4. ________ Jahr hat zwölf ______________.
5. Zweiundfünfzig ______________ sind ________ Jahr.
6. Hundert Jahre sind ________ ______________.

der Student, -en / das Horn, ¨er / der Professor, -en der Finger, - / die Hand, ¨e

7. Viele ______________ und ______________ sind ________ Universität.
8. ________ Mensch (m) *(human being)* hat zwei ______________ und zehn ______________, aber nur ________ Nase (f).
9. ________ Bulle (m) hat zwei ______________.

1-6 Fakten oder Meinungen? Choose the appropriate noun to complete each statement and precede it with the proper form of **kein.** Then indicate whether the statements are facts or subjective opinions. Note: **so ... wie** = *as . . . as.* (Strukturen 3, p. 9)

das Metall / die Frucht / die Sinfonie / die Jahreszeit / das Bier / das Land / der Tag / die Blume / der Kontinent / der Monet / der Tenor / der Planet / die Rockgruppe / der Wein / die Violine

				opinion	fact
1.	Kein	Bier	ist so gut wie Löwenbräu.	✔	____
2.	____	____	ist so lang wie der 21. Juni.	____	____
3.	____	____	ist so schön wie eine Rose.	____	____
4.	____	____	ist so gut wie Rheinwein.	____	____
5.	____	____	ist so heiß wie Indien.	____	____
6.	____	____	ist so rot wie der Mars.	____	____
7.	____	____	ist so schön wie Gold.	____	____
8.	____	____	singt so schön wie Pavarotti.	____	____
9.	____	____	hat so wenige Tage wie der Februar.	____	____
10.	____	____	kostet so viel wie eine Stradivari.	____	____
11.	____	____	ist so schön wie der Sommer.	____	____
12.	____	____	ist so gut wie eine Banane.	____	____
13.	____	____	ist so interessant wie Europa.	____	____
14.	____	____	spielt so gut wie *U2*.	____	____
15.	____	____	ist so schön wie Beethovens *Neunte.*	____	____

NAME: ______________________________ DATE: ______________

1-7 Kleine Gespräche. Complete the following exchanges by adding an appropriate verb from the list given. In each case rewrite the question and the response. Note that some verbs are used more than once. (☞ Strukturen 4, p. 10)

heiße / kommt / kommst / ist / scheint / sind / zeigt / geht / bin / regnet

1. > Woher du, Asha?
   < Ich aus Bombay.

   > Woher kommst du, Asha?

   < ______________________________

2. > es noch?
   < Nein, jetzt die Sonne wieder, aber es noch sehr windig.

   > ______________________________

   < ______________________________

3. > Wie heiß es heute?
   < Das Thermometer fast dreißig Grad.

   > ______________________________

   < ______________________________

4. > heute die Sonne?
   < Nein, heute es, und es kalt und sehr windig.

   > ______________________________

   < ______________________________

5. > Du, Martin, wer das?
   < Das Stephanie. Sie Amerikanerin, und sie aus Chicago.

   > ______________________________

   < ______________________________

6. > Guten Tag. Ich Ziegler.
   < Oh, Sie Herr Ziegler aus Göttingen. Wie es Ihnen?

   > ______________________________

   < ______________________________

1-8 Was sind die Fragen? Write the questions that elicit the following responses. The words or phrases in boldface indicate which question words you should use to introduce the questions. (☞ Strukturen 5, p. 10)

1. Wer ist Serena Williams?
Serena Williams ist **eine amerikanische Tennisspielerin.**

2. ______
Bryan Adams ist **aus Kanada.**

3. ______
Michaels Zimmer ist **sehr** groß.

4. ______
Der Januar hat **einunddreißig** Tage.

5. ______
Weihnachten ist **am 25. Dezember.**

6. ______
Dreißig minus drei ist **siebenundzwanzig.**

7. ______
Stephanie ist **neunzehn** Jahre alt.

8. ______
Peter geht heute Abend **ins Kino.**

9. ______
Eine Oboe ist **ein Musikinstrument.**

10. ______
Arnold Schwarzenegger kommt **aus Österreich.**

11. ______
Hannover ist **in Deutschland.**

12. ______
Claudia geht **in die Bibliothek.**

13. ______
Das Wetter ist heute **sehr schön.**

14. ______
Eddie Murphy ist **ein amerikanischer Komiker.**

15. ______
Kitzbühel ist **in Österreich.**

NAME: ______________________ DATE: ______________

1-9 Ergänzen Sie! Complete the following sentences, using the components provided. The verbs are given in the infinitive form. Add the proper endings to the verb stems. (☞ Strukturen 6, p. 10)

1. in Deutschland / studieren / nächstes Jahr

   Andrea studiert nächstes Jahr in Deutschland.

2. im Winter / fliegen / nach Spanien

   Zieglers ______________________

3. in die Vorlesung / jetzt / du / ?

   Gehst ______________________

4. du / heute / arbeiten / im Supermarkt / ?

   Wie lang ______________________

5. zu Angelikas Party / morgen Abend / ihr / ?

   Kommt ______________________

6. ins Bett / gehen / heute Abend um acht

   Ich ______________________

7. heute Abend / ihr / in die Kneipe / gehen / ?

   Wann ______________________

1-10 ***Ja oder nein?*** Respond positively or negatively, basing your response on the statement of fact that begins each set. (☞ Strukturen 7, p. 11)

1. Heute zeigt das Thermometer nur fünf Grad Celsius.
   > Ist es heute warm?

   < Nein, heute ist es nicht warm,

   heute ist es kalt.

2. Peter kommt aus Berlin.
   > Kommt Peter aus Bonn?

   < ________, Peter ________________ ________________ aus Bonn, sondern aus Berlin.

3. Berlin ist eine große Stadt.
   > Ist Berlin eine kleine Stadt?

   < ________, Berlin ________________ ________________ kleine Stadt, sondern

   ________________ sehr große Stadt.

4. Heute scheint die Sonne und der Himmel ist blau.
   > Ist es heute schön?

   < ________, heute ________________ ________________ sehr ________________.

5. Der Himmel ist grau und es regnet.
   > Scheint heute die Sonne?

   < ________, heute ________________ die Sonne ________________.

6. Claudia studiert in München.
   > Studiert Claudia in Köln?

   < ________, Claudia studiert ________________ ________________

   ________________. Sie ________________ in München.

7. In Hamburg scheint heute die Sonne.
   > Regnet es heute in Hamburg?

   < ________, in Hamburg regnet es ________________ ________________.

8. Das Ristorante Napoli ist ein schlechtes Restaurant.
   > Ist das Ristorante Napoli ein gutes Restaurant?

   < ________, das Ristorante Napoli ________________ ________________ gutes

   Restaurant.

NAME: ______________________________ **DATE:** ______________

1-11 Kleine Gespräche. Complete these short exchanges with the appropriate personal pronouns and/or forms of **sein.** (☞ Strukturen 8 & 9, p. 11–12)

1. > Kommt Peter aus Mannheim?

   < Nein, ___er___ ___ist___ aus Berlin.

2. > Wie __________ der Wein?

   < Gar nicht gut. __________ __________ viel zu sauer.

3. > Wie viel kostet die Jacke?

   < __________ kostet nur dreißig Euro.

4. > __________ der Pullover warm?

   < Ja, __________ __________ sehr warm.

5. > __________ Sie Herr Karlhuber aus Österreich?

   < Ja, __________ __________ Arnold Karlhuber und komme aus Salzburg.

6. > Woher __________ die Äpfel? __________ __________ sehr gut.

   < Ich glaube, __________ kommen aus Chile.

7. > Wer __________ ihr?

   < __________ __________ Stephanie und Claudia.

   > __________ __________ Schwestern?

   < Nein, __________ __________ Freundinnen.

8. > Wie __________ die Zimmer (pl) im Studentenheim?

   < __________ __________ sehr schön, nur die Betten __________ zu hart.

9. > __________ du Claudia?

   < Nein, __________ heiße Stephanie. Und wer __________ __________?

   > __________ __________ Bernd Neuner und __________ komme aus Dresden.

10. > Wie __________ der Film? __________ __________ so gut wie das Buch?

    < __________ __________ gut, aber nicht so gut wie das Buch.

11. > Der Kaffee __________ sehr gut. __________ __________ aus Kolumbien?

    < Nein, __________ __________ aus Nicaragua.

1-12 Kleine Gespräche. Complete the following short conversations with the correct forms of the appropriate verbs. You will have to use some verbs more than once. (Strukturen 10, p. 12)

kommen / studieren / heißen

1. > Ich __________ David und ich __________ aus Köln. Wie __________ du und woher __________ du?

   < Ich __________ Kurt, __________ aus Erfurt und __________ Geographie. Was __________ du, David?

   > Ich __________ Physik.

lernen / machen / gehen

2. > Was __________ Tanja heute Abend? __________ sie in die Disco?

   < Nein, heute Abend __________ sie in die Bibliothek und __________ Deutsch.

trinken / tanzen / sein / sitzen

3. > Warum __________ du nicht, Ralf? Warum __________ du hier und __________ Bier?

   < Ich __________ nur mit Tanja und Tanja __________ nicht hier.

kosten / fliegen

4. > Wie __________ Sie nach Finnland, Frau Ziegler?

   < Wir __________ mit Finnair. Mit Lufthansa __________ es zu viel.

finden / regnen

5. > Wie __________ ihr das Wetter hier in Hamburg?

   < Wir __________ es kalt und es __________ viel zu viel.

spielen / arbeiten / machen / schreiben

6. > Was __________ ihr morgen?

   < Ralf __________ im Supermarkt und ich __________ E-Mails.

   Und morgen Abend __________ wir dann mit Eva und Kurt Tennis.

NAME: ______________________________ DATE: ______________

1-13 Was passt? Supply appropriate verbs. (☞ Strukturen 10, p. 12)

1. ____Studiert____ Sabine Geographie oder Geologie?
2. ________________ du auch so gut Gitarre wie Andrea?
3. ________________ Sie mit Lufthansa oder mit KLM, Frau Ziegler?
4. Mein Ticket ________________ fast siebenhundert Dollar.
5. Was ________________ ihr heute Abend? ________________ ihr ins Kino oder ________________ ihr Tennis?
6. Im Sommer ________________ ich oft schwimmen.
7. Michael ist Programmierer und ________________ bei IBM.
8. Wann ________________ das Konzert heute Abend?
9. ________________ du es auch so kalt hier?
10. Ich ________________ Kathrin und komme aus Köln. Wie ________________ du und woher ________________ du?

Zum Verstehen

1-14 Was passt zusammen? Match in each group by writing the appropriate numbers in the spaces provided.

1. schreiben	___	Geld	5. gehen	___	wo?	9. spielen	___	Vorlesung
2. tanzen	___	Lufthansa	6. kommen	___	wohin?	10. studieren	___	Bus
3. kosten	___	Disco	7. sitzen	___	wie?	11. beginnen	___	Fußball
4. fliegen	___	Karte	8. heißen	___	woher?	12. reisen	___	Biologie

1-15 Was passt? Mark the appropriate answer to each question.

1. Wie heißt du?
   a. Das ist Stephanie.
   b. Ich heiße Stephanie.
   c. Sie heißt Stephanie.
2. Woher kommst du?
   a. Oh, du bist aus Amerika.
   b. Sie ist aus Amerika.
   c. Ich bin aus Amerika.
3. Kommt Kurt heute?
   a. Nein, Kurt kommt heute nicht.
   b. Nein, Kurt kommt morgen nicht.
   c. Nein, Kurt kommt heute.
4. Ist es heute sehr kalt?
   a. Nein, es ist sehr kalt.
   b. Nein, es ist nicht sehr kalt.
   c. Ja, es ist sehr warm.
5. Wie ist das Wetter heute?
   a. Ja, es ist windig.
   b. Nein, es ist kalt.
   c. Es ist kalt und windig.
6. Ist der Himmel heute blau oder grau?
   a. Ja, der Himmel ist heute blau.
   b. Heute ist der Himmel blau.
   c. Nein, heute ist der Himmel grau.

1-16 Ein kleines Gespräch. Write a conversation by putting the scrambled sentences in the proper order.

Aus Itzehoe? Wo ist das?

Ja, hier ist es auch oft regnerisch und windig.

Itzehoe ist in Norddeutschland.

Regnet es in Itzehoe auch so viel wie in Hamburg?

Wo in Norddeutschland? Bei Hamburg?

Das ist aber gar nicht schön.

Hallo, ich heiße Kirsten und ich komme aus Itzehoe.

Ja, ungefähr fünfzig Kilometer nordwestlich von Hamburg.

> Hallo, ich ______________________________

____

< ______________________________

> ______________________________

< ______________________________

> ______________________________

____

< ______________________________

> ______________________________

< ______________________________

NAME: ______________________________ DATE: ________________

1-17 Krista Gugenberger und Frank Becker. Read what Krista and Frank say about themselves and then complete the sentences below appropriately.

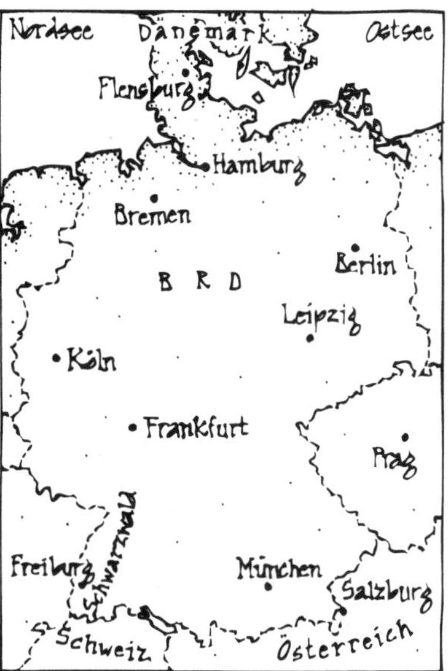

Ich heiße Krista Gugenberger und ich bin einundzwanzig Jahre alt. Ich bin Studentin und komme aus Salzburg. Salzburg ist in Österreich und es ist hier sehr, sehr schön. Von Salzburg ist es gar nicht weit *(far)* nach Deutschland und auch gar nicht weit nach Italien. Ich studiere aber nicht in Salzburg. Meine Mutter ist aus Bremen und ich studiere in Bremen Mathematik. Bremen ist in Norddeutschland, fast an der Nordsee, und es ist hier oft sehr kühl *(cool)* und regnerisch. Meine Adresse ist Mühlenweg 78, 28355 Bremen, und meine Telefonnummer ist (0421) 38 65 24.

Ich heiße Frank Becker und ich komme aus Flensburg. Flensburg ist im Norden von Deutschland, fast in Dänemark. Ich bin zwanzig Jahre alt und ich studiere in Freiburg Psychologie und Soziologie. Freiburg ist in Südwestdeutschland. Es ist sehr schön hier und von Freiburg ist es gar nicht weit zum Schwarzwald und auch gar nicht weit nach Frankreich und in die Schweiz. In Freiburg scheint oft die Sonne und im Sommer ist es hier sehr warm. Meine Adresse ist Rempartstraße 15, 79098 Freiburg, und meine Telefonnummer ist (0761) 47 15 38.

1. Frank Becker ist ____________________ Jahre alt.
   a. zwanzig b. neunzehn c. zweiundzwanzig
2. Kristas Mutter kommt aus ____________________.
   a. Freiburg b. Salzburg c. Bremen
3. Von Flensburg ist es gar nicht weit nach ____________________.
   a. Dänemark b. Frankreich c. Österreich
4. Von Freiburg ist es gar nicht weit ____________________.
   a. nach Deutschland b. nach Italien c. zum Schwarzwald
5. Bremen ist ____________________.
   a. fast in Italien b. fast an der Nordsee c. fast in Österreich
6. In Bremen ist es im Sommer oft sehr ____________________.
   a. warm und regnerisch b. kühl und regnerisch c. heiß und sonnig
7. In Freiburg ist der Sommer ____________________.
   a. sehr kühl b. sehr warm c. sehr regnerisch
8. Frank studiert ____________________.
   a. Biologie b. Mathematik c. Soziologie und Psychologie
9. Die Vorwahl von Freiburg ist ____________________.
   a. 47 15 38 b. 0761 c. 79098
10. Die Postleitzahl von Bremen ist ____________________.
   a. 28355 b. 38 65 24 c. 0421

Zum Übersetzen

1-18 Jahreszeiten. For the names of seasons and months, use **im** to translate *in.*

1. In spring it's often very windy and it also rains a lot. In spring my girlfriend and I play tennis.
2. In summer it's hot. The thermometer often reads thirty degrees. Then I don't play tennis, but go swimming.
3. In fall it's very beautiful. The fall colors *(one word!)* are red, yellow, and brown. My friends and I play soccer.
4. In winter it snows and it's often very cold. The sun doesn't shine so brightly. In January and in February we go skiing.

1-19 Zukunftspläne. For the names of seasons and months use **im** to translate *in (the),* for the names of cities use **in.**

TINA: What will you be doing in the summer?

TOM: I'm going to fly to Germany.

TINA: What will you be doing there?

TOM: In July and in August I'll be working in Munich.

TINA: And then?

TOM: Then I'll be traveling to England.

TINA: And what will you be doing in the fall?

TOM: In the fall I'm going to be studying in Austria, in Salzburg.

TINA: What will you be studying there?

TOM: I'm going to study music.

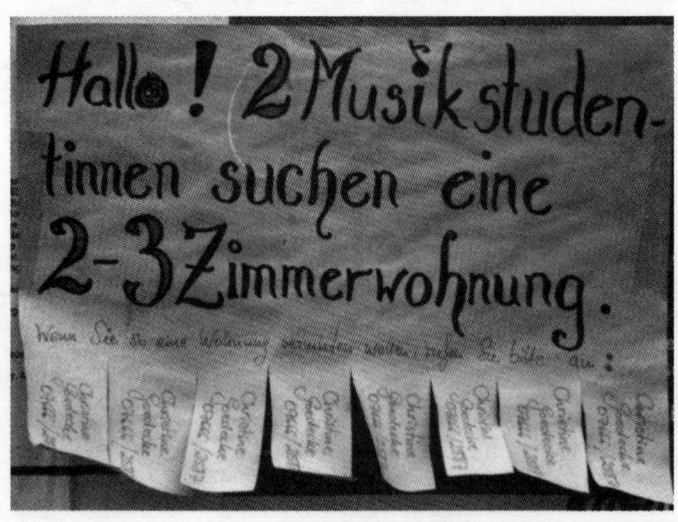

KAPITEL 2

Strukturen

Telling time

1. Official and colloquial time (☞ Übungen 2-1, 2-2, p. 31. Also read *Strukturen 2* before doing these exercises!)

OFFICIAL		COLLOQUIAL
13.00 Uhr	dreizehn Uhr	eins (ein Uhr)
13.05 Uhr	dreizehn Uhr fünf	fünf nach eins
13.15 Uhr	dreizehn Uhr fünfzehn	Viertel nach eins
13.20 Uhr	dreizehn Uhr zwanzig	zwanzig nach eins
13.25 Uhr	dreizehn Uhr fünfundzwanzig	fünf vor halb zwei
13.30 Uhr	dreizehn Uhr dreißig	halb zwei
13.35 Uhr	dreizehn Uhr fünfunddreißig	fünf nach halb zwei
13.40 Uhr	dreizehn Uhr vierzig	zwanzig vor zwei
13.45 Uhr	dreizehn Uhr fünfundvierzig	Viertel vor zwei
13.55 Uhr	dreizehn Uhr fünfundfünfzig	fünf vor zwei
14.00 Uhr	vierzehn Uhr	zwei (zwei Uhr)

2. Expressions of time referring to parts of the day (☞ Übungen 2-1, 2-2, p. 31)

morgens *in the morning*
vormittags *in the morning*
nachmittags *in the afternoon*
abends *in the evening*
nachts *at night*

3. Expressions of time referring to parts of a specific day (☞ Übung 2-3, p. 32)

heute Abend	*tonight*	**morgen früh**	*tomorrow morning*
gestern Nacht	*last night*	**am Montagnachmittag**	*on Monday afternoon*
heute Morgen	*this morning*	**am Dienstagabend**	*on Tuesday evening*

4. The present tense of *haben* (☞ Übung 2-4, p. 33)

singular		plural	
ich	habe	wir	haben
du	**hast**	ihr	habt
er/es/sie	**hat**	sie	haben
	Sie haben		

Expressing likes, dislikes, and preferences

5. Verb + *gern, nicht gern,* or *lieber* (☞ Übung 2-5, p. 33)

Alexander kocht **gern.**	*Alexander **likes to** cook.*
Nina geht **gern** tanzen.	*Nina **likes to** go dancing.*
Robert lernt **nicht gern.**	*Robert **doesn't like** studying.*
Was spielst du **lieber,** Karten oder Scrabble?	*What do you **prefer to** play, cards or Scrabble?*

Answering *who* or *what*

6. The nominative case: subject and subject completion (☞ Übung 2-6, p. 34)

German grammar assigns every noun or pronoun to one of four cases. These cases signal the function of the noun or pronoun in a sentence. The nominative case signals the function subject or subject completion. In the chart below, the nouns and the pronoun are in the *nominative case* and are subjects or subject completions.

subject		subject completion
Ninas Freund	heißt	**Alexander.**
Er	ist	**ein toller Tänzer.**

The following chart shows the nominative forms of the definite and indefinite article.

	masculine		neuter		feminine		plural	
	der		das		die		die	
NOMINATIVE	ein	Pulli	ein	Hemd	eine	Jacke	—	Schuhe
	kein		kein		keine		keine	

7. The interrogative pronouns *wer* and *was* (☞ Übung 2-7, p. 35)

The nominative forms of the interrogative pronouns **wer** *(who)* and **was** *(what)* correspond closely to the definite article forms **der** and **das.**

	definite article	interrogative pronoun	definite article	interrogative pronoun
NOMINATIVE	der	wer	das	was

Describing people, places, and things

8. *Der*-words in the nominative case (☞ Übung 2-8, p. 35)

	masculine	neuter	feminine	plural	
NOMINATIVE	der	das	die	die	*the*
	dieser	dieses	diese	diese	*this*
	jeder	jedes	jede	—[1]	*each, every*
	welcher	welches	welche	welche	*which*

[1]The plural of **jeder** is **alle.**

9. *Ein*-words in the nominative case: *ein, kein,* and the possessive adjectives (☞ Übungen 2-9, 2-10, p. 36)

masculine	neuter	feminine	plural	
ein	ein	eine	—	*a(n)*
kein	kein	keine	keine	*not a(n)*
mein	mein	meine	meine	*my*
dein	dein	deine	deine	*your*
sein	sein	seine	seine	*his*
ihr	ihr	ihre	ihre	*her*
unser	unser	unsere	unsere	*our*
euer	euer	eure	eure	*your*
ihr	ihr	ihre	ihre	*their*
Ihr	Ihr	Ihre	Ihre	*your*

- When an ending is added to **euer,** the **e** before the **r** is dropped: **eure.**
- Like the formal **Sie,** the formal **Ihr** is always capitalized.

10. Adjective endings in the nominative case (☞ Übungen 2-11, 2-12, p. 37)

Nominative endings of adjectives preceded by **der-*words***

	masculine	neuter	feminine	plural
NOMINATIVE	der rot**e** Pulli	das blau**e** Hemd	die weiß**e** Jacke	die braun**en** Schuhe

- In the nominative, these same endings occur after *all* **der**-words, e.g., **der** rot**e** Pulli, **dieses** blau**e** Hemd, **jede** weiß**e** Jacke, **welche** braun**en** Schuhe.
- If two or more adjectives come directly before a noun, they all have the same ending.

  Wie viel kosten diese beid**en** hübsch**en** Blusen?
- An adjective takes an ending even if the noun to which it refers is not repeated.

  Die rot**e** Bluse kostet 40 Euro und die gelb**e** kostet 55 Euro.

Nominative endings of adjectives preceded by **ein-*words***

	masculine	neuter	feminine	plural
NOMINATIVE	**ein** rot**er** Pulli	**ein** blau**es** Hemd	eine weiß**e** Jacke	keine braun**en** Schuhe

- In the nominative, these same endings occur after *all* **ein**-words, e.g., **mein** rot**er** Pulli, **sein** blau**es** Hemd, **ihre** weiß**e** Jacke, **Ihre** braun**en** Schuhe.
- If an adjective is preceded by an **ein**-word *without an ending,* the adjective itself shows the gender and case of the noun by taking the appropriate **der**-word ending: dies**er** Pulli, **ein** rot**er** Pulli; dies**es** Hemd, **ein** blau**es** Hemd.

Nominative endings of unpreceded adjectives

	masculine	neuter	feminine	plural
NOMINATIVE	gut**er** Kaffee	gut**es** Bier	gut**e** Milch	gut**e** Oliven

Adjectives that are not preceded by a **der**-word or an **ein**-word show the gender, number, and case of the noun by taking the appropriate **der**-word ending.

NAME: ______________________ DATE: ______________

Anwendung

Übungen

2-1 Anders gesagt. The following times of the day are expressed in colloquial terms. Rewrite them in words, using the official 24-hour system. (☞ Strukturen 1 & 2, p. 27)

1. zehn nach elf nachts dreiundzwanzig Uhr zehn
2. halb acht abends ______________________
3. zwanzig vor fünf nachmittags ______________________
4. Viertel nach zehn vormittags ______________________
5. fünf vor halb zwei nachmittags ______________________
6. zehn vor elf nachts ______________________
7. fünf nach halb sechs morgens ______________________
8. Viertel vor zehn abends ______________________

2-2 Wie viel Uhr ist es? In words, write the times given a. in official time; b. in colloquial time, using the appropriate adverbs of time to specify the part of the day. (☞ Strukturen 1 & 2, p. 27)

1. 13.35 Uhr a. dreizehn Uhr fünfunddreißig
   b. fünf nach halb zwei nachmittags
2. 20.15 Uhr a. ______________________
   b. ______________________
3. 23.45 Uhr a. ______________________
   b. ______________________
4. 9.10 Uhr a. ______________________
   b. ______________________
5. 16.30 Uhr a. ______________________
   b. ______________________
6. 19.45 Uhr a. ______________________
   b. ______________________

7. 0.15 Uhr a. ______________________

b. ______________________

8. 14.25 Uhr a. ______________________

b. ______________________

9. 7.40 Uhr a. ______________________

b. ______________________

10. 15.15 Uhr a. ______________________

b. ______________________

2-3 Tage und Tageszeiten. Imagine that it is Sunday noon. How would you refer to other parts of this day or the two days preceding and the two days following it? To specify the day, use the expressions **heute, gestern, vorgestern** *(the day before yesterday)*, **morgen, übermorgen** *(the day after tomorrow)*. Specify the part of the day by adding **Abend, Nacht, früh, Vormittag,** etc. for the clock times given below. Note that all clock times are given in official time. (☞ Strukturen 1 & 3, pp. 27–28)

1. Freitag, 20.00 Uhr acht Uhr vorgestern Abend
2. Montag, 10.00 Uhr ______________________
3. Sonntag, 7.00 Uhr ______________________
4. Samstag, 16.00 Uhr ______________________
5. Dienstag, 19.00 Uhr ______________________
6. Freitag, 23.00 Uhr ______________________
7. Sonntag, 15.00 Uhr ______________________
8. Montag, 6.00 Uhr ______________________
9. Samstag, 11.00 Uhr ______________________
10. Dienstag, 17.00 Uhr ______________________

NAME: ______________________________ DATE: ______________

2-4 Was haben diese Leute? Supply the correct forms of **haben.** (Strukturen 4, p. 28)

1. > __________ ihr ein Haus, Robert?

   < Ja, wir __________ ein kleines, aber sehr schönes Haus.

2. > __________ Ninas Freund Alexander ein Auto?

   < Nein, aber er __________ ein Motorrad.

3. > __________ du ein Fahrrad, Robert?

   < Klar! Ich __________ ein sehr schönes Fahrrad.

4. > Warum __________ dein Bruder denn keine Freundin, Nina?

   < Ich glaube, er __________ keine Zeit für Freundinnen.

5. > __________ Sie ein Auto, Frau Maier?

   < Nein, ich __________ kein Auto, aber ich __________ ein Motorrad.

6. > __________ Martin und Peter jetzt ein Zimmer?

   < Ja, sie __________ ein Zimmer in der Zennerstraße.

7. > __________ ihr Telefon?

   < Nein, wir __________ kein Telefon.

8. > __________ du heute Nachmittag Zeit, Peter?

   > Nein, heute Nachmittag __________ ich Vorlesungen.

2-5 *Gern, nicht gern* oder *lieber!* (Strukturen 5, p. 28)

1. > Warum gehen Bettina und Oliver nie in die Disco?

   < Ich glaube, Oliver tanzt ____nicht gern____ .

2. > Spielt David auch so __________ Squash wie du?

   < Nein, er spielt __________ Tennis.

3. > Was sind Bettinas Hobbies?

   < Sie geht __________ tanzen und fotografiert auch __________ .

4. > Hörst du __________ Jazz, Kurt?

   < Ja, aber Rock höre ich __________ .

5. > Tanzt Marias Freund auch so ________________ wie sie?

< Nein, er tanzt gar ________________. Er spielt ________________ Fußball.

6. > Was trinkst du, Antje, Bier oder Wein?

< Ein Glas Wein, bitte. Ich trinke ________________ Wein als Bier.

7. > Warum fliegt Frau Müller allein nach Schweden?

< Ich glaube, Herr Müller fliegt ________________.

8. > Spielst du ________________ Monopoly, Kathrin?

< Ja, aber Scrabble spiele ich ________________.

9. > Was machst du heute Abend? Gehst du in die Disco?

< Nein, ich gehe ________________ in die Bibliothek und lerne.

10. > Warum geht Günter nie in die Bibliothek?

< Ich glaube, er lernt ________________.

2-6 Was ist das? Supply the nominative endings of the definite or indefinite articles. Remember that the indefinite article does not always have an ending. (☞Strukturen 6, p. 28)

1. > Ist d____ *Stern* (m) ein____ Zeitung (f)?

< Nein, d____ *Stern* ist kein____ Zeitung, sondern ein____ Magazin (n).

2. > Ist d____ *Frankfurter Allgemeine* (f) ein____ Magazin?

< Nein, d____ *Frankfurter Allgemeine* ist kein____ Magazin, sondern ein____ Zeitung.

3. > Ist *D____ Frau und d____ Affe* (m) ein____ Film?

< Nein, *D____ Frau und d____ Affe* ist kein____ Film, sondern ein____ Buch.

4. > Ist *D____ Himmel über Berlin* (m) ein ____ Buch (n)?

< Nein, *D____ Himmel über Berlin* ist kein____ Buch, sondern ein____ Film (m).

5. > Sind *D____ Simpsons* (pl) ein____ Film?

< Nein, *D____ Simpsons* sind kein____ Film, sondern ein____ TV-Serie (f).

6. > Ist *D____ Nussknacker* (m) ein____ Oper (f)?

< Nein, *D____ Nussknacker* ist kein____ Oper, sondern ein____ Ballett (n).

7. > Ist *D____ Zauberflöte* (f) ein____ Ballett?

< Nein, *D____ Zauberflöte* ist kein____ Ballett, sondern ein____ Oper.

NAME: ____________________ DATE: ____________

2-7 *Wer* oder *was* ist das? Complete the questions with **wer** or **was** and the responses with the appropriate information from the list below. (Strukturen 7, p. 29)

ein deutscher Politiker / eine kanadische Provinz / eine österreichische Stadt / ein amerikanischer Autor / ein kanadischer Rockstar / ein russischer Komponist / ein großes Reptil / ein deutsches Bier / ein britischer Filmstar

1. _____ ist Löwenbräu? Löwenbräu ist ____________________.
2. _____ ist Stephen King? Stephen King ist ____________________.
3. _____ ist Gerhard Schröder? Gerhard Schröder ist ____________________.
4. _____ ist Salzburg? Salzburg ist ____________________.
5. _____ ist Bryan Adams? Bryan Adams ist ____________________.
6. _____ ist Hugh Grant? Hugh Grant ist ____________________.
7. _____ ist Ontario? Ontario ist ____________________.
8. _____ ist Tschaikowski? Tschaikowski ist ____________________.
9. _____ ist ein Krokodil? Ein Krokodil ist ____________________.

2-8 *Dies-, jed-* oder *welch-?* Supply appropriate **der**-words and correct endings. (Strukturen 8, p. 29)

1. Nicht ______________ Magazin ist so interessant wie der *Stern.*
2. ______________ Oper ist von Mozart, *Don Giovanni* oder *Carmen?*
3. Ist ______________ Film gut?
4. ______________ Briefmarken sind sehr schön.
5. ______________ Zeitung ist das, die *Frankfurter Allgemeine* oder die *Süddeutsche?*
6. Ist ______________ Buch interessant?
7. ______________ Wein ist besser, der Beaujolais oder der Chianti?
8. Nicht ______________ Frau kocht gern.
9. ______________ kalte Wetter ist gar nicht schön.
10. In Deutschland lernt fast ______________ Schüler Englisch.

2-9 Kleine Gespräche. From the lists provided, supply appropriate **ein**-words with correct endings. (☞ Strukturen 9, p. 29)

mein (2x) / dein (2x) / sein / unser / euer / ihr

1. MARIA: Wie heißt ____________ beste Freundin, Claudia?

CLAUDIA: ____________ beste Freundin heißt Stephanie. Sie ist ____________ Mitbewohnerin.

MARIA: Ist ____________ Zimmer im Studentenheim schön?

CLAUDIA: Ja, ____________ Zimmer ist sehr schön, aber es ist nicht sehr groß.

MARIA: Wohnt ____________ Freund Martin auch im Studentenheim?

CLAUDIA: Nein, Martin und ____________ Freund Peter wohnen in der Zennerstraße. ____________ Zimmer dort ist sehr groß und kostet nur 250 Euro im Monat.

mein / sein (2x) / ihr / Ihr (2x)

2. FRAU HOLZ: Wo lebt ____________ Sohn jetzt, Frau Berg?

FRAU BERG: Florian und ____________ zwei Kinder leben jetzt wieder hier in Bremen, aber ____________ Frau arbeitet noch in Hamburg und hat dort ein Zimmer. Sie ist aber jedes Wochenende hier in Bremen.

FRAU HOLZ: Und was machen ____________ beiden Töchter, Frau Berg?

FRAU BERG: ____________ Tochter Anna studiert in Leipzig Medizin und ____________ Schwester Beate arbeitet bei Daimler-Chrysler in Stuttgart.

2-10 Wer hat das bessere Zimmer? From the list below, supply appropriate **ein**-words with correct endings. (☞ Strukturen 9, p. 29)

mein (2x) / unser (2x) / euer (5x) / ihr (2x)

Sabine besucht ____________ Freundinnen Stephanie und Claudia. Die beiden fragen Sabine: „Wie findest du ____________ Zimmer?" Sabine antwortet: „Ich finde ____________ Zimmer toll. ____________ Zimmer ist nicht so groß und nicht so schön wie ____________ Zimmer." Dann fragt sie ____________ Freundinnen: „Was kostet denn ____________ Zimmer?" Stephanie antwortet: „ ____________ Zimmer kostet nur 200 Euro im Monat." Da sagt Sabine: „Was?! ____________ Zimmer kostet nur 200 Euro?! Dann kostet __________ kleines Zimmer ja fast so viel wie ____________ großes, schönes Zimmer!"

NAME: ______________________________ **DATE:** ______________

2-11 Adjektive. Supply the correct endings. (Strukturen 10, p. 30)

1. Berlin ist eine groß____ und sehr interessant____ Stadt.
2. Liechtenstein ist ein klein____ Land.
3. *Lola rennt* ist ein deutsch____ Film.
4. Woher sind diese schön____ Oliven?
5. Ist dein neu____ Wintermantel warm?
6. Chianti ist ein italienisch____ Rotwein.
7. Lang____ Röcke sind jetzt wieder modern.
8. Wie heißt Marias neu____ Freund?
9. Sind eure neu____ Nachbarn nett?
10. Stephanie ist eine sehr gut____ Studentin.
11. Frau Dr. Erdmann ist unsere best____ Professorin.
12. Deutsch____ Bier ist sehr gut.
13. Gut____ italienisch____ Salami (f) ist nicht billig.
14. Dieses blau____ Kleid ist sehr hübsch, aber viel zu teuer.
15. Ihre schwarz____ Schuhe sind sehr schick, Frau Merck.

2-12 Beschreiben. Choose at least four people, animals, or things, and describe them with as many adjectives as possible from the list below. Conclude each of your sentences with an appropriate noun, e.g., **Frau, Mann, Mädchen** (n!) *(girl),* **Junge** *(boy),* **Mensch** (m) *(human being),* **Tier** (n) *(animal),* **Fahrzeug** (n) *(vehicle).* (Strukturen 10, p. 30)

hübsch	groß	konservativ	sportlich	neu
schick	klein	modern	unsportlich	schwarz
schön	schlank	praktisch	interessant	weiß
elegant	mollig	unpraktisch	gut	braun
nett	intelligent	musikalisch	schlecht	grau
süß[1]	doof	unmusikalisch	alt	...

1. Meine Mutter ist eine moderne und sehr intelligente, ein bisschen mollige, aber sehr schöne und elegante Frau.

[1] *sweet*

2. Mein Vater ist ______________________________

____

3. Mein Bruder ist ______________________________

____

4. Meine Schwester ist ______________________________

____

5. Meine Freundin ist ______________________________

____

6. Mein Freund ist ______________________________

____

7. Meine Mitbewohnerin/Mein Mitbewohner ist ______________________________

____

8. Ich bin ______________________________

____

9. Mein Hund[2] ist ______________________________

____

10. Meine Katze ist ______________________________

____

11. Mein Auto ist ______________________________

____

12. Mein Motorrad ist ______________________________

____

13. Mein Fahrrad ist ______________________________

____

[2] *dog*

NAME: ______________________ DATE: ____________

Zum Verstehen

2-13 Sylvia fliegt nach Europa. Consult the map below as you read the following paragraph. Then do the activities that follow.

Sylvia fliegt Anfang[1] Juli nach Europa. Sie fliegt mit American Airlines nach Frankfurt und dann mit Lufthansa nach Bremen. In Bremen besucht sie ihre Kusine Barbara. Bremen ist sehr schön und sehr interessant und Sylvia bleibt[2] fast zwei Wochen dort. Mitte Juli fahren[3] Sylvia und Barbara nach Skandinavien. Sie haben nur wenig Geld und sie nehmen[4] deshalb den Bus. Sie fahren zuerst nach Lübeck, denn dort lebt Barbaras Freundin Ulrike. Sie bleiben drei Tage in Lübeck und fahren dann alle drei zu Ulrikes Freund Sven nach Kiel. Sven ist Hydrologe. Er hat ein Segelboot und am Freitag und Samstag gehen sie alle segeln. Am Sonntag fahren sie alle zusammen nach Kopenhagen und am Montag fahren Sylvia und Barbara dann nach Schweden. Schweden ist sehr teuer und die beiden Studentinnen haben nicht viel Geld. Aber Barbara hat in Schweden Freunde. Diese Freunde sind auch aus Bremen und haben bei[5] Kristianstad ein Sommerhaus. Das Wetter ist sehr schön, die Ostsee ist warm und die zwei Kusinen bleiben fast drei Wochen. Sie gehen schwimmen und sitzen am Strand und am Abend gehen sie oft mit Barbaras Freunden tanzen. Anfang August fahren Sylvia und Barbara nach Trelleborg. Dort nehmen sie die Fähre[6] nach Saßnitz und von dort sind sie in wenigen Stunden in Berlin. Sie bleiben fünf Tage in Berlin und fahren dann über Hannover wieder nach Bremen. Mitte August fliegt Sylvia dann wieder nach Amerika.

[1]*at the beginning of* [2]*stays* [3]*go* [4]*take* [5]*near* [6]*ferry*

A. Draw Sylvia's and Barbara's itinerary on the map below.

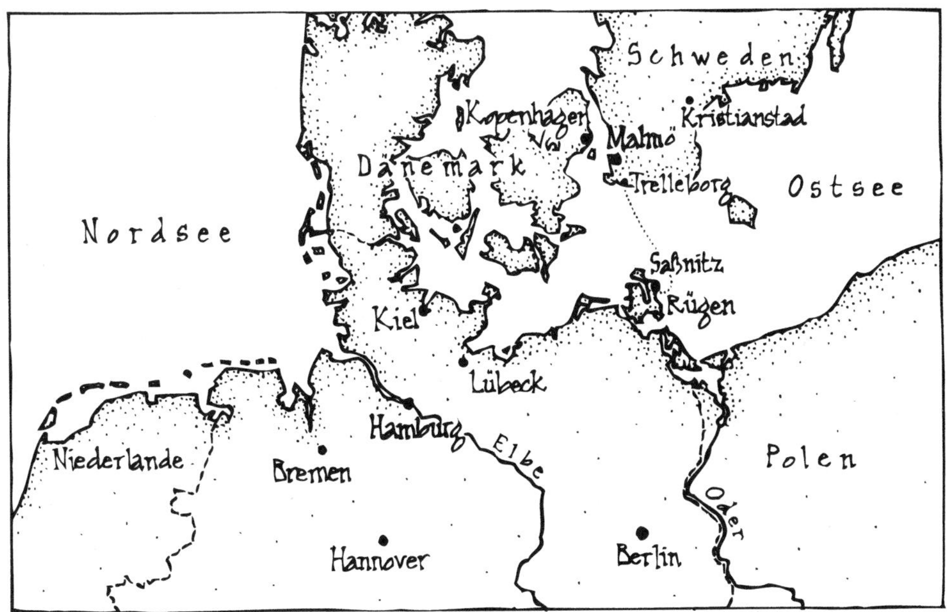

B. Complete the following sentences with the appropriate phrases.

1. Sven ist ______________________.
   a. Barbaras Freund b. Sylvias Kusine c. Ulrikes Freund

2. Barbaras Freunde haben ein Sommerhaus ______________________.
   a. bei Trelleborg b. bei Kristianstad c. bei Saßnitz

3. Ulrike lebt ______________________.
a. in Bremen b. in Lübeck c. in Kiel

4. In Trelleborg nehmen Sylvia und Barbara die Fähre ______________________.
a. nach Saßnitz b. nach Lübeck c. nach Kiel

5. In Berlin bleiben Sylvia und Barbara ______________________.
a. nur wenige Stunden b. fast drei Wochen c. fünf Tage

6. ______________________ fahren Sylvia und Barbara nach Skandinavien.
a. Mitte Juli b. Anfang August c. Anfang Juli

7. Sven hat ______________________.
a. nicht viel Geld b. ein Segelboot c. ein Sommerhaus in Schweden

8. Von Berlin fahren Sylvia und Barbara ______________________ wieder nach Bremen.
a. über Lübeck b. über Hannover c. über Saßnitz

9. Sven lebt ______________________.
a. in Kiel b. in Lübeck c. in Bremen

10. Sylvia ist ______________________ in Europa.
a. zwei Monate b. fast drei Monate c. etwa sechs Wochen

2-14 Wortsalat. Read across and down to find 11 additional adjectives or adverbs. Write them and their opposites in the spaces provided.

g	r	o	ß	d	s	ü	ß	r	h
u	k	h	v	o	y	z	o	e	e
f	e	u	s	r	l	a	n	g	i
r	i	c	h	t	i	g	e	p	ß
g	ö	l	w	f	b	f	u	n	i
w	t	e	u	e	r	d	ü	n	n
t	t	w	e	n	i	g	s	h	k
d	u	m	m	e	i	m	m	e	r

1. groß ______ klein ______
2. ______ ______
3. ______ ______
4. ______ ______
5. ______ ______
6. ______ ______
7. ______ ______
8. ______ ______
9. ______ ______
10. ______ ______
11. ______ ______
12. ______ ______

NAME: ______________________________ DATE: ______________

2-15 Kategorien. Enter the following nouns under the appropriate categories.

das Fahrrad / das Konzert / das Barometer / die Gitarre / der Herbst / die Milch / das Wasser / das Auto / das Eis / das Motorrad / das Bier / der Jazz / das Thermometer / die Rockgruppe / der Bus / der Wein / die Lokomotive / der Regen / der Kaffee / die Trompete

Fahrzeuge	Getränke
______________________	______________________
______________________	______________________
______________________	______________________
______________________	______________________
______________________	______________________

Musik	Wetter
______________________	______________________
______________________	______________________
______________________	______________________
______________________	______________________
______________________	______________________

Zum Übersetzen

2-16 Mein Freund Kurt. For the names of seasons, use **im** to translate *in*.

My boyfriend's name is Kurt. He studies geography and geology and he's very nice. Kurt is very athletic: in summer he swims and sails and he also plays tennis, and in winter he plays hockey. He likes to cook and he also collects stamps. Kurt is very musical: he plays guitar and sings very well. But Kurt is not perfect **(perfekt)**. I think his big motorcycle costs a bit too much. He often talks on the phone for hours, and he doesn't always like to study. But nobody **(niemand)** is as interesting as my Kurt.

2-17 Kleine Gespräche.

1. TOBIAS: What's Nina doing?

   ROBERT: She's talking on the phone with Alexander.

   TOBIAS: Who's Alexander?

   ROBERT: That's her dumb boyfriend.

2. JULIA: Where does your friend Anna live now?

   KIRSTEN: She and her husband live in Kiel.

   JULIA: Do they have an apartment or a house?

   KIRSTEN: They have a beautiful, big house. I'm going to visit Anna in the summer.

3. CHRISTINE: How much does this red coat cost?

   VERKÄUFERIN: The red coat? It costs only two hundred euros.

   CHRISTINE: That's much too expensive!

4. MARIA: What time does the film start?

   SVEN: At seven thirty. *(Use colloquial time.)*

   MARIA: And when is it over?

   SVEN: At nine.

KAPITEL 3

Strukturen

Answering *whom* or *what*

1. The accusative case: direct object (☞ Übungen 3-1, 3-2, 3-3, 3-4, pp. 47–49)

The noun or pronoun in a sentence that is the *target* of what is expressed by the verb is called the *direct object*. Direct objects are in the *accusative case.*

NOMINATIVE CASE	=	subject and subject completion
ACCUSATIVE CASE	=	direct object

	masculine		neuter		feminine		plural	
NOMINATIVE	der		das		die		die	
	ein	Rock	ein	Kleid	eine	Jacke	—	Schuhe
	kein		kein		keine		keine	
ACCUSATIVE	den		das		die		die	
	einen	Rock	ein	Kleid	eine	Jacke	—	Schuhe
	keinen		kein		keine		keine	

The *masculine* forms **der, ein,** and **kein** change, depending on whether the nouns they precede are the subject or the direct object of the verb.

2. The interrogative pronoun in the accusative case (☞ Übung 3-5, p. 50)

Wen *(whom)* and **was** *(what)* are the accusative forms of the interrogative pronoun.

	interrogative pronoun	
NOMINATIVE	wer	was
ACCUSATIVE	wen	was

3. *Der*-words in the accusative case (☞ Übung 3-6, p. 50)

In the accusative case, as in the nominative, the endings of **dieser** *(this),* **jeder** *(each, every),* and **welcher** *(which)* correspond closely to the forms of the definite article.

	masculine	neuter	feminine	plural
NOMINATIVE	dieser	dieses	diese	diese
ACCUSATIVE	diesen	dieses	diese	diese

4. *Ein*-words in the accusative case: *ein, kein,* and the possessive adjectives

(☞ Übung 3-7, p. 51)

The **ein**-words are **ein, kein,** and the possessive adjectives. All **ein**-words take the same case endings. The possessive adjectives are:

mein	*my*	**unser**	*our*
dein	*your*	**euer**	*your*
sein	*his, its*	**ihr**	*their*
ihr	*her, its*		
Ihr	*your*		

 Like the formal **Sie,** the formal **Ihr** is always capitalized.

In the following chart, the possessive adjective **mein** is used to show the nominative and accusative forms of *all* **ein**-words.

	masculine	neuter	feminine	plural
NOMINATIVE	mein Freund	mein Auto	meine Freundin	meine Eltern
ACCUSATIVE	mein**en** Freund	mein Auto	meine Freundin	meine Eltern

 When an ending is added to **euer,** the **e** before the **r** is dropped: **eure, euren.**

5. *Haben* versus *sein* (☞ Übung 3-8, p. 51)

The verb **haben** always takes an accusative object.

Müllers haben **einen** Esel. *The Müllers have a donkey.*

Subject completions after the verb **sein** always appear in the nominative case.

Günter ist **ein** Esel. *Günter is a nitwit.*

Describing people, places, and things

6. Adjective endings in the accusative case

Accusative endings of adjectives preceded by* der*-words (☞ Übung 3-9, p. 52)

	masculine	neuter	feminine	plural
NOMINATIVE	der neue Drucker	das teure Notebook	die große Festplatte	die tollen CDs
ACCUSATIVE	den neu**en** Drucker	das teure Notebook	die große Festplatte	die tollen CDs

- In the masculine accusative singular, the ending of an adjective preceded by a **der**-word is **-en.**
- The other accusative endings are identical to those in the nominative.
- Adjectives that end in **-er** or **-el** drop the **e** when they take an ending **(teu*er*: den teu*ren* Drucker; dunk*el*: das dunk*le* Sofa).**

Accusative endings of adjectives preceded by **ein-words** (☞ Übung 3-10, p. 53)

	masculine	neuter	feminine	plural
NOMINATIVE	**ein** neu**er** Drucker	**ein** teur**es** Notebook	ein**e** groß**e** Festplatte	mein**e** toll**en** CDs
ACCUSATIVE	**einen** neu**en** Drucker	**ein** teur**es** Notebook	ein**e** groß**e** Festplatte	mein**e** toll**en** CDs

- In the masculine accusative singular, the ending of an adjective preceded by an **ein**-word is **-en.**
- The other accusative endings are identical to those in the nominative.
- If an adjective is preceded by an **ein**-word *without an ending,* the adjective itself shows the gender and case of the noun by taking the appropriate **der**-word ending: dies**er** Drucker, **ein** neu**er** Drucker; dies**es** Notebook, **ein** teur**es** Notebook.

Accusative endings of unpreceded adjectives (☞ Übung 3-11, p. 53)

	masculine	neuter	feminine	plural
NOMINATIVE	gut**er** Kaffee	gut**es** Bier	gut**e** Salami	gut**e** Oliven
ACCUSATIVE	gut**en** Kaffee	gut**es** Bier	gut**e** Salami	gut**e** Oliven

- In the masculine accusative singular, the ending of an unpreceded adjective is **-en.**
- The other accusative endings are identical to those in the nominative.

Word order

7. A review of negation (☞ Übung 3-12, p. 54)

Negation in a sentence with a direct object follows the same rules you learned in *Kapitel 1:*

- If no word or expression is specifically negated, **nicht** stands at the end of the sentence. This means that **nicht** usually follows the direct object.

  Ich kenne diesen Mann **nicht.**
  Warum verstehen meine Eltern meine Probleme **nicht?**
  Meine Kusine kommt dieses Wochenende **nicht.**
  Warum antwortest du **nicht?**

- **Nicht** precedes words or expressions that are specifically negated.

adjectives	Meine Tante ist **nicht verheiratet.**
	Ich möchte **nicht** die **schwarze** Katze, sondern die weiße.
adverbs	Mein Onkel lacht **nicht oft.**
	Ich koche **nicht gern.**
prepositional phrases	Meine Eltern fliegen diesen Sommer **nicht nach Europa.**
	Ich gehe heute Abend **nicht ins Kino.**
subject completions	Rot ist **nicht meine Lieblingsfarbe.**
	Ich heiße **nicht Müller.**

- Use **kein** to negate a noun preceded by the indefinite article **ein** or by a noun without an article.

Hast du **eine** Katze?	Nein, ich habe **keine** Katze.
Hast du Geschwister?	Nein, ich habe **keine** Geschwister.

Expressing actions in the present and future

8. Verbs with stem-vowel changes in the present tense (☞ Übungen 3-13, 3-14, 3-15, 3-16, pp. 55–57)

Some German verbs have a stem-vowel change in the **du**-form and in the **er/es/sie**-form of the present tense.

e → i		e → ie		a → ä		au → äu	
SPRECHEN		LESEN		FAHREN		LAUFEN	
ich	spreche	ich	lese	ich	fahre	ich	laufe
du	sprichst	du	liest	du	fährst	du	läufst
er/es/sie	spricht	er/es/sie	liest	er/es/sie	fährt	er/es/sie	läuft
wir	sprechen	wir	lesen	wir	fahren	wir	laufen
ihr	sprecht	ihr	lest	ihr	fahrt	ihr	lauft
sie/Sie	sprechen	sie/Sie	lesen	sie/Sie	fahren	sie/Sie	laufen

These stem-vowel changes occur *only* in the **du**-form and in the **er/es/sie**-form.

NAME: ______________________ DATE: ______________

Anwendung

Übungen

3-1 Subjekte und direkte Objekte. Enter the subjects, subject completions, and direct objects from the following sentences in the chart below. Not all sentences have subject completions and direct objects. (☞ Strukturen 1, p. 43)

1. Sylvia fliegt im Juli nach Europa.
2. In Bremen besucht sie ihre Kusine Barbara.
3. Barbara hat in Lübeck eine gute Freundin.
4. Sie heißt Ulrike.
5. Ulrikes Freund lebt in Kiel.
6. Er hat ein Segelboot.
7. Barbara hat auch in Schweden Freunde.
8. Diese Freunde sind auch aus Bremen.
9. Barbaras Freunde haben bei Kristianstad ein Sommerhaus.
10. In Trelleborg nehmen Sylvia und Barbara die Fähre.
11. Von Saßnitz sind sie in wenigen Stunden in Berlin.
12. Mitte August fliegt Sylvia wieder nach Amerika.

	subjects or subject completions	direct objects
1.	Sylvia	
2.		
3.		
4.		
5.		
6.		
7.		
8.		
9.		
10.		
11.		
12.		

3-2 Auf dem Flohmarkt. The following people are at a flea market. What do they buy? (☞ Strukturen 1, p. 43)

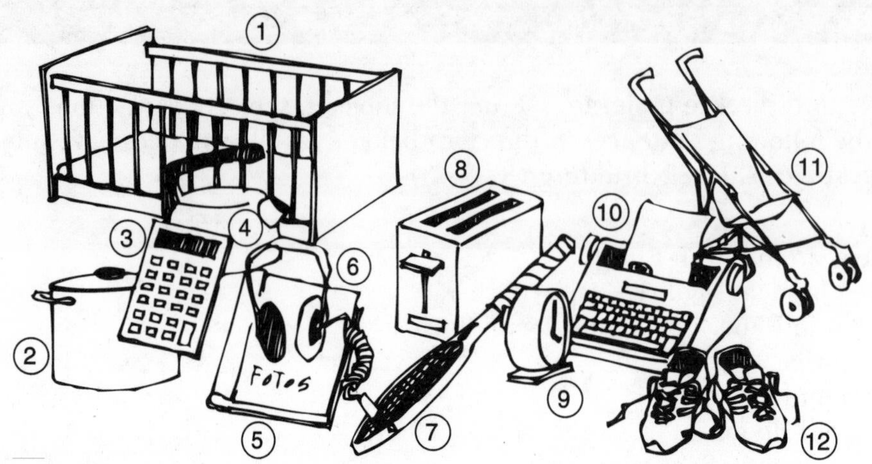

1. das Kinderbett
2. der Kochtopf
3. der Taschenrechner
4. der Teekessel
5. das Fotoalbum
6. der Kopfhörer
7. der Tennisschläger
8. der Toaster
9. der Wecker
10. die Schreibmaschine
11. der Kinderwagen
12. die Joggingschuhe

1. Robert trinkt viel Tee, isst *(eats)* gern Toast und er kocht auch sehr gern. Er kauft

   den Teekessel, ______________________ und

   ______________________.

2. Thomas kommt morgens immer zu spät in die Vorlesung. Er kauft deshalb

   ______________________.

3. Frau Krüger fotografiert gern. Sie kauft ______________________.

4. Ingrid ist sehr sportlich. Sie kauft ______________________ und

   ______________________.

5. Sebastian hört gern sehr laute Rockmusik. Sein Mitbewohner Matthias kauft deshalb für

   Sebastian ______________________.

6. Schmidts haben ein kleines Baby. Sie kaufen ______________________ und

   ______________________.

7. In Mathematik ist Stefan gar nicht gut. Er kauft deshalb ______________________.

8. Frau Denner ist 85 und schreibt ihre Memoiren. Sie tippt gut, aber sie ist nicht sehr

   modern. Deshalb kauft sie __________ alte ______________________.

NAME: ______________________ DATE: ______________

3-3 Was passt wo? Supply the most appropriate word and precede it with the correct form of **ein.** (☞ Strukturen 1, p. 43)

Job (m) / Visum (n) / Winterjacke (f) / Regenmantel (m) / Kamera (f)

1. Hier regnet es fast jeden Tag. Ich brauche einen Regenmantel.
2. Ich fotografiere gern. Ich brauche ______________.
3. Ich habe kein Geld. Ich brauche ______________.
4. Es ist sehr kalt. Ich brauche ______________.
5. Ich fliege nach China. Ich brauche ______________.

CD-Spieler (m) / Rucksack (m) / Fahrrad (n) / Film (m) / Pizza (f)

6. Ich habe eine Kamera. Jetzt brauche ich ______________.
7. Ich höre gern Musik. Ich brauche ______________.
8. Ich wandere gern. Ich brauche ______________.
9. Ich habe Hunger. Ich brauche ______________.
10. Zur Uni sind es fast fünf Kilometer. Ich brauche ______________.

3-4 Was passt wo? Supply the most appropriate word and precede it with the correct form of **kein.** (☞ Strukturen 1, p. 43)

Skier (pl) / Kamera (f) / Geld (n) / Pullover (m) / CDs (pl)

1. Heute ist es nicht kalt. Du brauchst keinen Pullover.
2. Ich reise gern, aber das kostet viel und ich habe ______________.
3. Ich fotografiere gern, aber ich habe ______________.
4. Ich laufe gern Ski, aber ich habe ______________.
5. Ich habe jetzt einen CD-Spieler, aber noch ______________.

Rucksack (m) / Gläser (pl) / Drucker (m) / Regenmantel (m) / Wecker (m)

6. Ich komme oft zu spät in die Vorlesung, denn ich habe ______________.
7. Wir haben Wein, aber ______________.
8. Ich habe einen Computer, aber noch ______________.
9. Ich wandere gern, aber ich habe ______________.
10. Es regnet nicht. Du brauchst ______________.

3-5 ***Wer, wen* oder *was?*** (Strukturen 2, p. 43)

1. __Was__ is Bettina Ziegler von Beruf?
2. ______ hat schicke Kleider und fährt ein rotes Sportcoupé?
3. ______ besucht Nina morgen, ihren Onkel oder ihren Opa?
4. ______ ist Alexander? Ist er Ninas Freund oder ihr Bruder?
5. ______ findet Robert doof, seine Schwester oder ihren Freund?
6. ______ studierst du?
7. ______ trinkt Kaffee, und ______ trinkt lieber Tee?
8. ______ trinkt ihr lieber, Bier oder Wein?
9. ______ spielt denn hier so gut Gitarre?
10. ______ findest du besser, John Grisham oder Stephen King?

3-6 **Kleider.** Supply the nominative or accusative forms of **dieser, jeder,** or **welcher.** (Strukturen 3, p. 43)

1. > Was kosten ____diese____ Sweatshirts?

   < Heute kostet hier ____jedes____ Sweatshirt (n) nur 10 Euro.

2. > Findest du ______________ Mantel (m) auch so schön?

   < Ja, ______________ Mantel ist sehr schön und gar nicht so teuer.

3. > ______________ Jacke (f) kaufst du?

   < Ich glaube, ich kaufe ______________ rote Jacke.

4. > ______________ Kleid (n) ist sehr schön, aber viel zu teuer. Ist denn hier ______________ Kleid so teuer?

   < Nein, ______________ Kleider hier sind nicht so teuer und sie sind auch sehr schön.

5. > ______________ Pulli (m) kaufst du? ______________ Mohair (m) hier?

   < Nein, ______________ Mohair Pullis sind viel zu teuer und auch viel zu warm.

NAME: ______________________________ DATE: ______________

3-7 Familie Ziegler. Supply appropriate possessive adjectives in the nominative or accusative case. (Strukturen 4, p. 44)

1. Robert sagt: Ich finde ___deinen___ Freund Alexander doof, Nina. Warum spielt er denn immer __________ blöde Gitarre? Aber __________ Motorrad finde ich ganz toll.
2. Nina sagt: Kennst du __________ Tante Bettina, Shauna? Sie ist __________ Lieblingstante. Ich finde __________ Kleider und __________ rotes Sportcoupé ganz toll.
3. Tante Bettina sagt: Heute Abend besuche ich __________ Bruder Klaus, __________ Frau Brigitte und __________ Kinder Nina und Robert.
4. Herr Ziegler sagt: Robert und Nina, warum macht ihr denn nie __________ Betten?
5. Herr und Frau Ziegler sagen: Kennen Sie __________ Kinder, Frau Meyer? Das ist __________ Tochter Nina und das ist __________ Sohn Robert.
6. Frau Berger sagt: Hat __________ Tochter schon einen Freund, Frau Ziegler?

3-8 Familie Müller. Complete with appropriate forms of **sein** or **haben** and with nominative or accusative endings where necessary. (Strukturen 5, p. 44)

1. > Wie viele Kinder ___haben___ Müllers?

   < Sie __________ ein_____ Tochter und ein_____ Sohn.
2. > __________ du ein_____ Schwester, Laura?

   < Nein, ich __________ nur ein_____ Bruder. Er heißt Tobias.
3. > __________ du schon ein_____ Freundin, Tobias?

   < Nein, ich __________ noch kein_____ Freundin. Aber meine Schwester __________ ein_____ Freund.
4. > Laura, dein Bruder sagt, du __________ ein_____ Freund. __________ es Dieter?

   < Nein, Dieter __________ nicht mein_____ Freund. Er __________ nur ein_____ Schulkamerad.

5. > ________________ ihr ein____ Katze, Tobias?

< Nein, wir ________________ ein____ Hund.

> Was für ein____ Hund ________________ es?

< Es ________________ ein____ Bernhardiner (m).

6. > ________________ Frau Müller ein____ Ford (m) oder ein____ Audi (m)?

< Ich glaube, sie ________________ ein____ Ford.

7. > Sie ________________ ein____ tollen Wagen, Frau Müller. ________________ das ein____ Audi?

< Nein, das ________________ kein____ Audi, das ________________ ein____ Ford.

3-9 Im Kaufhaus. Supply the appropriate adjective endings. (☞ Strukturen 6, p. 44)

1. > Welchen Mantel kaufst du? Den teur____ rot____ oder diesen preisgünstig____ blau____?

< Der rot____ Mantel ist sehr schön. Ich finde aber auch den blau____ gar nicht so schlecht.

> Ja, der blau____ Mantel ist auch sehr schick.

< Gut, dann nehme ich den blau____.

2. > Ich finde die preisgünstig____ Jacken hier gar nicht schön.

< Ja, und die schick____ Jacken sind viel zu teuer.

> Vielleicht ist dieses Kaufhaus dann nicht das richtig____ für uns Studenten.

3. > Haben Sie die neu____ CD von Robbie Williams?

< Nein, die ganz neu____ CDs kommen immer erst am Nachmittag.

> Ich brauche diese toll____ CD aber gleich jetzt.

< Warum gehen Sie dann nicht in das groß____ Musikgeschäft in der Geranienstraße? Vielleicht finden Sie sie dort.

4. > Welches Olivenöl finden Sie besser, dieses griechisch____ oder dieses italienisch____?

< Ich finde die griechisch____ Olivenöle (pl) alle sehr gut, aber die italienisch____ sind oft ein bisschen milder. Für Salate nehme ich deshalb immer dieses teur____, italienisch____ Olivenöl.

NAME: ______________________________ DATE: ______________

3-10 Meinungen. *(Opinions.)* Supply the appropriate adjective endings. (Strukturen 6, p. 45)

1. Nina sagt: Meine Tante Bettina ist eine sehr gut____ Physiotherapeutin. Sie fährt ein teur____, rot____ Sportcoupé (n) und hat ein toll____ Leben (n).
2. Robert sagt: Nina hat so einen doof____ Freund! Er ist oft stundenlang bei Nina und spielt seine blöd____ Gitarre. Aber sein neu____ Motorrad (n) ist ganz toll.
3. Frau Ziegler sagt: Beverly Harper ist meine best____ Freundin. Sie ist eine sehr gut____ Journalistin und mein Mann und ich lesen ihre interessant____ Artikel (pl) immer sehr gern.
4. Herr Ziegler sagt: Mein Bruder Alfred ist ein langweilig____ Mann. Er trägt immer einen teur____, grau____ Anzug und er fährt einen groß____, grau____ Mercedes.

3-11 Ein richtiger Gourmet. Supply the appropriate adjective endings. (Strukturen 6, p. 45)

Herr Ziegler sagt: Mein Bruder Alfred ist ein richtiger Gourmet. Gut____, französisch___ Rotwein (m) ist sehr teuer, aber Alfred verdient ja gut und er trinkt deshalb immer nur teur____, französisch____ Rotweine (pl). Bier trinkt er nicht oft, aber dann immer nur teur____, bayerisch____ Bier (n). Er kauft auch oft Kaviar. Russisch____ Kaviar (m) ist sehr teuer und sehr gut, aber Alfred findet iranisch____ Kaviar besser und kauft deshalb nur iranisch____ Kaviar. Er findet italienisch____ Oliven (pl) nicht so gut wie griechisch____, und deutsch____ Schokolade (f) nicht so gut wie belgisch____. Er kauft deshalb immer nur griechisch____ Oliven und teur____, belgisch____ Schokolade.

3-12 Immer negativ. Complete the negative responses to the questions below. (☞ Strukturen 7, p. 45)

1. > Gehst du jetzt nach Hause?

   < Nein, ich gehe jetzt nicht nach Hause, sondern in die Bibliothek.

2. > Verstehst du diesen Artikel?

   < Nein, ich verstehe ______________________________.

3. > Findest du dieses Buch interessant?

   < Nein, ich finde ______________________________.

4. > Kommst du heute Abend?

   < Nein, ich komme______________________________.

5. > Ist Günter heute Abend bei Tina?

   < Nein, er ist ______________________________, sondern bei Helga.

6. > Geht Claudia oft ins Kino?

   < Nein, sie geht ______________________________.

7. > Kennst du Stephanie?

   < Nein, ich kenne ______________________________.

8. > Wohnt ihr im Studentenheim?

   < Nein, wir wohnen ______________________________.

9. > Hast du einen Wagen?

   < Nein, ich habe ______________________________.

10. > Arbeitest du jeden Samstag?

    < Nein, ich arbeite ______________________________.

11. > Arbeitet Martin morgen?

    < Nein, er arbeitet ______________________________.

12. > Gehst du mit Bernd in die Disco?

    < Nein, ich gehe ______________________________, sondern mit Ralf.

3-13 Was passt zusammen? Match correctly by writing the appropriate number in the space provided. (☞ Strukturen 8, p. 46)

1.	Matthias liest	____ ein Bad.
2.	Bernd wäscht	____ gern Dokumentarfilme.
3.	Sylvia spricht	__1__ ein Buch.
4.	Stefan läuft	____ gern Schokolade.
5.	Martin isst	____ am Telefon.
6.	Angelika nimmt	____ seinen Wagen.
7.	Peter sieht	____ zum Bus.

3-14 Was passt zusammen? Match correctly by writing the appropriate number in the space provided. (☞ Strukturen 8, p. 46)

1.	Horst fährt	____ du die Katze nicht ins Haus, Robert?
2.	Claudia trägt	____ morgen ein Konzert.
3.	Warum lässt	____ Oma Ziegler morgen?
4.	Wie alt wird	____ sonntags immer bis zehn oder elf.
5.	Helga schläft	____ oft viel zu schnell.
6.	Unsere Rockgruppe gibt	____ der Bus hier nicht?
7.	Warum hält	____ gern schöne Kleider.

3-15 Kleine Gespräche. Complete the questions, using the correct forms of the appropriate verbs. (☞ Strukturen 8, p. 46)

werden / backen / lassen / sprechen

1. > Was für einen Kuchen ____bäckst____ du, Mutti?
   < Einen Apfelkuchen.

2. > Wann ____________________ ihr mit Professor Seidlmeyer?
   < Morgen Nachmittag um drei.

3. > Wie alt ____________________ Helga morgen?
   < Einundzwanzig.

4. > Warum ____________________ du Horst nie deinen Wagen fahren?
   < Er fährt viel zu schnell.

laufen / lesen / geben / fahren

5. > Was ____________________ du denn da?
   < Einen Artikel über Shakespeares *Romeo und Julia.*

6. > Was ____________________ es heute zu essen?
   < Spaghetti mit Tomatensoße.

7. > Was für einen Wagen ____________________ deine Freundin?
   < Einen Audi A4.

8. > Wohin ____________________ Martin?
   < Zum Bus.

schlafen / tragen / nehmen / sehen

9. > Warum ____________________ du denn keinen Kuchen, Anita?
   < Kuchen macht doch dick!

10. > Wann ____________________ du deinen Freund wieder?
    < Erst nächsten Sommer.

11. > ____________________ Monika immer so lang?
    < Nein, nur am Wochenende.

12. > Was ____________________ du zu Monikas Party?
    < Meinen schwarzen Rock und meinen neuen schwarzen Pullover.

NAME: ______________________ DATE: ______________

3-16 Das große Familienpicknick. Complete the following story using the correct forms of the appropriate verbs from the list preceding each paragraph. (☞ Strukturen 8, p. 46)

nehmen / fahren / tragen

Familie Ziegler __fährt__ heute zu Onkel Alfreds Wochenendhaus, denn dort ist heute – wie jeden Herbst – das große Familienpicknick. Robert ______________ seinen Fußball mit *(along)*, denn er und seine Vettern spielen bei Familienpicknicks immer stundenlang Fußball. Nina und Herr Ziegler ______________ das Essen, den Wein und Frau Zieglers Apfelstrudel zum Auto.

schlafen / werden / lesen / sehen / fahren

Im Auto ______________ Nina ein Buch, Robert ist müde *(tired)* und ______________, und beide ______________ deshalb die wunderbaren Herbstfarben nicht. Herr Ziegler ______________ wieder viel zu schnell und Frau Ziegler ______________ ganz nervös.

essen / lassen / sprechen / geben

Bei Onkel Alfreds Wochenendhaus ______________ Frau Ziegler dann noch ein paar Instruktionen:

„Nina, du ______________ bitte dein Buch im Auto. Robert, du ______________ nicht wieder so viel Apfelstrudel, und du, Klaus, du ______________ bitte nicht immer nur mit Onkel Alfred."

Zum Verstehen

3-17 Das ist Tina Hill. Mark is interviewing Tina. Tina's responses are given. Write Mark's questions.

MARK: Warum lernst du Deutsch, Tina?

TINA: Ich brauche es für mein Hauptfach *(major)*.

MARK: ______________________________?

TINA: Mein Hauptfach ist Philosophie.

MARK: ______________________________?

TINA: Nein, meine Eltern sprechen kein Wort Deutsch.

MARK: ______________________________?

TINA: Meine Mutter ist Fototechnikerin und mein Vater arbeitet für die Stadt.

MARK: ______________________________?

TINA: Ja, ich habe einen Bruder.

MARK: ______________________________?

TINA: Thomas ist sechsundzwanzig.

MARK: ______________________________?

TINA: Er ist Chemiker und er arbeitet bei Dupont.

MARK: ______________________________?

TINA: Ich lese gern und ich spiele oft mit David Scrabble.

MARK: ______________________________?

TINA: David ist mein Freund.

MARK: ______________________________?

TINA: Ja, er studiert Geographie.

3-18 Kathrin fliegt nach Amerika. Read the following narrative and then answer the questions.

Kathrin ist zwanzig Jahre alt und studiert in Marburg Physik. Im Juli ist das Sommersemester zu Ende und Kathrin packt dann gleich ihre Koffer und fährt nach Hannover, denn dort leben ihre Eltern und ihre Geschwister. Aber Kathrin bleibt nur wenige Tage und packt dann schon wieder ihre Koffer. Sie nimmt den ICE[1] nach Frankfurt und von dort die S-Bahn[2] zum Flughafen und fliegt nach Amerika.

Am Nachmittag landet Kathrins Flugzeug in Chicago. Dort wartet[3] auch schon ihr Onkel Gerd und sie fahren dann zusammen nach Milwaukee. Onkel Gerd ist der Bruder von Kathrins Vater. Er lebt schon viele Jahre in Amerika, ist Elektriker von Beruf und hat in Milwaukee ein kleines Elektrowarengeschäft. Onkel Gerd und Tante Ellen haben drei Kinder, zwei Töchter und einen Sohn. Kusine Lois ist zwei Monate jünger als Kathrin, Kusine Heather ist fünf Jahre jünger und Vetter Alex ist sechs Jahre älter. Lois studiert in Madison Soziologie, und sie lernt dort auch Deutsch, denn nächstes Jahr fliegt sie nach Deutschland und besucht dort Kathrin und Kathrins Familie. Jetzt im Sommer ist sie zu Hause, arbeitet in Onkel Gerds Geschäft und verdient Geld für ihr Studium.[4] Alex ist Ingenieur und lebt und arbeitet in Chicago, und Heather geht natürlich noch in die Schule. Tante Ellen ist Sozialarbeiterin und findet ihre Arbeit sehr interessant.

[1]InterCityExpress: *express train* [2]Schnellbahn: *fast commuter train* [3]*is waiting* [4]*studies*

Check the correct response to each of the following questions.

1. Wie viel älter ist Kathrin als ihre Kusine Heather?

   _____ zwei Monate _____ fünf Jahre _____ sechs Jahre

2. Was studiert Kathrins Kusine Lois?

   _____ Physik _____ Mathematik _____ Soziologie

3. Was ist Kathrins Vetter Alex von Beruf?

   _____ Sozialarbeiter _____ Ingenieur _____ Elektriker

4. Von Hannover nach Frankfurt nimmt Kathrin ...

   _____ die S-Bahn _____ ein Flugzeug _____ den ICE

5. Wo leben Kathrins Eltern?

   _____ in Marburg _____ in Frankfurt _____ in Hannover

6. Wo lebt Kathrins Kusine Lois im Winter?

   _____ in Madison _____ in Milwaukee _____ in Chicago

Zum Übersetzen

3-19 Kleine Gespräche.

1. HERR KAUL: Is that your car (*use* **Wagen**), Mr. Bürgli?

   HERR BÜRGLI: No, that's not my car. I don't have a car. I only have an old bicycle.

2. SOPHIA: How many siblings do you have?

   ANNE: I have one brother and two sisters.

3. FRAU BERG: How old is your daughter, Mr. Kuhn?

   HERR KUHN: Tomorrow she's going to be twenty.

4. OSMAN: We have a fine foods store. My whole family works there.

   STEFAN: What does your mother do there?

   OSMAN: She bakes fantastic cakes.

   STEFAN: And what do you do?

   OSMAN: I'm a sales clerk.

5. JULIA: I buy my clothes at **(bei)** Karstadt. Karstadt is an excellent department store.

   LISA: How are the prices there?

   JULIA: Not cheap but not too expensive either.

3-20 Mein Onkel Stefan.

Do you know my uncle Stefan? He's my favorite uncle. He's an auto mechanic by trade and he loves cars (*use* **Auto**). He drives an old Porsche and he likes to make old cars new again. Uncle Stefan likes to travel and his trips are never boring. He visits interesting countries and he also speaks many languages. Next year he's going to fly to Seattle. He's taking his mountain bike along **(mit)** and is going to ride into **(in)** the *Cascade Mountains.*

KAPITEL 4

Strukturen

Modifying the meaning of verbs: modal verbs

1. Modal verbs (☞ Übungen 4-1, 4-2, 4-3, 4-4, pp. 65–67)

Modal verbs modify the meaning of other verbs. The verbs modified by the modals appear in the infinitive form at the very end of the sentence.

Ich **muss** bessere Zensuren **bekommen.** — *I **have to get** better grades.*

können	*to be able to, to know how to, can*	**dürfen**	*to be allowed to, to be permitted to, may*
müssen	*to have to, must*	**mögen**	*to like*
wollen	*to want to*	**sollen**	*to be supposed to, should*

present tense of the modal verbs						
	können	müssen	wollen	dürfen	mögen	sollen
ich	kann	muss	will	darf	mag	soll
du	kannst	musst	willst	darfst	magst	sollst
er/es/sie	kann	muss	will	darf	mag	soll
wir	können	müssen	wollen	dürfen	mögen	sollen
ihr	könnt	müsst	wollt	dürft	mögt	sollt
sie/Sie	können	müssen	wollen	dürfen	mögen	sollen

- Except for **sollen,** all modals have a stem-vowel change in the **ich-, du-,** and **er/es/sie**-forms.
- The modals have no personal endings in the **ich**-form and the **er/es/sie**-form.
- When **können** is used to express mastery of a foreign language, it is not followed by an infinitive.

  Können Sie Deutsch? — ***Can** you speak German?*

- **Mögen** is usually used without an infinitive.

  Ich **mag** keinen Spinat. — *I don't **like** spinach.*

2. *Möchte* versus *mögen* (☞ Übungen 4-5, 4-6, pp. 68–69)

Ich **mag** Käsekuchen. — *I **like** cheesecake.*
Ich **möchte** ein Stück Käsekuchen. — *I **would like** a piece of cheesecake.*

Note that **ich möchte** is a more polite way of saying **ich will.**

singular		plural	
ich	möchte	wir	möchten
du	möchtest	ihr	möchtet
er/es/sie	möchte	sie	möchten
	Sie möchten		

3. Omission of the infinitive after modal verbs (☞ Übung 4-7, p. 70)

If the meaning of a sentence containing a modal is clear without an infinitive, the infinitive is often omitted.

Ich muss jetzt nach Hause. *I have to* **go** *home now.*

4. Position of *nicht* in sentences with modal verbs (☞ Übung 4-8, p. 70)

If no word or expression is specifically negated, **nicht** becomes the second-to-last element. It is placed directly before the infinitive, since the infinitive must stand at the end of the sentence.

Warum könnt ihr **nicht** kommen? *Why can't you come?*

Modifying the meaning of verbs: prefixes

5. Verbs with separable prefixes (☞ Übungen 4-9, 4-10, pp. 71–72)

Position of the separable prefix.

INFINITIVE:	**ausgehen**
PRESENT TENSE:	Ich **gehe** heute Abend **aus.**
WITH A MODAL:	Ich **möchte** heute Abend **ausgehen.**

Position of **nicht** (if no word or expression is specifically negated).

PRESENT TENSE:	Ich gehe heute Abend **nicht aus.**
WITH A MODAL:	Ich möchte heute Abend **nicht ausgehen.**

6. Verb-noun and verb-verb combinations (☞ Übung 4-11, p. 73)

Some verbs are so closely associated with a noun or another verb that they function like separable-prefix verbs.

Position of the noun or second verb in the combination.

INFINITIVE:	**Tennis spielen; windsurfen gehen**
PRESENT TENSE:	Peter **spielt** heute Nachmittag **Tennis.**
	Martin **geht** heute Nachmittag **windsurfen.**
WITH A MODAL:	Peter **möchte** heute Nachmittag **Tennis spielen.**
	Martin **möchte** heute Nachmittag **windsurfen gehen.**

Position of **nicht** (if no word or expression is specifically negated).

PRESENT TENSE:	Warum spielst du heute **nicht Tennis,** Peter?
WITH A MODAL:	Warum kannst du heute **nicht windsurfen gehen,** Martin?

Expressing commands and requests

7. Imperatives (☞ Übungen 4-12, 4-13, 4-14, 4-15, pp. 74–76)

German has three forms of address **(du, ihr, Sie)** and consequently it has three imperative forms.

	du-imperative	**ihr**-imperative	**Sie**-imperative
most verbs	Komm!	Kommt!	Kommen Sie!
verbs with stem vowel change **e → i (ie)**	Sprich! Lies!	Sprecht! Lest!	Sprechen Sie! Lesen Sie!
verbs with stem ending in **-d** or **-t**	Antworte!	Antwortet!	Antworten Sie!
separable-prefix verbs	Komm mit!	Kommt mit!	Kommen Sie mit!
sein	Sei!	Seid!	Seien Sie!

Word order

8. Position of the verb in independent and dependent clauses

Coordinating conjunctions (☞ Übung 4-16, p. 77)

Coordinating conjunctions connect independent clauses, i.e., clauses that can stand alone as complete sentences.

und	*and*	**aber**	*but*
denn	*because, for*	**sondern**	*but (rather), but (. . . instead)*
oder	*or*		

Coordinating conjunctions do not affect the position of the verb.

independent clause	conjunction	independent clause
Bernd hat endlich ein Zimmer	**und**	es kostet nur 150 Euro im Monat.
Es ist nur ein kleines Zimmer,	**aber**	es ist groß genug für Bernd.
Bernd geht nicht zu Fuß zur Uni,	**sondern**	er nimmt den Bus.

- The conjunctions **aber** and **sondern** are always preceded by a comma.
- The clause preceding **sondern** states what is *not* happening. The clause following **sondern** states what is happening *instead.*

Subordinating conjunctions (☞ Übungen 4-17, 4-18, pp. 78–79)

Subordinating conjunctions introduce dependent clauses, i.e., clauses that make sense only in connection with an independent clause.

bis	*until*	**sobald**	*as soon as*
bevor	*before*	**weil**	*because*
damit	*so that*	**wenn**	*if; when*
obwohl	*although; even though*		

Subordinating conjunctions affect the position of the verb: the verb stands at the end of the clause.

independent clause	dependent clause
Bernd möchte das Zimmer,	**weil** es sehr schön und sehr preisgünstig **ist.**
Er möchte das Zimmer,	**obwohl** es von dort zur Uni sehr weit **ist.**

In clauses introduced by a subordinating conjunction, modal verbs appear at the end of the clause and separable-prefix verbs are not separated.

independent clause	dependent clause
Bernd möchte einen Wagen,	**damit** er nicht stundenlang Bus fahren **muss.**
Er möchte einen Wagen,	**weil** seine Vorlesungen oft sehr früh **anfangen.**

 A dependent clause is always separated from the independent clause by a comma.

Dependent clause preceding independent clause (☞ Übung 4-19, p. 79)

dependent clause	independent clause
Bevor ich **aufstehe,**	**sehe** ich meistens eine halbe Stunde **fern.**
Wenn du fit bleiben **willst,**	**musst** du viel mehr Sport machen.

 The conjugated verbs of both clauses appear side by side, separated by a comma.

NAME: ______________________________ DATE: ______________

Anwendung

Übungen

4-1 Ergänzen Sie. Rewrite, correctly inserting the modals and the modified verbs given. Do not rearrange the items in the sentence fragments. Capitalize wherever necessary. (☞ Strukturen 1, p. 61)

1. wollen / studieren: Tanja nächstes Jahr in Berlin.

   Tanja will nächstes Jahr in Berlin studieren.

2. müssen / arbeiten: du morgen?

   ____

3. können / kochen: Kurt sehr gut.

   ____

4. mögen: du Wiener Schnitzel?

   ____

5. dürfen / trinken: warum Sie denn keinen Kaffee

   ______________________________, Frau Borg?

6. sollen / regnen: morgen es.

   ____

7. wollen / sprechen: warum du mit Professor Weber?

   ____

8. können / waschen: ihr bitte meinen Wagen?

   ____

9. mögen: ihr eure neue Professorin?

   ____

10. dürfen / fahren: du immer noch nicht Auto?

    ____

4-2 Kleine Gespräche. Complete with the correct forms of the appropriate modal verbs. (☞ Strukturen 1, p. 61)

mögen / dürfen

1. > Warum _darf_ deine Schwester heute Abend nicht tanzen gehen?

   < Meine Eltern _mögen_ ihren Freund nicht.

müssen / sollen

2. > Warum ______________ du denn schon gehen?

   < Ich ______________ in zehn Minuten bei Professor Seidlmeyer sein.

wollen / mögen

3. > Warum ______________ du denn kein Bier?

   < Ich ______________ kein Bier. Es ist so bitter.

sollen / können

4. > Morgen ______________ es sehr heiß werden.

   < Toll! Dann ______________ wir schwimmen gehen.

wollen / dürfen

5. > Warum ______________ du denn keinen Wein?

   < Ich ______________ keinen Alkohol trinken.

wollen / können

6. > ______________ Maria Deutsch?

   < Nein, aber sie ______________ es lernen.

können / müssen

7. > Warum ______________ du heute Abend nicht tanzen gehen?

   < Ich ______________ Deutsch lernen.

NAME: ______________________________ DATE: ______________

4-3 Was passt zusammen? *a.* Complete the questions and responses with the correct verb forms. *b.* Mark the appropriate response to each question by writing the number in the space provided. (☞ Strukturen 1, p. 61)

1.	lernen:	Warum __________ du Deutsch?	____ können:	Ich __________ kein Spanisch.
2.	kaufen:	Warum __________ du ein Fahrrad?	____ müssen:	Ich __________ ein Referat schreiben.
3.	fliegen:	Warum __________ Sie nicht nach Peru, Frau Borg?	____ sollen:	Ich __________ mehr Sport machen.
4.	gehen:	Warum __________ du in die Bibliothek?	____ wollen:	Ich __________ nächstes Jahr in Berlin studieren.

4-4 Was passt zusammen? *a.* Complete the questions and responses with the correct verb forms. *b.* Mark the appropriate response to each question by writing the number in the space provided. (☞ Strukturen 1, p. 61)

1.	trinken:	Warum __________ Sie denn keinen Wein, Herr Kohl?	____ mögen:	Ich __________ seine Freunde nicht.
2.	arbeiten:	Warum __________ du so oft im Supermarkt?	____ dürfen:	Ich __________ keinen Alkohol trinken.
3.	nehmen:	Warum __________ Sie keinen Nachtisch, Frau Haag?	____ wollen:	Ich __________ einen Wagen kaufen.
4.	gehen:	Warum __________ du nicht auf Günters Party?	____ sollen:	Ich __________ nicht so viel essen.

4-5 ***Möcht- versus mögen.*** Supply **mögen** or **möcht-** appropriately, so that sentence *b* has approximately the same meaning as sentence *a.* (Strukturen 2, p. 61)

1. a. Willst du ein Stück Schokolade?

   b. Möchtest ____________________ du ein Stück Schokolade?

2. a. Ich esse gern Schokolade.

   b. Ich ____________________ Schokolade.

3. a. Habt ihr eure neue Professorin gern?

   b. ____________________ ihr eure neue Professorin?

4. a. Was wollt ihr heute Abend essen?

   b. Was ____________________ ihr heute Abend essen?

5. a. Mein kleiner Bruder will jetzt auch ein Fahrrad.

   b. Mein kleiner Bruder ____________________ jetzt auch ein Fahrrad.

6. a. Ich trinke Mineralwasser lieber als Cola.

   b. Ich ____________________ Mineralwasser lieber als Cola.

7. a. Wollt ihr lieber einen Hund oder eine Katze?

   b. ____________________ ihr lieber einen Hund oder eine Katze?

8. a. Ich habe Hunde viel lieber als Katzen.

   b. Ich ____________________ Hunde viel lieber als Katzen.

NAME: ______________________________ **DATE:** ______________

4-6 Kleine Gespräche. Complete these short conversations, using appropriate modal verbs from the choices given. (☞ Strukturen 1 & 2, p. 61)

dürfen / können / mögen / müssen

1. > Warum machst du denn dein tolles Chili con carne nie mehr, Bettina? Ich mag es doch so gern.

   < Mein Chili con carne? Das braucht viel zu viel Zeit. Aber du ______________ es gern selbst kochen.

   > Ich? Ich ______________ doch nicht kochen.

   < Dann ______________ du es so schnell wie möglich lernen.

wollen / mögen / können

2. > Warum ______________ du denn deine Mitbewohnerin nicht, Monika?

   < Brigitte ______________ immer laute Musik hören und ich ______________ deshalb nie richtig lernen.

dürfen / wollen / mögen

3. > Warum ______________ du denn deine Mitbewohnerin nicht, Brigitte?

   < Monika ______________ immer nur lernen und ich ______________ deshalb nie laute Musik hören.

können (2x) / müssen (2x) / möcht-

4. > Gehst du heute Abend auch tanzen, Claudia?

   < Ich ______________ gern, aber ich ______________ nicht. Ich ______________ bis morgen zwei Bücher lesen. ______________ ihr denn nicht morgen Abend tanzen gehen?

   > Nein, morgen Abend ______________ wir für eine Klausur in Mathe lernen.

müssen / dürfen (2x) / möcht- (2x)

5. > ______________ wir heute Abend fernsehen, Mutti?

   < Was ______________ ihr denn sehen?

   > Zuerst ______________ wir *Star Trek* sehen und dann die *Simpsons.*

   < Das ______________ ihr, aber zuerst ______________ ihr eure Hausaufgaben machen.

möcht- / sollen (2x)

6. > Was ______________ wir heute Abend machen? ______________ wir in die Kneipe gehen oder ins Kino?

   < Ich ______________ heute lieber mal früh ins Bett.

4-7 Ergänzen Sie. Supply the correct form of the appropriate modal. (Strukturen 3, p. 62)

1. können / mögen: ___Magst___ du Brokkoli?
2. dürfen / wollen: ________ ich heute Abend in die Disco, Mutti?
3. möcht- / müssen: ________ Sie Kaffee oder Tee?
4. sollen / mögen: Wann ________ die Kinder ins Bett?
5. mögen / müssen: Ich ________ jetzt in die Vorlesung.
6. können / möcht-: Herr Ziegler ________ sehr gut Italienisch.
7. müssen / mögen: Wen ________ du lieber, Martin oder Peter?
8. wollen / mögen: Warum ________ ihr denn schon nach Hause?

4-8 Immer negativ. Complete the responses. (Strukturen 4, p. 62)

1. > Wollen deine Eltern das Haus kaufen?

   < Nein, sie ___wollen das Haus nicht kaufen___.

2. > Möchtest du tanzen?

   < Nein, ich ________________________.

3. > Mögt ihr das Schnitzel?

   < Nein, wir ________________________.

4. > Müsst ihr heute in die Vorlesung?

   < Nein, wir ________________________.

5. > Müsst ihr jeden Tag in die Vorlesung?

   < Nein, wir ________________________.

6. > Können Zieglers morgen Abend kommen?

   < Nein, Zieglers ________________________.

7. > Möchtest du in Wien studieren?

   < Nein, ich ________________________.

8. > Dürfen wir heute Abend ins Kino, Mutti?

   < Nein, Kinder, ihr ________________________.

NAME: ______________________ **DATE:** ______________

4-9 Am Mittwoch hat Günter so viel zu tun! Using the separable-prefix verbs given in parentheses, complete the story about Günter and his relationship to Helga and Tina. (Strukturen 5, p. 62)

Mittwochs ___fangen___ Günters Vorlesungen schon um acht ___an___ (anfangen) und er muss deshalb schon um sieben ___aufstehen___ (aufstehen) und um halb acht ___weggehen___ (weggehen). Um zwölf isst Günter zu Mittag und um halb eins ______________ er dann mit seiner Freundin **Helga** ______________ (spazieren gehen). Kurz vor drei ______________ **Helga** und Günter wieder ______________ (zurückkommen), denn Günters Übung in Botanik ______________ Punkt drei ______________ (anfangen). Die Botanikübung geht bis halb sechs und so ______________ Günter mittwochs erst um sechs ______________ (heimkommen). Er isst schnell zu Abend, ______________ dann **Helga** ______________ (anrufen) und sagt: „Ich gehe jetzt in die Bibliothek und lerne dort bis zwölf Uhr nachts."

Tina muss mittwochs nicht früh ______________ (aufstehen), denn ihre erste Vorlesung ______________ erst nachmittags um halb zwei ______________ (anfangen). Um zehn oder halb elf geht sie meistens zum Supermarkt und manchmal ______________ sie erst kurz vor eins ______________ (zurückkommen). Zehn nach eins muss sie ______________ (weggehen), denn der Bus zur Uni ______________ Punkt ein Uhr zwanzig ______________ (abfahren). **Tinas** letzte Vorlesung ist um halb sieben zu Ende. Sie ______________ dann schnell ______________ (heimgehen) und macht ein gutes Abendessen. Um halb acht kommt dann ihr Freund Günter, denn mittwochs ______________ **Tina** und Günter immer abends miteinander ______________ (ausgehen).

4-10 Fragen und Antworten. Write questions using the components correctly. Then choose the appropriate responses from those listed below by writing the numbers of the questions in the spaces provided. (Strukturen 5, p. 62)

1. Sie / einkaufen / auch so gern / bei A&P / Frau Schürer / ?

   Kaufen Sie auch so gern bei A&P ein, Frau Schürer?

2. warum / ich / dürfen / fernsehen / denn nicht / Mutti / ?

   ____

3. du / aufstehen / immer so spät / ?

   ____

4. was / du / vorhaben / nächstes Wochenende / ?

   ____

5. wie / Tinas neuer Freund / aussehen / ?

   ____

6. du / können / aufräumen / nicht mal ein bisschen / Claudia / ?

   ____

7. um wie viel Uhr / Sie / ankommen / in Frankfurt / Herr O'Brien / ?

   ____

8. warum / ihr / ausgehen / heute Abend / nicht / ?

   ____

9. wann / das Wintersemester / anfangen / in Deutschland / ?

   ____

10. dürfen / ich / anprobieren / das Kleid / ?

    ____

ANTWORTEN:

_____ Du hast zu viele Hausaufgaben.

_____ Nein, nur am Wochenende.

_____ Ja, bitte.

_____ Morgens um halb sieben.

_____ Da besuche ich meinen Freund.

_____ Mitte Oktober.

_____ Er ist groß und schlank.

_____ Wir müssen lernen.

_____ Ja, das Gemüse ist dort so frisch.

_____ Klar! Aber nicht heute.

NAME: ________________________ DATE: ______________

4-11 Stefan ist sehr musikalisch und sehr sportlich. The check marks in the chart show which instruments Stefan plays and which sports he does. Answer the questions about Stefan in complete sentences. (Strukturen 6, p. 62)

INSTRUMENTE		SPORTARTEN	
___	Flöte	✓	Ski
___	Saxophon	___	wandern
___	Trompete	✓	Motorrad
✓	Gitarre	✓	windsurfen
✓	Klavier	___	Fußball
___	Cello	✓	Eishockey

1. Läuft Stefan Ski?

   Ja, er läuft Ski.

2. Kann Stefan Flöte spielen?

   Nein, er kann nicht Flöte spielen.

3. Spielt Stefan Gitarre?

   ____

4. Geht Stefan windsurfen?

   ____

5. Kann Stefan Trompete spielen?

   ____

6. Kann Stefan Klavier spielen?

   ____

7. Spielt Stefan Eishockey?

   ____

8. Geht Stefan wandern?

   ____

9. Fährt Stefan Motorrad?

   ____

10. Spielt Stefan Saxophon?

    ____

4-12 Eltern. David is about to go off to university and his parents give him last-minute instructions. Using appropriate verbs, write these instructions in the form of commands. (☞ Strukturen 7, p. 63)

mit·nehmen / aus·geben / vergessen / schreiben / auf·stehen

1. nicht so viel Geld für Bier

   VATI: Gib nicht so viel Geld für Bier aus!

2. uns bitte jede Woche eine E-Mail

   MUTTI: ______________________________

3. dein Adressbuch nicht

   VATI: ______________________________

4. auch warme Kleider

   MUTTI: ______________________________

5. morgens nicht immer so spät

   VATI: ______________________________

sitzen / waschen / sein / auf·räumen / essen

6. auch jeden Morgen ein gutes Frühstück

   MUTTI: ______________________________

7. ja nie weiße Hemden zusammen mit Jeans

   MUTTI: ______________________________

8. bitte nicht den ganzen Tag vor dem Fernseher

   VATI: ______________________________

9. auch manchmal dein Zimmer

   MUTTI: ______________________________

10. bitte nie so taktlos wie hier zu Hause

    VATI: ______________________________

NAME: ______________________ DATE: ______________

4-13 Auf Wiedersehen! You are in the driveway saying good-bye to friends who have spent the weekend with you. Use the appropriate words in the imperative to give final words of farewell. (☞Strukturen 7, p. 63)

kommen / grüßen / wieder·kommen / haben / schreiben / fahren

1. vielen Dank für euren Besuch

   Habt vielen Dank für euren Besuch!

2. bitte nicht zu schnell

   ____

3. gut nach Frankfurt

   ____

4. bitte gleich eine E-Mail, wenn ihr heimkommt

   ____

5. auch alle meine Freunde in Frankfurt

   ____

6. bald mal

   ____

4-14 Eine Fahrstunde. Paula Berg is having a driving lesson. Say what her driving instructor tells her to do by adding the imperative forms of the appropriate verbs. (☞Strukturen 7, p. 63)

fahren / auf·passen / sein / parken / nehmen

1. doch besser, Frau Berg

   Passen Sie doch besser auf, Frau Berg!

2. doch nicht so nervös

   ____

3. doch nicht so schnell

   ____

4. bitte den Fuß vom Gas

   ____

5. bitte dort vor dem blauen BMW

   ____

4-15 Kleine Szenen. After reading each of the following scenarios, write three commands by matching the verbs and the other components appropriately. Be sure to use the proper level of address. (☞ Strukturen 7, p. 63)

1. You are the parent of two teenagers who are going to a party tonight. When they are about to leave, you say:

trinken	bitte nicht so viel Junkfood
sein	ja keinen Alkohol
essen	bitte vor Mitternacht zu Hause

Trinkt ja keinen Alkohol!

____

____

2. The student with whom you are sharing an apartment is terribly sloppy. Today you have had enough. Since you know that she/he will be home before you, you write the following requests on a piece of paper:

auf·räumen	heute bitte mal dein Bett
machen	doch endlich mal dein Zimmer
auf·hängen	bitte deine Kleider

____

____

____

3. You are a German professor and you ask your class to do the following:

sprechen	diesen Artikel bis morgen bitte
durch·lesen	bitte gut
zu·hören	doch bitte ein bisschen lauter

____

____

____

NAME: ______________________________ DATE: ____________________

4-16 ***Und, oder, aber, sondern, denn?*** Supply the appropriate conjunctions.
(Strukturen 8, p. 63)

1. Gehst du heute Abend tanzen ______________ musst du lernen?
2. Ich möchte gern tanzen gehen, ______________ ich muss noch stundenlang lernen.
3. Ich kann heute nicht tanzen gehen, ______________ ich muss noch stundenlang lernen.
4. Wir gehen heute Abend nicht in die Disco, ______________ ins Konzert.
5. Wann fährst du nach Zürich ______________ wen besuchst du dort?
6. Ich fahre nicht nach Zürich, ______________ nach Bern, ______________ meine Freunde leben jetzt in Bern.
7. Ich habe einen Wagen, ______________ nach Bern nehme ich lieber den Zug.
8. Ich nehme den Zug, ______________ im Zug kann ich lesen oder schlafen.
9. Ich komme um 18.30 in Bern an ______________ nehme dann ein Taxi.
10. > Möchtest du lieber den Pulli ______________ die Jacke?

    < Ich möchte den Pulli ______________ die Jacke!

4-17 ***Damit, weil* oder *wenn?*** Of the two responses given, select the appropriate one and introduce it with **damit, weil,** or **wenn.** (Strukturen 8, p. 64)

1. > Warum stehst du denn so früh auf, Florian?

   < Damit ich noch joggen gehen kann.

Ich kann noch joggen gehen. / Ich kann nicht joggen gehen.

2. > Warum frühstückt Eva nie?

   < ____

Sie steht immer zu früh auf. / Sie steht immer zu spät auf.

3. > Kommt Peter heute Abend?

   < ____

Er muss nicht arbeiten. / Er muss arbeiten.

4. > Warum kauft Bernd einen Wagen?

   < ____

Er muss nicht mehr Bus fahren. / Er muss mehr Bus fahren.

5. > Wann gehst du nach Hause?

   < ____

Meine letzte Vorlesung fängt an. / Meine letzte Vorlesung ist zu Ende.

6. > Warum arbeitet Paul den ganzen Sommer?

   < ____

Er kann im Herbst nicht weiterstudieren. / Er kann im Herbst weiterstudieren.

7. > Warum kaufst du das Fahrrad nicht?

   < ____

Ich habe nicht genug Geld. / Ich habe zu viel Geld.

NAME: ______________________ DATE: ______________

4-18 Was ist die richtige Konjunktion? Connect the clauses in the sentences below with the most appropriate conjunction. (☞Strukturen 8, p. 64)

sobald / obwohl / bis

1. Ich muss hier bleiben, ______________ Anna nach Hause kommt.
2. Ich kann gehen, ______________ Anna zu Hause ist.
3. Ich muss jetzt gehen, ______________ Anna immer noch nicht zu Hause ist.

obwohl / bevor / sobald

4. Bernd will den Wagen nicht kaufen, ______________ der Scheck von seinen Eltern kommt.
5. Bernd will den Wagen kaufen, ______________ der Scheck von seinen Eltern hier ist.
6. Aber dann kauft Bernd den Wagen, ______________ der Scheck von seinen Eltern immer noch nicht hier ist.

4-19 Sagen Sie es anders! Combine the two sentences into a single sentence that begins with the dependent clause. (☞Strukturen 8, p. 64)

1. Ich komme in Frankfurt an. Ich rufe gleich meine Kusine an.

   Wenn ich in Frankfurt ankomme, rufe ich gleich meine Kusine an.
2. Kurt hat genug Geld. Er will einen Wagen kaufen.

   Sobald ______________________________
3. Du gehst weg. Du musst dein Zimmer aufräumen.

   Bevor ______________________________
4. Du gehst immer so spät ins Bett. Du wirst krank.

   Wenn ______________________________
5. Sein Wagen ist kaputt. Bernd nimmt den Bus.

   Weil ______________________________
6. Claudia hat Fieber. Sie geht nicht zum Arzt.

   Obwohl ______________________________

Zum Verstehen

4-20 Assoziationen. Choose the appropriate words from the list to complete the associations in the word sets.

die Vorlesung / lesen / die Schüssel / der Nachtisch / spielen das Glas / die Bibliothek / trinken / die Scheibe / fahren

1. der Tee - die Tasse
   die Milch - das Glas
2. das Gemüse - essen
   der Kaffee - trinken
3. der Toast - das Frühstück
   das Eis - ____________
4. der Kuchen - das Stück
   das Brot - ____________
5. essen - die Mensa
   lesen - ____________
6. die E-Mail - schreiben
   die Zeitung - ____________
7. die CD - hören
   die Gitarre - ____________
8. das Flugzeug - fliegen
   der Zug - ____________
9. der Bäcker - das Brot
   der Professor - ____________
10. der Jogurt - der Becher
    das Müsli - ____________

4-21 Ein schwieriger Gast. Julia finds that her uncle Gerd is a house guest who is hard to please. Reconstruct her pre-breakfast conversation with her uncle by numbering the exchanges appropriately.

___ GERD: Aber Tee mag ich doch nicht.

___ JULIA: Du kannst morgens nicht so viel essen? Warum denn nicht?

___ JULIA: Und Milch? Magst du Milch?

___ GERD: Nein danke, Julia. Ich darf keinen Kaffee trinken.

1 JULIA: Und was möchtest du essen? Ein Ei und ein paar Scheiben Toast?

___ JULIA: Möchtest du Kaffee zum Frühstück, Onkel Gerd?

___ GERD: Ich will nicht dick werden.

___ GERD: Ja, ein Glas Milch trinke ich gern.

___ JULIA: Dann mache ich Tee.

___ GERD: Kein Ei, bitte, und nur *eine* Scheibe Toast. Ich kann morgens nicht so viel essen.

NAME: ______________________________________ DATE: ________________

4-22 Beate Fischer. Read the narrative below and then answer the questions.

Beate Fischer ist siebzehn und sie geht noch aufs Gymnasium. Sie ist eine gute Schülerin, besonders in Englisch und in Französisch. Englisch kann sie aber noch besser als Französisch, weil sie als Austauschschülerin[1] ein ganzes Jahr in Amerika war. Beate will später Dolmetscherin[2] werden, weil das ein sehr interessanter Beruf ist und weil es in Europa für Dolmetscher viel Arbeit gibt.

Heute Nachmittag hat Beate keine Schule und ist schon um eins zu Hause. Sie isst schnell zu Mittag und geht dann in die Stadtbibliothek, denn morgen soll sie im Englischkurs über die amerikanische Europapolitik sprechen, und das natürlich[3] auf Englisch. Die Stadtbibliothek hat gute amerikanische Zeitungen und Beate liest dort den ganzen Nachmittag und macht Notizen für ihr Referat.

Beates Eltern kommen heute schon früh nach Hause und gehen beide gleich in die Küche[4]. Dort macht Herr Fischer das Abendessen. Es gibt Spaghetti mit Tomatensoße, weil die Tomatensoße schon fertig ist. Frau Fischer hat viel mehr zu tun. Sie bäckt einen Apfelkuchen und eine Schwarzwälder Kirschtorte, denn morgen hat Beate Geburtstag.

Um sechs kommt Beate nach Hause. Sie will schnell essen und dann ihr Referat fertig schreiben, aber da klingelt[5] das Telefon. Es ist David, ihr Freund. Er möchte heute Abend mit Beate ins Kino, aber sie kann heute natürlich nicht.

„Warum gehen wir nicht morgen, David?“ fragt sie, „übermorgen habe ich kein Referat und übrigens ist morgen ein ganz besonderer Tag.“ „Ein ganz besonderer Tag?“ fragt David. „Du vergisst auch alles, David! Ich werde doch morgen achtzehn!“

[1]als ... : *as an exchange student* [2]*interpreter* [3]*of course* [4]*kitchen* [5]*rings*

Write **R** in the appropriate spaces to indicate which of the three responses to each of the following questions are **richtig.** Note that a question can have more than one correct response.

1. Ist Beate Studentin?
   _____ a. Nein, sie ist Schülerin.
   _____ b. Nein, sie ist Dolmetscherin.
   _____ c. Nein, sie geht noch aufs Gymnasium.
2. Warum kann Beate so gut Englisch?
   _____ a. Sie ist Dolmetscherin.
   _____ b. Sie geht oft in die Stadtbibliothek.
   _____ c. Sie war ein ganzes Jahr in Amerika.
3. Was machen Beates Eltern, sobald sie zu Hause sind?
   _____ a. Ihre Mutter kocht und ihr Vater bäckt.
   _____ b. Sie kochen und backen.
   _____ c. Ihre Mutter bäckt und ihr Vater kocht.

4. Warum geht Beate in die Stadtbibliothek?

_____ a. Sie braucht Informationen für ihr Referat.

_____ b. Die Stadtbibliothek hat gute amerikanische Zeitungen.

_____ c. Sie muss morgen im Englischkurs über die amerikanische Europapolitik sprechen.

5. Warum kann Beate heute Abend nicht ins Kino?

_____ a. Sie wird morgen achtzehn.

_____ b. Sie hat übermorgen ein Referat.

_____ c. Sie muss ihr Referat fertig schreiben.

Zum Übersetzen

4-23 Kleine Gespräche.

1. MARTIN: Should we go dancing tonight?

   CLAUDIA: I can't. I have to finish writing my report.

2. TOM: Why do you want to sell your car, Ralf?

   RALF: I don't want to, I have to. I need money.

3. KATHRIN: What are you eating for dessert? Ice cream or a piece of cake?

   MARTINA: I prefer to eat fruit. I'd like to stay slim.

4. PAUL: Why don't you take any sausage?

   DAVID: Because I'm not allowed to eat meat.

5. ANNE: Will you be at home this afternoon?

   KEVIN: No, today I'm not coming home until seven-thirty. *(Use colloquial time.)*

6. FLORIAN: Do you always watch so much TV?

   TINA: No, only on the weekend.

4-24 Lebensgewohnheiten.

Lukas is very fit, and because he wants to stay fit, he always gets up early and goes jogging. When he has time, he also goes cycling. But he doesn't just do sports. He eats very little meat, but a lot of fruit and fresh vegetables. For breakfast he doesn't eat cheese, sausage, and eggs, but a big bowl of muesli. Because Lukas lives so healthy, he also looks **(aus·sehen)** very healthy.

KAPITEL 5

Strukturen

Talking about persons or things without naming them

1. Personal pronouns in the accusative case (☞ Übungen 5-1, 5-2, 5-3, pp. 87–89)

personal pronouns							
NOMINATIVE				ACCUSATIVE			
ich	*I*	**wir**	*we*	**mich**	*me*	**uns**	*us*
du	*you*	**ihr**	*you*	**dich**	*you*	**euch**	*you*
er	*he, it*			**ihn**	*him, it*		
es	*it*	**sie**	*they*	**es**	*it*	**sie**	*them*
sie	*she, it*			**sie**	*her, it*		
Sie	*you*			**Sie**	*you*		

Expressing direction, destination, time, manner, and place

2. Accusative prepositions (☞ Übungen 5-4, 5-5, 5-6, pp. 90–91)

durch	*through*	Nächsten Sommer möchte ich mit David **durch die Schweiz** reisen.
für	*for*	**Für wen** sind diese Reisebroschüren, **für mich?**
gegen	*against*	Meine Eltern haben nichts **gegen diese Reise.**
	around	Morgen planen wir die Reise. Ich komme **gegen zwei.**
ohne	*without*	Mach ja keine Pläne **ohne mich!**
um	*at*	**Um acht** läuft beim Studentenwerk ein Dokumentarfilm über die Schweiz.
	around	Das Studentenwerk ist **um die nächste Ecke.**

- There are two German equivalents for *around:*

gegen	*around (in a temporal sense)*	**gegen** zwei
um	*around (in a spatial sense)*	**um** die Ecke

- In colloquial German the prepositions **durch, für,** and **um** are often contracted with the article **das: durchs, fürs, ums.**

3. *Dafür* and *dagegen* (☞ Übung 5-7, p. 91)

The German equivalents of the prepositional phrases *for it* and *against it* are **dafür** and **dagegen.**

HERR ZIEGLER:	Wer ist fürs Campen am Grundlsee?	*Who is for going camping at the Grundlsee?*
KINDER:	Wir sind **dafür.**	*We are **for it.***
FRAU ZIEGLER:	Und ich bin **dagegen.**	*And I'm **against it.***

Making comparisons

4. The comparative of adjectives and adverbs (☞ Übungen 5-8, 5-9, pp. 92–93)

The comparative of *all* adjectives and adverbs is formed by adding **-er** to the base form. The German equivalent of *than* is **als.**

Paul ist **kleiner als** Bernd.	*Paul is* ***shorter than*** *Bernd.*
Bernd ist **sportlicher als** Paul.	*Bernd is* ***more athletic than*** *Paul.*

For many adjectives and adverbs of more than one syllable, English uses *more* to form the comparative. German never uses **mehr.**

Most German one-syllable adjectives or adverbs with the vowels **a, o,** or **u** are umlauted in the comparative.

BASE FORM	COMPARATIVE	
warm	wärm**er**	*warmer*
oft	öft**er**	*more often*
jung	jüng**er**	*younger*

As in English, a few adjectives and adverbs have irregular comparative forms.

gut	**besser**	*better*
viel	**mehr**	*more*
hoch	**höher**	*higher*
gern	**lieber**	

Remember that the meaning of **lieber** depends on its context:

Ich esse Äpfel **lieber** als Birnen.	*I like apples better than pears. (I prefer apples to pears.)*

Adjectives or adverbs ending in **-er** or **-el** drop the **e** in the comparative.

teuer	**teurer**	*more expensive*
dunkel	**dunkler**	*darker*

Adjectives in the comparative that precede nouns take adjective endings.

Florian hat einen schneller**en** Wagen als Stefan.

5. The superlative of adjectives and adverbs (☞ Übung 5-10, p. 94)

- Unless the superlative precedes a noun, it is formed by using the pattern **am _____(e)sten.**
- An **e** is added before the **st** if the base adjective or adverb ends in **-d, -t,** an **s**-sound, a vowel, or a vowel plus **h**.
- Most one-syllable adjectives or adverbs with the stem vowels **a, o,** or **u** are umlauted in the superlative.

⚠ For many adjectives and adverbs of more than one syllable, English uses *most* to form the superlative. German uses the pattern **am _____(e)sten** with *all* adjectives and adverbs.

BASE FORM	COMPARATIVE	SUPERLATIVE	
schnell	schneller	**am** schnell**sten**	*fastest*
kalt	kälter	**am** kält**esten**	*coldest*
heiß	heißer	**am** heiß**esten**	*hottest*
neu	neuer	**am** neu**esten**	*newest*
früh	früher	**am** früh**esten**	*earliest*
interessant	interessanter	**am** interessant**esten**	*most interesting*

A few adjectives and adverbs have irregular superlative forms.

gut	besser	**am besten**	*best*
viel	mehr	**am meisten**	*most*
groß	größer	**am größten**	*largest*
hoch	höher	**am höchsten**	*highest*
gern	lieber	**am liebsten**	

 Remember that the meaning of **am liebsten** depends on its context:

Was isst du **am liebsten?** — *What's your favorite food?*

6. An adjective in the superlative before a noun (☞ Übungen 5-11, 5-12, pp. 94–95)

If an adjective in the superlative precedes a noun, it does not use the pattern **am _____(e)sten.** It takes the ending **-(e)st** plus an adjective ending. Remember that the adjective takes an ending even if the noun to which it refers is not repeated.

David hat den neu**esten** Computer, aber Lauras Computer ist immer noch der schnell**ste.** — *David has the latest computer, but Laura's computer is still the fastest one.*

Word order

7. Object clauses introduced by *dass* (☞ Übung 5-13, p. 97)

The object of a verb can be a clause. Object clauses introduced by the conjunction **dass** *(that)* are dependent clauses. The conjugated verb appears at the end of the clause.

Ich hoffe, ***dass* du bald einen guten Job *findest.***

8. Questions as object clauses (☞ Übung 5-14, p. 98)

Questions that are introduced by phrases like **Könnten Sie mir bitte sagen, … ?** or **Weißt du, …** are object clauses. The conjugated verb appears at the end of the clause.

INFORMATION QUESTION: Könnten Sie mir bitte sagen, ***wann* das Konzert heute Abend *anfängt?***
YES/NO QUESTION: Weißt du, ***ob* wir morgen eine Klausur *schreiben?***

⚠ If a yes/no question is an object clause, it is introduced by the conjunction **ob** *(whether).*

Talking about what and whom you know

9. The verb *wissen* (☞ Übung 5-15, p. 99)

The present tense of **wissen** *(to know)* is irregular in the singular.

singular		plural	
ich	**weiß**	wir	wissen
du	**weißt**	ihr	wisst
er/es/sie	**weiß**	sie	wissen
	Sie wissen		

The object of the verb **wissen** is often a dependent clause. It can also be a pronoun like **das, es, alles,** or **nichts.**

ANN: Weißt du, **wie viel Uhr es ist?**
LISA: Nein, ich weiß **es** leider auch nicht.

10. *Wissen* versus *kennen* (☞ Übung 5-16, p. 99)

wissen	*to know (something as a fact)*	+	object clause, **das, es, alles,** or **nichts**
kennen	*to know (be acquainted with someone; be familiar with something)*	+	direct object

Talking about events in the past

11. The simple past of *sein, haben,* and the modals (☞ Übungen 5-17, 5-18, pp. 100–101)

	sein	haben	dürfen	können	mögen	müssen	sollen	wollen
ich	war	hatte	durfte	konnte	mochte	musste	sollte	wollte
du	warst	hattest	durftest	konntest	mochtest	musstest	solltest	wolltest
er/es/sie	war	hatte	durfte	konnte	mochte	musste	sollte	wollte
wir	waren	hatten	durften	konnten	mochten	mussten	sollten	wollten
ihr	wart	hattet	durftet	konntet	mochtet	musstet	solltet	wolltet
sie	waren	hatten	durften	konnten	mochten	mussten	sollten	wollten
Sie	waren	hatten	durften	konnten	mochten	mussten	sollten	wollten

- The modals form the simple past by adding the past tense marker **-t-** to the verb stem.
- For **dürfen, können, mögen,** and **müssen,** the umlaut of the infinitive form is dropped in the simple past.
- The **g** of **mögen** becomes **ch.**

NAME: ______________________________ **DATE:** ______________

5-3 Kleine Gespräche. Supply the appropriate personal pronouns or possessive adjectives. (☞ Strukturen 1, p. 83)

ihren / du / sie / er

1. > Du, Sabine, weißt ____________ vielleicht, warum Monika ____________ Wagen verkauft?

   < Ich glaube, ____________ kostet ____________ zu viel.

mich / Ihr / meine

2. > Fährt ____________ Sohn Sie nach Berlin, Frau Schneider?

   < Nein, diesmal fährt ____________ ____________ Tochter.

wir / seine / euren / ihn

3. > Mögt ihr ____________ neuen Professor?

   < Ja, ____________ finden ____________ und ____________ Vorlesungen sehr interessant.

dein / dich / mein / mich / dich

4. > Soll ich ____________ abholen, Tina, oder holt ____________ Freund ____________ ab?

   < Heute holt ____________ Freund ____________ ab.

sie / ihr / Sie / sie

5. > Warum verkaufen Vogels ____________ Haus? Brauchen ____________ Geld?

   < Warum fragen ____________ ____________ denn nicht selbst, Frau Dollinger?

uns / euch / sie / eure

6. > Gibt ____________ Professorin ____________ auch so viele Hausaufgaben?

   < Nein, aber ____________ gibt ____________ jede Woche ein Quiz.

5-4 Was passt wo? Supply the appropriate accusative prepositions. (☞ Strukturen 2, p. 83)

durch (2x) / für (2x) / gegen (3x) / ohne (3x) / um (3x)

1. Warum willst du ein Motorrad kaufen? Ein Fahrrad ist doch viel besser ____________ dich.
2. Warum geht Brigitte jetzt oft ____________ ihren Freund aus? Liebt sie ihn nicht mehr?
3. Die neue Straße soll mitten ____________ den Park gehen.
4. Ich bin ____________ Experimente an Ratten und Mäusen.
5. ____________ wie viel Uhr fängt das Konzert an, ____________ acht?
6. Wir haben noch keine Karten ____________ das Konzert. Aber vielleicht können wir ____________ die Sekretärin noch ein paar Karten bekommen.
7. ____________ Mittag werde ich immer sehr hungrig.
8. Kevin joggt jeden morgen zweimal ____________ den großen See im Stadtpark.
9. Ich trinke meinen Kaffee mit viel Milch, aber ____________ Zucker.
10. Was hast du denn ____________ Brigitte? Ich finde sie sehr nett.
11. Heute müsst ihr ____________ mich ausgehen. Ich muss mein Referat fertig schreiben.

5-5 Was passt wo? Supply the appropriate prepositions and personal pronouns from the list below. (☞ Strukturen 1 & 2, p. 83)

durch / für (2x) / gegen (2x) / ohne (2x) — mich / dich (2x) / sie / ihn (2x) / Sie

1. Wie will dieser Mann denn Präsident werden? Die Frauen sind doch fast alle ____________ ____________.
2. Ich mache das sehr gern ____________ ____________, Frau Meyer.
3. Was hast du denn ____________ ____________ abine? Liebst du mich nicht mehr?
4. Ich kann ____________ ____________ nic , Sabine!
5. Hier ist ein Brief ____________ __ r.
6. Martin sagt, er hat morgen n heute ____________ ____________ schwimmen gehen.
7. Di rt ____________ ____________

NAME: ______________________________ **DATE:** ______________

5-6 Ergänzen Sie! Complete with prepositions from the list below and with accusative endings. (☞ Strukturen 2, p. 83)

durch / für (2x) / gegen / ohne (2x) / um (2x)

1. Heute gehen wir mal mitten ____________ d____ Englischen Garten (m) nach Hause.
2. Der Zug nach Bonn fährt ____________ 16.35 Uhr ab.
3. Bist du ____________ oder ____________ d____ Kapitalismus (m)?
4. Hoffentlich kommen Maiers diesmal ____________ ihr____ großen Bernhardiner (m)!
5. Nächsten Sommer machen wir eine Radtour ____________ d____ Bodensee (m).
6. Warum fliegt Herr Borg denn ____________ sein____ Frau nach Florida?
7. ____________ sein____ Hobbys hat Thomas immer Zeit.

5-7 Claudias Freizeitpläne. Read what Claudia is planning for a day off. Complete Martin's reactions appropriately by supplying **dafür** or **dagegen.** (☞ Strukturen 3, p. 83)

1. Claudia möchte morgen mit Martin beim Donisl zu Mittag essen.
   Martin ist ________________, denn er isst lieber beim Schnellimbiss.
2. Am Nachmittag will Claudia mit Martin ins Deutsche Museum.
   Martin ist nicht ________________, denn er möchte lieber in die Alte Pinakothek.
3. Vom Deutschen Museum möchte Claudia dann zum Englischen Garten fahren.
   Martin ist ________________, denn auch er möchte zum Englischen Garten.
4. Im Englischen Garten möchte Claudia mit Martin spazieren gehen.
   Martin ist ________________, denn er möchte im Eisbach baden gehen.
5. Zum Abendessen möchte Claudia dann ins Mövenpick.
   Martin ist gar nicht ________________, denn er will zu Hause zu Abend essen.
6. Zuletzt will Claudia dann mit Martin tanzen gehen.
   Martin ist ________________, denn er möchte viel lieber ins Kino.

5-8 Du und ich. Write questions and responses as in the model. Remember to use the comparative form of the adverbs in all responses. (☞ Strukturen 4, p. 84)

1. gern essen

   > Isst du auch so gern wie ich?

   < Ich esse viel lieber als du.

2. lang schlafen

   > ______________________________

   < ______________________________

3. gern lesen

   > ______________________________

   < ______________________________

4. viel backen

   > ______________________________

   < ______________________________

5. oft waschen

   > ______________________________

   < ______________________________

6. schnell fahren

   > ______________________________

   < ______________________________

7. gut Deutsch sprechen

   > ______________________________

   < ______________________________

NAME: ______________________ DATE: ______________

5-9 Vergleiche. Read the statements and then complete the comparisons as shown in the example. (Strukturen 4, p. 84)

1. Der Porsche kostet 60 000 Euro und der Ford kostet nur 22 000 Euro.
   a. Der Porsche ist teurer als der Ford.
   b. Der Porsche ist der teurere Wagen.
2. Bei A&P kostet der Liter Eis € 3,49 und bei Tengelmann kostet er nur € 3,19.
   a. Bei Tengelmann ist der Liter Eis 30 Cent billiger als bei A&P.
   b. Tengelmann hat das billigere Eis.
3. Florians Zimmer ist 25 Quadratmeter[1] groß und Bernds Zimmer ist nur 22 Quadratmeter groß.
   a. Florians Zimmer ist drei Quadratmeter grösser al Bernds Zimmer.
   b. Florian hat das grössere Zimmer.
4. Müllers Haus hat fünf Zimmer und Maiers Haus hat acht.
   a. Müllers Haus ist kleiner Maiers Haus.
   b. Müllers haben das kleinered Haus.
5. Evas Referat ist zwölf Seiten[2] lang und Kurts Referat ist nur acht Seiten lang.
   a. Evas Referat ist vier Seiten länger als Kurts Referat.
   b. Eva hat das längere Referat.
6. Der Januar hat einunddreißig Tage und der Februar nur achtundzwanzig oder neunundzwanzig.
   a. Der Februar ist zwei oder drei Tage kürzer als der Januar.
   b. Der Februar ist der kürzwer Monat.
7. Frau Schulte ist fünfundvierzig Jahre alt und Frau Denner ist neununddreißig.
   a. Frau Schulte ist sechs Jahre älter als Frau Denner.
   b. Frau Schulte ist die älterer Frau.
8. Der Mount Everest ist 8848 Meter hoch und der Fudschijama nur 3776.
   a. Der Mount Everest ist 5072 Meter höher als der Fudschijama.
   b. Der Mount Everest ist der höherer Berg.

[1]*square meters* [2]*pages*

5-10 Der Superlativ (I). Supply the appropriate adjectives or adverbs in the superlative.
(Strukturen 5, p. 84)

schnell / schön / gern / grün

1. Welche Rockgruppe magst du am ______________________?
2. In Müllers Garten sind die Blumen am ______________________, aber bei Schultes ist das Gras am ______________________.
3. Wie komme ich von Hamburg am ______________________ nach Berlin?

früh / interessant / viel

4. Kurt steht immer am ______________________ auf.
5. Ralf gibt immer am ______________________ Geld aus.
6. Welchen Artikel findest du am ______________________?

teuer / voll / schick / preisgünstig

7. In der Mensa isst man am ______________________.
8. Professor Webers Vorlesungen sind immer am ______________________.
9. Ich finde diese rote Jacke am ______________________, aber sie ist natürlich auch am ______________________.

5-11 Der Superlativ (II). Supply the appropriate adjectives in the superlative.
(Strukturen 6, p. 85)

heiß / kurz / lang / berühmt / kalt

1. In Deutschland ist der Juli der ______________________ Monat und der Januar ist der ______________________.
2. Die ______________________ Tage sind im Juni und die ______________________ sind im Dezember.
3. Schloss Neuschwanstein ist Deutschlands ______________________ Schloss.

teuer / jung / elegant / hoch / groß

4. Das ist mein ______________________ und ______________________ Kleid.
5. Ich bin zehn Jahre älter als mein ______________________ Bruder, aber mit eins fünfundneunzig ist er der ______________________ in der ganzen Familie.
6. Die Zugspitze ist Deutschlands ______________________ Berg.

gut / glücklich / billig / reich

7. Meine Mutter macht den ______________________ Kaffee.
8. Kauf bitte nicht wieder den ______________________ Wein, Klaus!
9. Ich möchte nicht so viel Geld, denn die ______________________ Menschen sind nicht immer die ______________________.

NAME: ______________________ DATE: ______________

5-13 ***Dass, weil* oder *wenn?*** Complete the dependent clauses with the conjunctions **dass, weil,** or **wenn,** and with the italicized verb forms in the sentences in parentheses. (☞ Strukturen 7, p. 85)

1. (Du *willst* schlank bleiben.)

   Wenn du schlank bleiben willst, darfst du nicht so viel essen.

2. (Sie *will* schlank bleiben.)

   Isst Antje so wenig, __________ sie schlank bleiben __________?

3. (Antje *isst* viel zu wenig.)

   Denkst du auch, __________ Antje viel zu wenig __________?

4. (Ich *stehe* früher *auf.*)

   Meine Mitbewohnerin will, __________ ich früher __________.

5. (Ich *stehe* immer zu spät *auf.*)

   Ich frühstücke nie, __________ ich immer zu spät __________.

6. (Anna *steht* morgens *auf.*)

   __________ Anna morgens __________, ist es meistens noch dunkel.

7. (Du *liest* es nicht.)

   Gib das Buch doch zurück, __________ du es nicht __________!

8. (Sie *soll* das Buch heute noch zurückgeben.)

   Sag deiner Mitbewohnerin, __________ sie das Buch heute noch zurückgeben __________.

9. (Irene *hat* morgen Geburtstag.)

   Weißt du, __________ Irene morgen Geburtstag __________?

10. (Sie *wird* einundzwanzig.)

    __________ Irene morgen einundzwanzig __________, gibt sie für alle ihre Freunde eine große Party.

5-14 Fragen, Fragen, Fragen. In *a.*, supply the appropriate question word where necessary. In *b.*, use the question in *a.* as an object clause. (☞ Strukturen 8, p. 85)

1. a. ___Wo___ ist der Bahnhof?

   b. Könnten Sie mir bitte sagen, ___wo der Bahnhof ist___?

2. a. Ist das der Zug nach Bonn?

   b. Könnten Sie mir bitte sagen, ___ob das der Zug nach Bonn ist___?

3. a. Um __________ Uhr fährt dieser Zug ab?

   b. Könnten Sie mir bitte sagen, __________?

4. a. Ist der Zug sehr voll?

   b. Könnten Sie mir bitte sagen, __________?

5. a. __________ spät ist es jetzt?

   b. Könnten Sie mir bitte sagen, __________?

6. a. Ist Ralf heute Abend zu Hause?

   b. Weißt du, __________?

7. a. __________ macht Ralf heute Abend?

   b. Weißt du, __________?

8. a. __________ fängt das Konzert an?

   b. Weißt du, __________?

9. a. Durch __________ können wir noch Karten bekommen?

   b. Weißt du vielleicht, __________?

10. a. Holt Ralf uns ab?

    b. Weißt du, __________?

11. a. Geht Bernd auch in dieses Konzert?

    b. Weißt du, __________?

NAME: ______________________________ **DATE:** ______________

5-15 Wer weiß das? Supply the correct forms of **wissen!** (Strukturen 9, p. 86)

1. HOLGER: ______________ du, wo Stephanie ist?
   CLAUDIA: Nein, das ______________ ich auch nicht, aber dort ist Peter, und Peter ______________ es bestimmt.
2. FRAU OTT: ______________ Sie vielleicht, wann das Fußballspiel beginnt?
   POLIZIST: Nein, das ______________ ich auch nicht.
   FRAU OTT: Aber als Polizist müssen Sie das doch ______________!
   POLIZIST: Wir Polizisten ______________ leider auch nicht alles.
3. BERND: ______________ ihr, wann das Konzert beginnt?
   CLAUDIA: Ich ______________ es nicht. ______________ du es vielleicht, Martin?
   MARTIN: Nein, aber dort sind Stephanie und Peter. Ich ______________, sie haben Karten für das Konzert und sie müssen deshalb auch ______________, um wie viel Uhr es beginnt.
4. EVA: ______________ Günters Eltern, dass er fast nie in seine Vorlesungen geht?
   TINA: Nein, und sie sollen es auch nicht ______________.

5-16 *Wissen* oder *kennen?* Supply the proper forms of **wissen** or **kennen.** (Strukturen 10, p. 86)

1. > Ist Claudias Mitbewohnerin nett?
   < Ich ______________ es nicht. Ich ______________ sie noch nicht.
   > Aber ______________ du vielleicht, woher sie ist?
   < Ja, das ______________ ich. Sie ist Amerikanerin und sie kommt aus Chicago.
2. > ______________ du Peter Ackermann?
   < Nicht persönlich, aber ich ______________, dass er Martins Mitbewohner ist.
   > Und Martin, ______________ du Martin?
   < Ja, ich ______________ ihn sehr gut.
3. > ______________ ihr, ob Professor Seidlmeyer heute Sprechstunden hat?
   < Nein, das ______________ wir auch nicht. Aber warum fragst du nicht seine Sekretärin, sie ______________ es bestimmt.

4. > Wie gut _______________ Sie Frau Koch, Herr Krüger?

   < Nicht sehr gut. Ich _______________ nicht mal, wo sie wohnt.

5. > _______________ du, wie viel die Konzertkarten kosten?

   < Zwanzig Euro. Aber du _______________ doch Osman Gürlük. Durch Osman kannst du sie für fünfzehn Euro bekommen.

6. > Wie gut _______________ ihr München?

   < Gar nicht gut. Wir _______________ nur, wo die Uni ist.

7. > _______________ Sie, was eine Postkarte nach Kanada kostet?

   < Nein, das _______________ ich leider auch nicht.

8. > _______________ du den Film *Lola rennt?*

   < Ja. _______________ du, ob es noch andere Filme von Tom Tykwer gibt?

5-17 Kleine Gespräche. Supply the appropriate forms of **sein** and **haben** in the simple past. (Strukturen 11, p. 86)

1. > Warum _______________ du nicht auf Monikas Party?

   < Ich _______________ zu viel zu tun.

2. > Wo _______________ ihr letztes Wochenende?

   < Da _______________ wir in Hamburg.

   > _______________ ihr schönes Wetter?

   < Nein, es _______________ kühl und sehr regnerisch.

3. > Warum _______________ du gestern keine Vorlesungen?

   < Unsere Professorin _______________ krank.

4. > Wie _______________'s in Irland?

   < Schön, nur _______________ wir zu viel Regen.

5. > Warum _______________ Sie denn letzten Winter nicht in Spanien, Frau Beck?

   < Mein Mann und ich _______________ beide zu viel Arbeit.

6. > Warum _______________ Heike und Beate heute Morgen nicht beim Frühstück?

   < Heike _______________ keinen Hunger und Beate _______________ noch zu müde.

NAME: ______________________________ DATE: ______________

5-18 Freizeit – Ferienzeit. Complete, using appropriate modal verbs from the choices given. Use the simple past. (Strukturen 11, p. 86)

1. Martin ______________ Claudia wieder in die Alte Pinakothek schleppen.
   (mögen / wollen)

2. Aber diesmal ______________ er das mal nicht, sondern ______________ mit
   (dürfen / müssen) (mögen / müssen)

   Claudia zuerst zum Donisl und dann ins Deutsche Museum.

3. Die Weißwürste beim Donisl waren so gut, dass auch Martin sie ______________.
   (dürfen / mögen)

4. Frau Ziegler ______________ dieses Jahr mal nicht campen gehen.
   (wollen / sollen)

5. Herr Ziegler ______________ deshalb ein schönes Hotel suchen und es
   (sollen / mögen)

   ______________ nicht das billigste sein.
   (mögen / dürfen)

6. Nina und Robert ______________ diesen Plan gar nicht, weil sie dann ihre
   (mögen / sollen)

   Freunde nicht wiedersehen ______________.
   (können / müssen)

7. Das Hotel ______________ deshalb nicht weit vom Campingplatz weg sein.
   (dürfen / mögen)

8. So ______________ Nina und Robert auch dieses Jahr ihre Freunde
   (können / wollen)

   wiedersehen und Herr Ziegler war in ein paar Minuten beim See und ______________
   (mögen / können)

   dort angeln gehen.

9. Günter ______________ mit Monika ins Kino gehen, aber Monika
   (wollen / mögen)

   ______________ Günter nicht und sie hatte deshalb nie Zeit für ihn.
   (wollen / mögen)

10. Monika ______________ Patrick viel lieber als Günter.
    (müssen / mögen)

Zum Verstehen

5-19 Beim Winterschlussverkauf. The winter sales are on and Monika is in a department store looking for a jacket. Write Monika's questions or statements that would elicit the following responses from the sales clerk.

MONIKA: Das sind mal schöne Jacken hier.

VERKÄUFERIN: Ja, diese Winterjacken sind sehr schön und die Preise sind alle reduziert.

MONIKA: ______________________________

VERKÄUFERIN: Die rote Jacke? Sie kostet 90 Euro.

MONIKA: ______________________________

VERKÄUFERIN: Aber natürlich dürfen Sie sie anprobieren. – Sieht gut aus, nicht?

MONIKA: ______________________________

VERKÄUFERIN: Gut. Das macht dann 90 Euro. Übrigens, wir haben auch sehr schöne Pullover, alle zum halben Preis. Möchten Sie sie sehen?

MONIKA: ______________________________

VERKÄUFERIN: Ja, das kenne ich. Meine Tochter ist auch Studentin und sie hat auch nie genug Geld.

5-20 Synonyme. Find the synonyms for the words and expressions in the box below and write them in the appropriate spaces.

der Vormittag	schwimmen	das Auto	ich heiße
täglich	mögen	anrufen	Tschüs!
elegant	fantastisch	anfangen	Ich habe Hunger.
die Menschen	Wie spät ist es?	machen	ein bisschen

telefonieren	______________	ein wenig	______________
Ich bin hungrig.	______________	der Morgen	______________
baden	______________	gern haben	______________
die Leute	______________	mein Name ist	______________
beginnen	______________	Wie viel Uhr ist es?	______________
Auf Wiedersehen!	______________	jeden Tag	______________
der Wagen	______________	toll	______________
schick	______________	tun	______________

NAME: ______________________________ **DATE:** ______________

5-21 Wir fliegen nach Europa. Look at the ad from the *Deutsche Presse,* a German language weekly from Toronto. Mark the correct responses to the questions below.

NEUE VOKABELN

der Sonderflug, ¨e	*special flight*
die Ermäßigung	*reduction*
das Mietauto, -s	*rental car*
unbegrenzt	*unlimited*

Europa Sonderflüge von Toronto

nach:	Min.	Max.	
AMSTERDAM	499.-	699.-	Apr 3 - Okt.16
KOPENHAGEN	779.-	839.-	Mai 11 - Jun.14
DÜSSELDORF	499.-	798.-	Apr 5 - Okt.18
FRANKFURT	548.-	798.-	Apr 2 - Okt.16
HANNOVER	598.-	848.-	Mai 1 - Okt.16
LONDON/GATWICK	499.-	699.-	Mai 5 - Dez.6
MÜNCHEN	598.-	848.-	Mai 5 - Okt.16
MAILAND	749.-	749.-	Mai 4 - Okt.19
MALAGA	649.-	899.-	Mai 4 - Okt.19
PARIS	509.-	679.-	Jun.8 - Sep.28
ROM/VENEDIG	769.-	1199.-	Mai 4 - Okt.19
STOCKHOLM	859.-	939.-	Mai 11 - Jun.14

Sonderflüge nach Toronto

von DÜSSELDORF			Apr.5 - Okt.18
FRANKFURT	€ 495,-	€ 745,-	Apr.1 - Okt.16
HANNOVER			Mai 1 - Okt.16
MÜNCHEN			Mai 5 - Okt.18

Das Ab- und Rückflugsdatum bestimmt den genauen Preis
Änderungen sind vorbehalten (Zusätzlich Flughafensteuer)
Fragen Sie nach Kinder- & Seniorenermäßigung
MIETAUTOS ab **$ 121.00** *(pro Woche / Unbegrenzte Kilometer)*

EURAIL PASS	ab	**$ 288.00**	(15 Tage)
JUGENDPASS	ab	**$ 456.00**	(1 Monat)
GERMAN RAIL PASS		**$ 78.00**	(4 Tage Junior)

1. Was ist billiger, der Flug nach Frankfurt oder der Flug nach Düsseldorf?

   ___ der Flug nach Frankfurt
   ___ der Flug nach Düsseldorf

2. Was kostet ein Flug von Toronto nach München in der Hochsaison?

   ___ $ 598. ___ $ 848.

3. Wie viel kostet ein Flug von Hannover nach Toronto in der Hochsaison?

   ___ € 745,- ___ € 495,-

4. Wer bekommt Ermäßigung?

   ___ Kinder ___ Studenten
   ___ Senioren

5. Sie sind zwei Wochen in Europa und brauchen ein billiges Mietauto. Wie viel kostet das?

   ___ $ 121. ___ $ 242.

6. Frau Jones hat ein Mietauto für eine Woche und Frau Smith hat auch ein Mietauto für eine Woche. Frau Jones fährt tausend Kilometer und Frau Smith fährt zweitausend Kilometer.

   Wie viel kostet Frau Jones' Mietauto?

   ___ $ 242. ___ $ 121.

   Wie viel kostet Frau Smiths Mietauto?

   ___ $ 242. ___ $ 121.

Zum Übersetzen

5-22 Kleine Gespräche.

1. SABINE: Do you need the car (*use* **Wagen**) every Saturday?
   HOLGER: No, next Saturday I don't need it.

2. TINA: Robert is working in Austria next summer.
   OLIVER: Who is he working for there?
   TINA: For his uncle.

3. FRAU BLUM: Do you know the novel *Die Firma?*
   HERR ROTH: No, I don't know it. I only know the film.

4. VANESSA: Where would you like to go on vacation this year?
   FLORIAN: I'd like to go camping in the **(im)** Black Forest.
   VANESSA: Good, then we don't have to spend so much money.
   FLORIAN: I know a couple of fantastic campgrounds there.
   VANESSA: And *I* know how beautiful the landscape is there: the mountains and the valleys, the fields and the forests, and the pretty little villages.

5. LUKAS: Florian is crazy! He is supposed to be studying for a test, and what is he doing? He's sitting in front of the TV and watching soap operas.
   JULIA: I know, but I think that he'll get an A **(eine Eins)** anyway.

6. LAURA: Why weren't you at **(auf)** Lisa's party last night?
   MARIA: I didn't have time, because I had to study for a test.
   LAURA: Why couldn't you study in the afternoon?
   MARIA: Because I work at Denner's fast food stand every afternoon.

5-23 Ferienreisen.

My friend Sebastian always goes on the most interesting and fantastic trips. Last year he was in Nepal and for next summer he wants to book a flight to Bhutan.

My friend Moritz also likes to travel, but only in Europe, and he always stays (*use* **übernachten**) in hotels. I find my friend Moritz a bit boring. I find a youth hostel or a campsite much more interesting than a hotel, because one gets to know more people there.

KAPITEL 6

Strukturen

Talking about events in the past

1. The perfect tense of regular verbs (☞ Übung 6-1, p. 111)

The perfect tense is used to talk about past events in conversational situations. It consists of an auxiliary verb (usually **haben**) that takes personal endings and a past participle that remains unchanged.

singular		plural	
ich	habe gespielt	wir	haben gespielt
du	hast gespielt	ihr	habt gespielt
er/es/sie	hat gespielt	sie	haben gespielt
	Sie haben gespielt		

Position of auxiliary and past participle

MAIN CLAUSE:		Ich **habe** die ganze Nacht **gelernt.**
DEPENDENT CLAUSE:	Ich bin müde,	weil ich die ganze Nacht **gelernt habe.**

Position of* nicht *if no word or expression is specifically negated

MAIN CLAUSE:		Ich **habe** heute Morgen **nicht gefrühstückt.**
DEPENDENT CLAUSE:	Ich bin hungrig,	weil ich heute Morgen **nicht gefrühstückt habe.**

past participle: regular verbs

INFINITIVE	PAST PARTICIPLE	PREFIX	VERB STEM	ENDING
lernen	gelernt	ge	lern	t
arbeiten	gearbeitet	ge	arbeit	et
baden	gebadet	ge	bad	et
regnen	geregnet	ge	regn	et
reparieren	repariert		reparier	t

- Past participles of regular verbs end in **-t** or **-et.**
- Past participles of verbs ending in **-ieren** do not have the prefix **ge-.**

2. The perfect tense of irregular verbs (☞ Übung 6-2, p. 111)

past participle: irregular verbs				
INFINITIVE	PAST PARTICIPLE	PREFIX	VERB STEM	ENDING
finden	gefunden	ge	fund	en
nehmen	genommen	ge	nomm	en
schlafen	geschlafen	ge	schlaf	en

- The verb stem often shows a vowel change and sometimes a consonant change as well.
- Past participles of irregular verbs end in **-en.**

3. The verb *sein* as auxiliary in the perfect tense (☞ Übungen 6-3, 6-4, 6-5, 6-6, pp. 113–116)

singular		plural	
ich	bin gekommen	wir	sind gekommen
du	bist gekommen	ihr	seid gekommen
er/es/sie	ist gekommen	sie	sind gekommen
	Sie sind gekommen		

Sein is used as auxiliary

- for verbs expressing a change of location:

fahren	**ist gefahren**	kommen	**ist gekommen**
fliegen	**ist geflogen**	reisen	**ist gereist**
gehen	**ist gegangen**	wandern	**ist gewandert**

- for verbs expressing a change of condition:

werden	**ist geworden**	*to become*
sterben	**ist gestorben**	*to die*
passieren	**ist passiert**	*to happen*

- for the verbs **bleiben** and **sein:**

bleiben	**ist geblieben**	*to stay; to remain*
sein	**ist gewesen**	*to be*

Verbs with **sein** as auxiliary in the perfect tense can be regular or irregular.

More on the past

4. The perfect tense of verbs with separable prefixes (☞ Übung 6-7, p. 117)

regular verbs		irregular verbs	
INFINITIVE	PERFECT TENSE	INFINITIVE	PERFECT TENSE
anhören	hat **angehört**	**fern**sehen	hat **ferngesehen**
abreisen	ist **abgereist**	**mit**singen	hat **mitgesungen**
ausprobieren	hat **ausprobiert**	**auf**stehen	ist **aufgestanden**

- Verbs with separable prefixes can be regular or irregular.
- Past participles of regular verbs ending in **-ieren** do not add **ge-** to the verb stem.
- Verbs that express a change of location or condition use **sein** as an auxiliary.
- Separable prefixes are *stressed* in pronunciation.

5. The perfect tense of verbs with inseparable prefixes (☞ Übungen 6-8, 6-9, pp. 118–119)

The three most common inseparable prefixes are **be-, er-,** and **ver-.**

regular verbs		irregular verbs	
INFINITIVE	PERFECT TENSE	INFINITIVE	PERFECT TENSE
besuchen	hat **besucht**	bekommen	hat **bekommen**
erzählen	hat **erzählt**	ertrinken	ist **ertrunken**
verkaufen	hat **verkauft**	verstehen	hat **verstanden**

- Verbs with inseparable prefixes can be regular or irregular.
- The auxiliary can be **haben** or **sein.**
- Inseparable prefixes are *unstressed* in pronunciation.

6. The perfect tense of mixed verbs (☞ Übungen 6-10, 6-11, pp. 120–121)

infinitive	perfect tense	
bringen	hat **gebracht**	*to bring*
denken	hat **gedacht**	*to think*
kennen	hat **gekannt**	*to know (be acquainted with)*
nennen	hat **genannt**	*to name, to call*
rennen	ist **gerannt**	*to run*
wissen	hat **gewusst**	*to know (a fact)*

- The past participles of mixed verbs have a stem change.
- The past participles of mixed verbs end in **-t.**
- **Rennen** is the only mixed verb that uses **sein** as auxiliary.

Ranking people and things

7. Ordinal numbers and dates (☞ Übung 6-12, p. 123)

der **erste**	der **siebte**	der dreizehnte	der zwanzigste
der zweite	der **achte**	der vierzehnte	der einundzwanzigste
der **dritte**	der neunte	der fünfzehnte	der zweiundzwanzigste
der vierte	der zehnte	der sechzehnte	der dreißigste
der fünfte	der elfte	der siebzehnte	der vierzigste
der sechste	der zwölfte	der achtzehnte	...
		der neunzehnte	

- For the numbers 1 through 19, the ordinal numbers are formed by adding **-t-** and an adjective ending to the cardinal number.
- From the number 20 on, the ordinal numbers are formed by adding **-st-** to the cardinal numbers.
- Note the four irregular forms that are indicated in boldface.

The following expressions are used to ask for and give the date:

Der Wievielte ist heute?
Heute ist der Fünfzehnte.

Den Wievielten haben wir heute?
Heute haben wir den Fünfzehnten.

Am wievielten Mai ist Lisas Geburtstag?
Lisas Geburtstag ist am 23. (dreiundzwanzigsten) Mai.
Lisa ist am 23. 5. (dreiundzwanzigsten Fünften) 1984 geboren.

- When written as a number, the ordinal number is indicated by a period.
- When writing dates, the day always precedes the month.

Writing personal letters

8. Conventions in writing personal letters (☞ Übung 6-13, p. 124)

In personal letters, dates are written as follows: **München, den 5. Oktober 2003**

- The article appears in the accusative case.
- There is no comma between the month and the year.
- Writing a personal letter is considered a conversational situation. The writer can therefore use the perfect tense to relate past events. (But remember that the modals and **haben** and **sein** are typically used in the simple past tense.)

Indicating direction away from and toward

9. *Hin* and *her* as directional suffixes and prefixes (☞ Übung 6-14, p. 125)

> **Hin** indicates motion or direction *away from* the speaker.
> **Her** indicates motion or direction *toward* the speaker.

The question words **wohin** and **woher** can be written as one word or split.

Wohin gehst du?	**Wo** gehst du **hin?**
Woher kommst du?	**Wo** kommst du **her?**

Hin and **her** are also used as separable prefixes or as parts of separable prefixes.

hinfahren	**her**fahren
hineingehen	**heraus**kommen

NAME: ______________________ DATE: ______________

Anwendung

Übungen

6-1 Sylvias freier Tag. Supply appropriate verbs in the perfect tense from the choices given. (☞ Strukturen 1, p. 105)

kochen / regnen / frühstücken / hören

Gestern hatte Sylvia einen freien Tag. Und wie war das Wetter? Richtig, es _hat_ den ganzen Tag _geregnet_. (An Sylvias freien Tagen regnet es immer!) Weil Sylvia sehr müde war, _hat_ sie im Bett noch eine Stunde lang Radio _gehort_, und sie _hat_ dann erst um zehn Kaffee _gekocht_ und _gefrühstückt_.

reparieren / lernen / telefonieren / spielen / machen / füttern

Später _hat_ Sylvia dann ihre Katze _gefüttert_, ihr Bett _gemacht_ und fast eine Stunde lang mit ihrer Kusine Kathrin _telefoniert_. Nachmittags _hat_ Sylvia ihr Fahrrad _repariert_ und dann stundenlang Solitär _gespielt_. Heute Morgen hatte Sylvia im Englischkurs ein Vokabelquiz und sie denkt, dass sie eine schlechte Zensur bekommt, denn ihre englischen Vokabeln _hat_ sie gestern leider nicht _gelernt_.

6-2 Ergänzen Sie! Rewrite, adding the appropriate verb in the perfect tense. Changes in the verb stem are indicated in parentheses. Do not change the sequence of the sentence elements provided. (☞ Strukturen 2, p. 106)

gebacken

schreiben (ie) / backen / liegen (e)

lag, hat geliegen

1. Günter wieder den ganzen Morgen im Bett?

   Hat Günter wieder den ganzen Morgen im Bett gelegen?

2. Weißt du, wer diesen Artikel?

   Weißt du, _wer diesen Artikel geschrieben hat_

3. Heute Morgen ich einen Apfelkuchen.

   Heute morben habe ich einen Apfelkuchen gebacken.

gießen (oss) / essen (gess) / lesen / sprechen (o)

4. Wer meinen Apfel?

____

5. Die Blumen sind alle kaputt, weil du sie nicht.

Die Blumen sind alle kaputt, ______________________________

6. du mit Professor Müller Deutsch?

____

7. Gestern ich ein tolles Buch.

____

schneiden (itt) / singen (u) / waschen / trinken (u)

8. Sobald ihr den Wagen, dürft ihr Fußball spielen.

______________________________, dürft ihr Fußball spielen.

9. ihr schon Kaffee?

____

10. Thomas wieder mal die Fingernägel nicht.

____

11. Welcher Tenor besser, Pavarotti oder Carreras?

______________________________, Pavarotti oder Carreras?

NAME: ______________________ **DATE:** ______________

6-3 Warum *sein* als Hilfsverb? *a.* Rewrite, adding the appropriate verb in the perfect tense. Changes in the verb stem are indicated in parentheses. Regular verbs are followed by (R). *b.* Decide whether the verb denotes a change of location (L), a change of condition (C), or neither (N) by writing L, C, or N in the spaces provided. (Strukturen 3, p. 106)

kommen (a) / bleiben (ie) / passieren (R) / werden (o)

wurde geworden

1. Paul gestern zwanzig.

Paul ist gestern zwanzig geworden. C

2. du gut nach Hause?

Bist du gut nach Hause gekommen L

3. Warum Claudia zu Hause?

Warum ist Claudia zu Hause geblieben. N

4. Weißt du, was auf Bernds Party?

Weißt du, was auf Bernds Party passiert ist. ____

sein (wes) / sterben (o) / fliegen (o) / werden (o) / fahren / gehen (gang)

war gewese, starb gestorben, flog geflogen, wurde geworden, fuhr gefahren, ging gegangen.

5. Wie Frau Berg denn so krank?

Wie ist Frau Berg denn so krank geworden ____

6. Wissen Sie schon, dass Frau Berg?

Wissen Sie schon, dass Frau Berg gestorben ist. ____

7. Wann du gestern Abend ins Bett?

Wann bist du gestern Abend ins Bett gegangen ____

8. In Deutschland ich viel Rad.

In Deutschland bin ich viel Rad gefahren. ____

9. Wo ihr gestern Abend?

Wo seid ihr gestern Abend gewesen ____

10. Warum ihr nicht mit Lufthansa?

Warum seid ihr nicht mit Lufthansa geflogen. ____

6-4 Was fehlt hier? Supply the missing verb forms. (Strukturen 2 & 3, p. 106)

INFINITIVE	PRESENT TENSE	PAST PARTICIPLE
finden	er findet	hat gefunden
singen	er sang	hat gesungen
Schlaffen	er schläft	geschlaffen
gehen	er ging	ist gegangen
bleiben	er blieb	ist geblieben
scheinen	die Sonne schien	hat geschienen
liegen	er lag	hat gelegen
sehen	er sieht	hat gesehen
fahren	er fuhr	ist gefahren
Waschen	er wusch	hat gewaschen
nehmen	er namm	hat genommen
stehen	er stand	hat gestanden
lesen	er lass	hat gelesen
essen	er ass	hat gegessen
kommen	er kamm	ist gekommen
sitzen	er sass	hat gesessen
sprechen	er sprach	hat gesprochen

NAME: ______________________________ DATE: ________________

6-5 Ralfs freier Tag. From the choices below, supply appropriate irregular verbs in the perfect tense. (☞ Strukturen 2 & 3, p. 106)

trinken / gehen / scheinen / waschen / essen / nehmen / schlafen / backen

Gestern hatte Ralf einen freien Tag. Und wie war das Wetter? Richtig, die Sonne __hat__ __geschienen__. (Für Ralf scheint immer die Sonne!) Ralf ______ nur bis sieben __________, denn an freien Tagen hat er immer viel vor. Er __hat__ ein Bad __genommen__ und zum Frühstück __hat__ er Müsli __gegessen__ und Orangensaft __getrunken__. Weil Ralf gern Kuchen isst und gern bäckt, __hat__ er dann einen Apfelkuchen __gebacken__. Um zehn __ist__ Ralf zum Waschsalon __gegangen__ und __hat__ dort seine Wäsche __gewaschen__.

essen / schreiben / schlafen / kommen / gehen / sprechen / trinken / sehen

Um zwölf __ist__ Ralf wieder nach Hause __gekommen__, __hat__ Kaffee __getrunken__, ein Stück Apfelkuchen __gegessen__ und im Fernsehen einen interessanten Dokumentarfilm __gesehen__. Am Nachmittag __hat__ Ralf für Professor Hagen ein Referat über die politische Situation in Osteuropa __geschrieben__. Dann __hat__ er noch lange mit Nicole am Telefon __gesprochen__. Um 23 Uhr __ist__ Ralf ins Bett __gegangen__ und __hat__ bald süß __geschlafen.__.

6-6 Ein Gespräch um drei Uhr morgens. Lutz and Frank tell Bernd about the party he had to miss. Use the components given to write this story in the perfect tense, but remember to use the simple past for the verbs **haben, sein,** and **müssen.** (Strukturen 1, 2, & 3, pp. 105–106)

1. Gestern Abend / Lutz und Frank / fahren / mit Bernds Wagen zu Annas Party / .

   Gestern Abend sind Lutz und Frank mit Bernds Wagen zu Annas Party gefahren.

2. Bernd / sein / krank / und / bleiben / deshalb zu Hause / .

   Bernd war krank und hat deshald zuHause gebicbt.

3. Lutz und Frank / kommen / erst morgens um drei nach Hause / .

   Lutzund Frank haben erst morgens um drei nach Hause gekommen.

4. Bernd / fragen / die beiden dann viel / .

   Bernd hat die beiden dann viel gefragt.

5. Bernd: Was / ihr / machen / denn so lange / ?

   ~~Ber~~ Was habt ihr denn solange gemacht.

6. Lutz: Zuerst / wir / tanzen / bis halb zwei / .

   Zuerst haben wir bis halb zwei getanzt

7. Frank: Und dann / wir / fahren / noch zu Nicole / .

   Und dann haben wir noch zu Nicole gefahrt.

8. Bernd: Zu Nicole? / Warum / Nicole / sein / denn nicht auf Annas Party / ?

   Zu Nicole? Warum war Nicole denn nicht auf Annas Party?

9. Lutz: Sie / haben / keine Zeit. / Sie / müssen / schreiben / ein paar wichtige E-Mails / .

   Sie hattekein zeit. Sie musste schreiben ein paar wichtige EMails.

10. Bernd: Nicole / kochen / für euch Kaffee / ?

    Nichole hat für euch Kaffee gekocht.

11. Frank: Nein / wir / trinken / Cola / und Pizza / essen / .

    Nein, Wir haben Cola getrunken und Pizza gegessen.

NAME: ______________________ **DATE:** ______________

6-7 Kleine Gespräche. Rewrite, adding the appropriate separable-prefix verb in the perfect tense. Do not change the sequence of the sentence elements provided. (Strukturen 4, p. 107)

heimkommen / ausprobieren / aufstehen / fernsehen

1. > Warum du heute Morgen so spät?

   Warum bist du heute morgen so spät aufgestanden?

   < Weil ich gestern erst um zwölf.

   ____

   > Du dann bestimmt noch stundenlang. fern gesehen

   ____

   < Nein, aber ich meinen neuen Scanner. ausprobiert.

   ____

abfahren / ankommen

angekommen

2. > Warum ihr erst um Mitternacht in Berlin?

   ____

   < Weil wir erst am Abend in Bremen. abgefahrt.

   ____

ausgehen / anhören / anrufen

3. > Gestern Abend Bernd mich.

   ____

   < ihr zusammen?

   ____

   > Nein, wir meine neuen CDs.

   ____

6-8 Fragen und Antworten. Rewrite, adding the appropriate separable- or inseparable-prefix verb in the perfect tense. Do not change the sequence of the sentence elements provided. (☞ Strukturen 4 & 5, p. 107)

ankommen / bekommen

1. > du meine Postkarte?

   Hast du meine Postkarte bekommen?

   < Nein sie noch nicht.

   Nein, sie ist noch nicht angekommen.

erklären / erzählen

2. > Professor Schwarz heute wieder nur Anekdoten?

   < Nein, heute er den Akkusativ.

ausprobieren / bestellen

3. > Kurt deinen neuen Scanner?

   < Ja, und er gleich auch einen. bestellt.

versuchen / besuchen

4. > ihr in München Stephanie Braun?

   < Wir es, aber sie war nicht zu Hause.

bezahlen / einkaufen

5. > Gestern ich im Supermarkt gleich für vierzehn Tage.

   < Und wie du das alles?

NAME: ______________________________________ **DATE:** ________________

6-12 Daten. Supply cardinal numbers and endings. Write all numbers as words. (☞ Strukturen 7, p. 108)

1. > Heute ist der Zehn__te__. Den Wieviel__ten__ haben wir dann in einer Woche?

   < In einer Woche wir dann den ____Siebzehnten____.

2. > Wenn heute der Vier_______ ist, den Wieviel_______ hatten wir dann gestern?

   < Dann hatten wir gestern den ________________________.

3. > Wenn wir morgen den Zwanzig_______ haben, der Wieviel_______ ist dann heute?

   < Dann ist heute der ________________________.

4. > Heute haben wir den Neunundzwanzig_______. Der Wieviel_______ war dann vorgestern?

   < Dann war vorgestern der ____.

5. > Wenn heute der Vierzehn_______ ist, der Wieviel_______ ist dann übermorgen?

   < Dann ist übermorgen der ________________________.

6. > Ralf ist am erst_______ Zwölf_______ neunzehnhundertfünfundsiebzig geboren. Seine Schwester Petra ist genau ein Jahr und einen Tag älter als er. Wann ist Petra geboren?

   < Am ________________________ ________________________ neunzehnhundertvierundsiebzig.

7. > Christa ist am einunddreißig_______ Fünf_______ neunzehnhundertvierundsiebzig geboren. Ihr Bruder Markus ist genau ein Jahr und einen Tag jünger als sie. Wann ist Markus geboren?

   < Am ________________________ ________________________ neunzehnhundertfünfundsiebzig.

8. > Wie oft hat man Geburtstag, wenn man am neunundzwanzig_______

   Zwei_______ geboren ist?

   < Eigentlich nur jedes ________________________ Jahr.

9. > Wann ist der Valentinstag?

   < Am ________________________ ________________________.

6-13 Ein Brief aus Berlin. Stephanie is visiting Peter's family in Berlin. Complete her letter to Claudia, using the appropriate verbs in the perfect tense. (Strukturen 8, p. 109)

gehen / einschlafen / ankommen / machen / sitzen

Berlin, den 1. Mai 2004

Liebe Claudia,

vorgestern Nacht um halb zwölf __sind__ wir hier bei Peters Eltern __angekommen__. Peters Mutter __hat__ uns schnell etwas zu essen __gemacht__ und dann __haben__ wir noch lange im Wohnzimmer __gesass__ und erzählt. Um drei Uhr nachts __haben__ wir endlich ins Bett __gegangen__ und ich __habe__ sofort __eingeschlaft.__.

laufen / fotografieren / essen / aufstehen

Gestern Morgen __~~haben~~ sind__ wir erst sehr spät __aufgestanden__ und __haben__ ein tolles Frühstück __gegessen__. Dann __sind__ wir stundenlang durch Berlin __gelaufen__. Peter hat viel erklärt und ich __habe__ viel __fotografiert.__.

aufbleiben / einladen / ausfragen *(to quiz)* / besuchen / arbeiten / kennen

Für den Abend __hat.__ Peter dann ein paar gute Freunde __eingeladen__. Seinen Freund Omar __habe__ ich schon __gekannt__, weil er uns in München mal __besucht__ __hat__. Wir __sind__ wieder bis spät in die Nacht __aufgeblieben__ und Peters Freunde __hat__ mich über Amerika __aufgefragt.__. Heute Nachmittag fahren wir nach Potsdam. Peter sagt, das Schloss dort ist ganz toll (ich glaube, es heißt Sanssouci). Nächste Woche sind wir dann wieder zurück in München. Hoffentlich __hast__ du nicht die ganze Zeit nur __gearbeitet__.

Viele liebe Grüße

Stephanie

6-14 Ein freier Tag. Supply **hin** or **her.** (☞ Strukturen 9, p. 109)

Gestern früh um sieben hat Holger mich angerufen. „Heute wird das Wetter echt toll," hat er gesagt. „Warum kommst du nicht _______über? Dann fahren wir zusammen zu Anja _______über. Vielleicht fährt sie mit uns zum Starnberger See _______aus." „Gute Idee!" habe ich gesagt, bin schnell aufgestanden und zu Holger _______übergerannt.

Vor Anjas Haus hat Holger _______aufgerufen: „Anja! Anja!" Anja hat das Fenster aufgemacht und gerufen: „Kommt doch _______auf, ihr zwei! Ich mache euch schnell eine Tasse Kaffee." Weil wir aber so schnell wie möglich zum See _______aus wollten, sind wir nicht _______aufgegangen und haben gerufen: „Komm lieber _______unter, Anja, und fahr mit uns zum Starnberger See _______aus."

Am Starnberger See hat die Sonne schon sehr warm geschienen, aber das Wasser war noch kalt und Holger und ich wollten nicht _______ein. Anja ist aber sofort _______eingesprungen und hat gerufen: „Kommt doch _______ein, ihr zwei! Es ist gar nicht so kalt, wie ihr denkt." Dann ist sie weit in den See _______ausgeschwommen.

Zum Verstehen

6-15 Assoziationen. Choose the appropriate words from the list to complete the associations in the word sets.

der Arm / die Zähne / die Haare / die Universität / die Zehe / die Ohren / das Flugzeug / der Hörsaal / die Lösung / der Mund

1. das Gymnasium – das Klassenzimmer
   die Universität – der Hörsaal
2. der Schüler – das Gymnasium
   der Student – die Universität
3. die Frage – die Antwort
   das Problem – die Lösung
4. die Hand – der Finger
   der Fuß – die Zehe
5. das Knie – das Bein
   der Ellbogen – der Arm
6. die Zahnpasta – die Zähne
   das Shampoo – die Haare
7. sehen – die Augen
   essen – der Mund
8. riechen[1] – die Nase
   hören – die Ohren
9. denken – der Kopf
   beißen[2] – die Zähne
10. fahren – das Auto
    fliegen – das Flugzeug

[1]*to smell* [2]*to bite*

6-16 Aus Karl Ottmanns Tagebuch. Read the following excerpts from the diary of a German emigrant to North America and then answer the questions below.

Im Norden von Kanada, den 21. Oktober 1930

Die letzten zweieinhalb Monate hatte ich keine Zeit für mein Tagebuch. Ich habe bis Ende September bei Farmer Dunnigan gearbeitet, schwere Arbeit, und nur fürs Essen und ein miserables Bett. Dann hat er mich weggeschickt, denn im Herbst und Winter brauchen Farmer keine Hilfe[1], und nächsten Sommer gibt es wieder neue hungrige Einwanderer. Ich habe gehört, dass es im Norden Arbeit gibt. Sie bauen eine Straße durch ganz Kanada und brauchen Holzfäller. Ich bin gleich hinaufgefahren und fälle jetzt von morgens bis abends Bäume. Wenn die Arbeitskollegen dann am Abend Bier trinken und Karten spielen, schleife[2] ich ihre Äxte oder wasche und flicke[3] ihre Socken und verdiene extra Geld. Viele Kollegen sind auch Einwanderer und viele kommen aus Deutschland. Wir sprechen oft Deutsch, ich habe viele neue Freunde, verdiene ziemlich gut und kann fast nichts ausgeben. Bis Frühling habe ich bestimmt genug Geld für eine eigene[4] kleine Werkstatt[5] und kann dann endlich wieder als Schlosser arbeiten.

Waterloo, den 10. Mai 1931

Ich war den ganzen Winter im Norden und habe viel Geld gespart. Dann bin ich mit ein paar Freunden hierher nach Waterloo gefahren. Hier leben viele Deutsche und die Farmer sind oft

Mennoniten und sprechen Deutsch. Ich habe hier eine kleine Werkstatt gemietet und mit meinen Ersparnissen[6] ein paar alte Maschinen gekauft. Über der Werkstatt sind zwei kleine Zimmer. Ich habe das eine vermietet[7] und das andere ist meine Wohnung. Mein Mieter ist auch aus Deutschland und wir sind gute Freunde.

Das Wetter ist wunderbar. Die Farmer arbeiten schwer und pflügen[8] und säen[9] und da geht oft etwas kaputt. Ein paar mennonitische Farmer wissen schon, wie gut ich repariere, und sie sprechen lieber Deutsch als Englisch. Sie erzählen anderen von mir[10] und so geht mein Geschäft von Tag zu Tag ein bisschen besser. Für die Leute in Waterloo schleife ich Messer[11] und Scheren[12] und repariere Rasenmäher. Das bringt auch ein bisschen Geld und vielleicht kann ich bald bessere Maschinen kaufen.

Gestern habe ich meiner lieben Maria geschrieben. Sie kann jetzt auch nach Kanada kommen und wir können endlich heiraten.

[1] *help* [2] *sharpen* [3] *mend* [4] *own* [5] *workshop* [6] *savings* [7] *rented out* [8] *are ploughing* [9] *are seeding* [10] *about me* [11] *knives* [12] *scissors*

Write **R** in the appropriate spaces to indicate which of the three responses to each of the following questions are **richtig.** Note that a question can have more than one correct response.

1. Warum arbeitet Karl jetzt nicht mehr bei Farmer Dunnigan?
   _____ a. Weil Farmer Dunnigan im Herbst und im Winter keine Hilfe braucht.
   _____ b. Weil er hier keine Zeit für sein Tagebuch hat.
   _____ c. Weil Farmer Dunnigan ihn weggeschickt hat.
2. Was macht Karl im Norden von Kanada?
   _____ a. Er fällt Bäume.
   _____ b. Er schleift Äxte.
   _____ c. Er wäscht und flickt Socken für seine Arbeitskollegen.
3. Karl denkt, dass er nächsten Frühling genug Geld für eine eigene kleine Werkstatt hat. Warum denkt er das?
   _____ a. Weil er bei Farmer Dunnigan so viel gespart hat.
   _____ b. Weil er jetzt ziemlich gut verdient und fast nichts ausgeben kann.
   _____ c. Weil er dann endlich wieder als Schlosser arbeiten kann.
4. Was hat Karl im Frühling 1931 gemacht?
   _____ a. Er ist nach Waterloo gefahren.
   _____ b. Er hat in Waterloo eine kleine Werkstatt gemietet.
   _____ c. Er hat mit seinen Ersparnissen bessere Maschinen gekauft.
5. Warum kommen viele mennonitische Farmer zu Karl Ottmann?
   _____ a. Weil sein Geschäft von Tag zu Tag ein bisschen besser geht.
   _____ b. Weil Karl ein guter Schlosser ist.
   _____ c. Weil sie mit Karl Deutsch sprechen können.
6. Warum hat Karl gestern nach Deutschland geschrieben?
   _____ a. Weil seine Frau jetzt auch nach Kanada kommen soll.
   _____ b. Weil er dort bessere Maschinen kaufen will.
   _____ c. Weil seine Freundin jetzt auch nach Kanada kommen soll.

Zum Übersetzen

6-17 Kleine Gespräche.

1. LISA: Why haven't you packed your suitcase yet?
   SARAH: Because I don't know how much I should take along.

2. FRAU SMITH: Where are your ancestors on your mother's side from?
   FRAU JONES: My grandmother is from Austria and my grandfather is from Germany.
   FRAU SMITH: When did they emigrate to America?
   FRAU JONES: My grandfather emigrated (in) 1948 and my grandmother arrived here six years later.

3. OLIVER: What's the date today?
   PAUL: Today's the nineteenth.

4. LEHRER: When did the First World War **(der Weltkrieg)** begin?
   SCHÜLER: On the twenty-eighth of July 1914.

5. OLIVIA: What kind of a summer job did you have last year?
   SAM: I worked for a painter and earned a lot of money.

6-18 Aus Stefans Tagebuch.

21.6.99 Today was a bad day. It already started in the morning. Because I didn't hear my alarm **(der Wecker),** I slept until eleven. My first lecture started at half-past nine and at half-past ten I was supposed to hand in **(abgeben)** my report for philosophy.

At twelve I had an interview for a summer job as a salesperson at Computer World. I ran like crazy and arrived at Computer World one minute after twelve. Unfortunately the interview didn't go well at all, and I don't think that I'll get the job. The personnel manager is going to call me tomorrow morning.

22.6.99 I can hardly believe it! I got the job and the pay isn't bad at all. I can start the day after tomorrow.

KAPITEL 7

Strukturen

Indicating the person *to whom* or *for whom* something is done

1. The dative case: the indirect object (☞ Übungen 7-1, 7-2, pp. 135–136)

The indirect object indicates *to whom* or *for whom* something is done, and is therefore almost always a *person.* In German the indirect object is signaled by the *dative case.* Don't use the preposition **zu** *(to)* with the indirect object.

	masculine		neuter		feminine		plural	
NOMINATIVE	der / mein	Vater	das / mein	Kind	die / meine	Mutter	die / meine	Kinder
ACCUSATIVE	den / meinen	Vater	das / mein	Kind	die / meine	Mutter	die / meine	Kinder
DATIVE	**dem** / **meinem**	Vater	**dem** / **meinem**	Kind	**der** / **meiner**	Mutter	**den** / **meinen**	Kinder**n**

 In the dative plural all nouns add the ending **-n** unless the plural form ends in **-n** or **-s.**

2. The interrogative pronoun in the dative case (☞ Übungen 7-3, 7-4, pp. 137–138)

The dative form of the interrogative pronoun **wer** has the same ending as the dative form of the masculine definite article.

	interrogative pronoun	definite article
NOMINATIVE	wer	der
ACCUSATIVE	wen	den
DATIVE	**wem**	**dem**

3. Personal pronouns in the dative case (☞ Übung 7-5, p. 139)

nominative	accusative	dative
ich	mich	**mir**
du	dich	**dir**
er	ihn	**ihm**
es	es	**ihm**
sie	sie	**ihr**
wir	uns	**uns**
ihr	euch	**euch**
sie	sie	**ihnen**
Sie	Sie	**Ihnen**

4. Word order: sequence of objects (☞ Übung 7-6, p. 140)

		DATIVE	ACCUSATIVE	
Peter	schenkt	**seinem Vater**	**ein Buch**	zum Vatertag.
Er	schenkt	**ihm**	**ein Kochbuch.**	
		ACCUSATIVE	DATIVE	
Er	kann	**es**	**seinem Vater**	nicht persönlich geben.
Er	muss	**es**	**ihm**	schicken.

⚠
- The dative object (the indirect object) precedes the accusative object (the direct object) *unless the accusative object is a pronoun.*
- Note that pronoun objects always precede noun objects, regardless of case.

5. Dative verbs (☞ Übung 7-7, p. 141)

There are a few German verbs that take a dative object only.

antworten	Warum antwortest du **mir** nicht?	*Why don't you answer* ***me?***
danken	Ich danke **dir** für deine Hilfe.	*I thank* ***you*** *for your help.*
gehören	Gehört dieser Wagen **dir**?	*Does this car belong* ***to you?***
gratulieren	Ich gratuliere **Ihnen** zu Ihrem Erfolg!	*I congratulate* ***you*** *on your success!*
helfen	Kannst du **mir** bitte helfen?	*Can you help* ***me*** *please?*

6. The dative case with adjectives and in idiomatic expressions (☞ Übung 7-8, p. 142)

The dative case is often used with adjectives to express a personal opinion, taste, or conviction.

Rockmusik ist **meiner Oma** zu laut. *Rock music is too loud* ***for my grandma.***

The dative case also appears in the following idiomatic expressions:

Wie geht es **Ihnen?**	*How are you?*
Es tut **mir** Leid.	*I'm sorry.*
Das ist **mir** egal.	*I don't care.*
Mir fällt nichts ein.	*I can't think of anything.*
Wie gefällt **dir** mein Mantel?	*How do you like my coat?*
Diese Jacke steht **dir.**	*This jacket looks good on you.*

Expressing origin, destination, time, manner, and place

7. The dative prepositions (☞ Übungen 7-9, 7-10, pp. 143–144)

aus	*out of*	aus dem Kühlschrank	**seit**	*since*	seit ein Uhr
	from	aus der Schweiz		*for*	seit einem Jahr
außer	*except for*	außer meinem Freund	**von**	*from*	von meinem Freund
bei	*for*	bei der Post		*of*	(ein Freund) von Peter
	at the home of	bei meinen Eltern		*about*	(erzählen) von ihm
	near	bei Berlin	**zu**	*to*	zu meinen Eltern
mit	*with*	mit meiner Freundin		*for*	zu meinem Geburtstag
	by	mit dem Zug		*with*	(Milch) zum Tee
nach	*after*	nach dem Frühstück			
	to	nach Hamburg			

8. Contractions (☞ Übung 7-11, p. 145)

The following contractions of prepositions and definite articles are commonly used.

bei + dem	=	**beim**	Brigitte ist heute Vormittag **beim** Zahnarzt.
von + dem	=	**vom**	Sind diese Eier wirklich **vom** Osterhasen?
zu + dem	=	**zum**	Fährt dieser Bus **zum** Bahnhof?
zu + der	=	**zur**	Seit wann fährst du denn mit dem Fahrrad **zur** Uni?

9. *Da*-compounds (☞ Übung 7-12, p. 146)

Personal pronouns that are objects of prepositions can refer only to people. For things or ideas, **da**-compounds are used.

mit meiner Freundin	→	mit ihr
mit meinem Handy	→	damit

- The **da**-compounds with dative prepositions are **daraus, dabei, damit, danach, davon,** and **dazu.**
- Note that an **r** is added to **da** if the preposition begins with a vowel: **da*r*aus.**

10. *Nach* versus *zu* and *aus* versus *von* (☞ Übungen 7-13, 7-14, pp. 147–148)

When **nach** and **zu** indicate a point of destination, they both mean *to.*

nach		zu	
to a city	nach Leipzig	*to a building*	zum Bahnhof
to a country	nach Luxemburg	*to an institution*	zur Uni
		to a place of business	zum Supermarkt
		to someone's residence	zu Zieglers

When **aus** and **von** indicate a point of origin, they both mean *from.*

aus		von	
from a city	aus Leipzig	*from a building*	vom Bahnhof
from a country	aus Luxemburg	*from an institution*	von der Uni
		from a person	von meinem Freund
		from a point of departure	von Berlin nach Potsdam

11. The preposition *seit* (☞ Übung 7-15, p. 149)

seit (point in time)	=	*since*	**seit** Montag
seit (period in time)	=	*for*	**seit** einem halben Jahr

Describing people, places, and things

12. Adjective endings in the dative case

(☞ Übungen 7-16, 7-17, 7-18, p. 150)

Dative endings of adjectives preceded by **der-*words***

	masculine	neuter	feminine	plural
NOM.	der junge Mann	das kleine Kind	die junge Frau	die kleinen Kinder
ACC.	den jungen Mann	das kleine Kind	die junge Frau	die kleinen Kinder
DAT.	dem jung**en** Mann	dem klein**en** Kind	der jung**en** Frau	den klein**en** Kindern

Dative endings of adjectives preceded by **ein-*words***

	masculine	neuter	feminine	plural
NOM.	ein junger Mann	ein kleines Kind	eine junge Frau	keine kleinen Kinder
ACC.	einen jungen Mann	ein kleines Kind	eine junge Frau	keine kleinen Kinder
DAT.	einem jung**en** Mann	einem klein**en** Kind	einer jung**en** Frau	keinen klein**en** Kindern

 Adjectives that are preceded by a **der**-word or an **ein**-word in the dative case always take the ending **-en.**

Dative endings of unpreceded adjectives

	masculine	neuter	feminine	plural
NOMINATIVE	guter Kaffee	gutes Bier	gute Salami	gute Äpfel
ACCUSATIVE	guten Kaffee	gutes Bier	gute Salami	gute Äpfel
DATIVE	gut**em** Kaffee	gut**em** Bier	gut**er** Salami	gut**en** Äpfeln

NAME: ______________________ DATE: ______________

Anwendung

Übungen

7-1 Margaret war in Österreich. In each sentence of this narrative, find all the subjects, indirect objects, and direct objects and write them under the appropriate headings in the table below. Not all sentences have indirect and/or direct objects. (Strukturen 1, p. 129)

1. Margaret war zwei Monate lang in Österreich und hat dort ihre Großeltern und ihren Onkel Bernhard besucht.
2. Sie hat viel Deutsch gelernt und auch viele Fotos gemacht.
3. Sie hat ihren Freundinnen viele Postkarten geschrieben.
4. Letzte Woche ist Margaret wieder nach Hause geflogen.
5. Gestern hatten ihre Freundinnen eine kleine Party für sie.
6. Margaret hat ihren Freundinnen ihre Fotos gezeigt.
7. Sie hat auch jeder Freundin ein kleines Geschenk mitgebracht.

	SUBJEKTE	INDIREKTE OBJEKTE	DIREKTE OBJEKTE
1.	Margaret		ihre Großeltern
			ihren Onkel Bernhard
2.			
3.			
4.			
5.			
6.			
7.			

7-2 Indirektes Objekt und direktes Objekt. Complete the sentences appropriately, using the nouns that precede each section as indirect or direct objects. (Strukturen 1, p. 129)

sein Kind, ein Stück (n) Schokolade / die Studenten, der Dativ / ihre Eltern, ein Kuchen (m)

1. Die Professorin erklärt den Studenten den Dativ.
2. Helga bäckt ihren Eltern einen Kuchen.
3. Der Vater gibt seinem Kind ein Stück Schokolade.

ihr Freund, ein Pullover (m) / der Hund, die ganze Wurst / seine Freunde, eine Runde Bier

4. Hast du dem Hund die ganzen Wurst gefüttert?
5. Thomas hat seinen Freunden eine Runde Bier bezahlt.
6. Eva hat ihrem Freund einen Pullover gekauft.

seine Tochter, ein Fahrrad (n) / ihre Kinder, die Haare / meine Eltern, eine E-Mail

7. Herr Koch hat seiner Tochter ein Fahrrad geschenkt.
8. Gestern Abend habe ich meinen Eltern einem EMail geschrieben.
9. Frau Sperber hat ihren Kindern die Haare gewaschen.

ihr Sohn, ein Paket (n) / seine Freundin, fünf rote Rosen / seine Frau, das Frühstück

10. Peter hat seiner Freundin fünf rote Rosen gebracht.
11. Frau Berger schickt ihrem Sohn ein Packet.
12. Herr Teuscher macht ____________.

deine Mutter, eine Tasse Kaffee / unsere Professorin, eine Postkarte / ihre Eltern, tausend Euro

13. Sollen wir ____________ schreiben?
14. Bring ________ doch bitte ________, Helga!
15. Maria schuldet ____________.

NAME: ______________________ DATE: ______________

7-3 Fragen und Antworten? Supply the interrogative pronouns **wer, wen, wem,** or **was** in the questions and appropriate case endings in the responses. Note that sometimes no ending is required. (Strukturen 1 & 2, p. 129)

1. > ___Was___ schenken Sie Ihrem Sohn zum Geburtstag, Herr Merck?

   < Ein_en_ Fußball (m).

2. > ___Wem___ schenken Sie diesen Fußball, Herr Merck?

   < Mein_em_ Sohn.

3. > ___Was___ schreibst du, Stephanie?

   < Ein_en_ Brief (m).

4. > ___Wem___ schreibst du, Stephanie?

   < Mein_en_ Eltern.

5. > ___Wen___ holt Sie in Frankfurt ab, Frau Vogel?

   < Unser___ Sohn und sein_e_ Frau.

6. > ___Wen___ holst du in Frankfurt ab, Florian?

   < Mein_e_ Eltern.

7. > ___________ will denn deine Fotos sehen?

   < Mein____ Freunde.

8. > ___Wem___ willst du denn deine Fotos zeigen?

   < Mein_en_ Freunde_n_.

9. > ___Was___ willst du deinen Freunden zeigen?

   < Mein_e_ Fotos.

7-4 ***Wer, wen, wem* oder *was?*** Supply the proper interrogative pronoun for each question. Then answer the questions appropriately, using the choices given. (☞ Strukturen 1 & 2, p. 129)

Meinen Freund / Mein Vater / Meiner Mutter

1. > Wer hat denn vorher angerufen?

   < Mein Vater.

2. > __________ schreibst du denn den langen Brief?

   < ______________________________.

3. > __________ hast du vorher angerufen?

   < ______________________________.

Ihr Freund Kurt / Meiner Freundin / Rote Rosen

4. > __________ für Blumen kaufst du?

   < ______________________________.

5. > __________ schickst du diese Rosen?

   < ______________________________.

6. > __________ hat denn unserer Tochter rote Rosen geschickt?

   < ______________________________.

NAME: ______________________________ DATE: ______________

7-5 Ergänzen Sie! Supply the appropriate pronouns in the nominative, accusative, or dative case. (Strukturen 3, p. 129)

ich (4x) / du (2x) / mich / mir / dich / dir / es

1. JENS: Kannst ___du___ ___mir___ hundert Euro leihen, Kurt?

   KURT: Ja, aber zuerst muss __________ auf die Bank. Heute Nachmittag kann __________ __________ das Geld dann geben.

2. LUTZ: Wann soll __________ __________ abholen, Nina? Um halb sieben?

   NINA: Erst um halb sieben?! Nein, __________ glaube, __________ ist besser, __________ holst __________ eine halbe Stunde früher ab.

Sie (2x) / ich (2x) / Ihnen (2x) / mir / ihr (2x)

3. HERR MERCK: Soll __________ __________ eine Tasse Kaffee bringen, Frau Kuhn?

   FRAU KUHN: Ja, Herr Merck, und bringen __________ __________ doch bitte auch ein Stück Kuchen mit.

4. FRAU LANG: Herr Merck! Hat Frau Kuhn __________ gesagt, dass __________ __________ eine Tasse Kaffee bringen sollen?

   HERR MERCK: Ja, und __________ soll __________ auch ein Stück Kuchen mitbringen.

du / ich (2x) / dich / uns (3x) / euch (2x)

5. MUTTI: Soll __________ __________ ein Märchen erzählen, Kinder?

   FLORIAN: Ja, Mutti, erzähl __________ doch das Märchen von Hänsel und Gretel.

6. MIEKE: Kannst __________ __________ drei heute Abend nach Hause fahren, Frank?

   FRANK: Wen? __________, Markus und Petra?

   MIEKE: Ja, __________ drei.

   FRANK: Ja natürlich, __________ nehme __________ gern mit.

wir / ich (2x) / du / ihn / ihm (2x) / ihnen / sie

7. EVA: Was soll __________ denn meinen Eltern zu Weihnachten schenken?

   ANTJE: Kauf __________ doch einen neuen Fernseher. Und deinem Bruder schenkst __________ ein schönes Hemd.

   EVA: Aber das habe __________ __________ doch schon zum Geburtstag geschenkt.

   ANTJE: Dann kauf __________ doch ein paar Tennisbälle.

8. DIRK: Sollen __________ auch Günter und Tina zu unserer Fete einladen?

   BEATE: __________ nicht, nur __________.

7-6 Kleine Gespräche. Complete with the direct and indirect objects in proper sequence. (☞ Strukturen 4, p. 130)

das Buch , Ihnen / mir, es

1. > Hat Peter ___Ihnen das Buch___ zurückgegeben, Frau Meyer?

   < Nein, aber er hat gesagt, er gibt ______________________ heute Nachmittag zurück.

Michael, ein Buch / eine CD, ihm

2. > Ich schenke ______________________.

   < Und ich kaufe ______________________.

ein Motorrad, ihrem Sohn / ihm, einen Wagen

3. > Letztes Jahr haben Bergers ______________________ gekauft.

   < Ja, und dieses Jahr wollen sie ______________________ kaufen.

zwanzig Euro, mir / mir, sie

4. > Kannst du ______________________ leihen, Monika?

   < Ja, aber du musst ______________________ morgen früh wieder zurückgeben.

dir, den schönen Pullover / mir, ihn

5. > Wer hat ______________________ geschenkt?

   < Meine Mutter hat ______________________ gekauft.

NAME: ______________________ DATE: ______________

7-7 Was passt in jeder Gruppe zusammen? In each group, match the questions and responses by writing the appropriate numbers in the spaces provided. (Strukturen 5, p. 130)

A.

1.	Wem gehört dieses Buch?	5	Vielleicht hat er sie gar nicht bekommen.
2.	Warum antwortest du mir nicht?		Nein, er hat es wieder mal vergessen.
3.	Wann hilfst du mir bei meinem Referat?		Du hast mich doch gar nichts gefragt.
4.	Hat Horst dir zum Geburtstag gratuliert, Maria?	1	Mir.
5.	Kurt hat uns für die 100 Euro nie gedankt.	3	Heute Abend.

B.

1.	Hilfst du mir bei meinem Referat?	____	Ja, das ist mein Buch.
2.	Warum hat Maria heute so viel Post bekommen?	____	Aber Frau Horb! Da gibt's doch nichts zu danken!
3.	Gehört dieses Buch dir?	____	Warum schreibst du ihr dann noch?
4.	Sabine antwortet mir nie.		Ja, aber erst heute Abend.
5.	Wie kann ich Ihnen danken, Frau Blum?	2	Weil sie Geburtstag hat und ihre Freunde ihr alle gratulieren wollen. 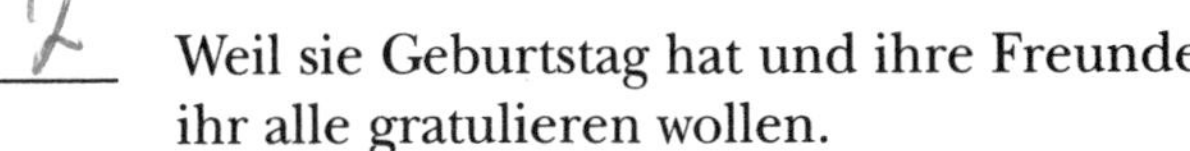

7-8 Fragen und Antworten. In each set, choose the correct responses to the questions and write them in the spaces provided. Complete the responses with the appropriate personal pronoun in the dative case. (Strukturen 6, p. 130)

es tut ___ Leid	jetzt geht es ___ wieder besser
sie war ___ zu teuer	es war ___ zu kalt

1. > Warum hat Nicole die Jacke nicht gekauft?

   < Sie war ihr zu teuer.

2. > Ist dein Großvater immer noch so krank, Renate?

   < Nein, ______________________________

3. > Warum habt ihr denn gestern Nachmittag nicht Tennis gespielt?

   < ______________________________

4. > Kannst du mir wirklich nicht helfen, Anita?

   < Nein, Günter, wirklich nicht. ______________________________

fällt ___ im Moment nicht ein	es steht ___ sehr gut
das ist ___ egal	es ist ___ zu weit

5. > Mir gefällt Barbaras neues Kleid gar nicht.

   < Und ich finde, ______________________________

6. > Kennst du den Mann dort, Sabine?

   < Ja, aber sein Name ______________________________

7. > Warum fahren deine Verwandten dich nicht nach Frankfurt?

   < Ich glaube, ______________________________

8. > Es tut mir Leid, Julia, aber dein neuer Freund gefällt mir gar nicht.

   < ______________________________. Mir gefällt er sehr gut.

7-9 ***Aus, außer, bei* oder *mit?*** Complete with the appropriate prepositions and endings. (☞ Strukturen 7, p. 131)

1. > Was hast du zu trinken?

   < __Außer__ dies_em_ Rotwein habe ich leider nichts.

2. > __Mit__ w_em_ gehst du heute Abend ins Konzert?

   < __Mit__ mein_er_ Schwester.

3. > Woher ist diese tolle Schokolade?

   < ____________ d____ Schweiz.

4. > ____________ w____ hat Stefan in Hamburg gewohnt?

   < ____________ sein____ Tante.

5. > Seid ihr ____________ d____ Zug nach Berlin gefahren?

   < Nein, ____________ d____ Wagen.

Großmama kommt uns besuchen, mit Bus & Bahn und einem Kuchen.

BUSSE & BAHNEN. GRÜNE WELLE FÜR VERNUNFT.

6. > Woher ist Stephanie?

   < Sie kommt ____________ d____ USA (pl).

7. > Arbeitet dein Vater ____________ d____ Post (f)?

   < Nein, ____________ d____ Bank (f).

8. > Wo war die Party gestern Abend? ____________ dir, Tina?

   < Ja, und ____________ dir waren alle meine Freunde da.

9. > Hast du ____________ d____ Direktorin gesprochen?

   < Nein, nur ____________ ihr____ Sekretärin.

10. > Woher hast du die fünfzig Euro, Gerd?

    < ____________ dein____ Geldtasche.

11. > Ist Potsdam ____________ Hamburg?

    < Nein, ____________ Berlin.

12. > Was gibt's ____________ dir zu essen, Beate?

    < ____________ Käse und ein bisschen Wurst habe ich leider gar nichts.

7-10 ***Nach, seit, von oder zu?*** Complete with the appropriate prepositions and endings. (☞ Strukturen 7, p. 131)

1. > ____________ w____ ist der Brief?
   < ____________ mein____ Eltern.
2. > Wann gehst du ____________ Hause?
   < Gleich ____________ mein____ letzten Vorlesung.
3. > ____________ wann bist du so krank?
   < ____________ d____ Abendessen bei Kathrin!
4. > Bist du morgen früh ____________ Hause?
   < Nur bis neun. Ich gehe gleich ____________ d____ Frühstück ____________ mein____ Freundin.
5. > Was machen wir ____________ dies____ Klausur?
   < Wir kommen alle ____________ dir und trinken ein Glas Bier.
6. > ____________ w____ hast du diese CD?
   < ____________ ein____ guten Freund ____________ mir.
7. > Besucht Ihre Tochter sie oft, Frau Bühler?
   < Nein, ____________ Weihnachten war sie nicht mehr ____________ Hause.
8. > Wann fahrt ihr ____________ Starnberg?
   < Gleich ____________ d____ Mittagessen.
9. > Haben Sie den BMW schon lange, Frau Strohmann?
   < Nein, erst ____________ ein____ halben Jahr.
10. > Was hast du ____________ dein____ einundzwanzigsten Geburtstag alles bekommen?
    < ____________ mein____ Eltern habe ich einen Farbfernseher bekommen und ____________ mein____ Bruder einen CD-Spieler.
11. > ____________ wann sind Bettina und Gerd so gute Freunde?
    < ____________ d____ Party bei Sylvia.
12. > Was möchtest du ____________ mir ____________ Weihnachten?
    < ____________ dir möchte ich ein schönes Sweatshirt.

NAME: ______________________ DATE: ______________

7-11 ***Wo? Wohin? Woher?*** Write questions that begin with **wo, wohin,** or **woher.** Begin each response with one of the following contractions: **beim, vom, zum, zur.** (☞ Strukturen 8, p. 131)

1. gehen / du — Zahnarzt (m)

   > Wohin gehst du? < Zum Zahnarzt.

2. kommen / du — Zahnarzt

   > ______________ < ______________

3. sein / Silke — Zahnarzt

   > ______________ < ______________

4. haben / du / dieses gute Brot — Bäcker Müller

   > ______________ < ______________

5. fahren / der Bus — Flughafen (m)

   > ______________ < ______________

6. kommen / der Bus — Flughafen

   > ______________ < ______________

7. rennen / du — Bus (m)

   > ______________ < ______________

8. sein / das Hotel Merkur — Bahnhof

   > ______________ < ______________

9. fahren / ihr — Hotel Merkur (n)

   > ______________ < ______________

10. gehen / du — Uni (f)

    > ______________ < ______________

11. sein / Martin und Claudia — Mittagessen

    > ______________ < ______________

12. kommen / ihr — Schwimmen (n)

    > ______________ < ______________

7-12 ***Präposition + Pronomen* oder *da-Form?*** Respond to the questions appropriately, replacing the phrases in bold face with a preposition + pronoun or a **da**-compound. (☞ Strukturen 9, p. 131)

1. Warum frißt denn die Katze nicht **aus dieser Schüssel?**

   Weil der Hund vorher schon ____daraus____ gefressen hat.

2. Wohin gehst du heute Abend **mit Ralf?**

   Heute Abend gehe ich ____________ in die Disco.

3. Ist Moritz wieder **mit meinem Fahrrad** zur Uni gefahren?

   Nein, er ist nur schnell ____________ zum Supermarkt gefahren.

4. Was macht ihr **nach dem Fußballspiel?**

   Wir fahren gleich ____________ nach Hause.

5. Hat Julia dir **von ihren Problemen mit Michael** erzählt?

   Nein. sie hat mir nichts ____________ erzählt.

6. Was hat Julia dir **von Michael** erzählt?

   Sie hat mir nichts ____________ erzählt.

7. Telefonierst du viel **mit deinem Handy?**

   Nein, ich telefoniere nur selten ____________.

8. Ist Moritz oft **bei Beate?**

   Ja, er ist fast jeden Abend ____________.

9. Was gibt es heute **zu deinem Wiener Schnitzel,** Beate?

   Heute gibt es Pommes frites und Brokkoli ____________.

10. Warst du auch **bei der Demonstration?**

    Nein, ich konnte leider nicht ____________ sein.

NAME: ______________________________ DATE: ______________

7-13 ***Nach, zu, aus* oder *von?*** Complete the responses with the appropriate prepositions and endings. (Strukturen 10, p. 132)

1. > Woher hast du diesen schönen Rucksack?

   < Von__________ mein_en_ Eltern.

2. > Woher kommt Stephanie?

   < __________ Chicago.

3. > Wohin fährt Stephanie nächstes Wochenende?

   < __________ ihr____ Verwandten __________ Köln.

4. > Woher kommen diese Orangen?

   < __________ Florida.

5. > Wohin reisen Sie diesen Winter, Frau Koch?

   < __________ Israel.

6. > Wie lang braucht der ICE-Sprinter

   __________ Frankfurt __________ Berlin?

   < Er braucht nur dreieinhalb Stunden.

7. > Wohin gehst du?

   < __________ Professor Weber.

8. > Woher kommt ihr?

   < __________ Professor Seidlmeyer.

9. > Woher ist dieser Brief?

   < __________ dein____ Uni.

10. > Wohin geht ihr heute Abend?

    < __________ Stefans Party.

7-14 Reisepläne. Complete the conversation by writing the questions and responses in the proper sequence. Where necessary, supply appropriate prepositions. (☞ Strukturen 7 & 10, pp. 131–132)

Nein, ich fliege ____________ Düsseldorf.

Wie lange bleibst du ____________ deinen Großeltern?

Landest du in Frankfurt?

Morgen fliege ich ____________ meinen Großeltern nach Deutschland.

Zwei Wochen. Dann fahre ich ____________ Österreich.

Wo leben deine Großeltern?

Und wie kommst du ____________ Düsseldorf ____________ Lehrte?

Warum ____________ Österreich?

Ich fahre ____________ dem Zug.

In Lehrte ____________ Hannover.

Mein Großvater ist ____________ Österreich und ich habe auch dort viele Verwandte.

> Morgen fliege ich ...

< Wo leben deine Großeltern?

> ____________

< Landest du in Frankfurt?

> ____________

< Und wie kommst du ...

> ____________

< ____________

> ____________

< ____________

> ____________

____

NAME: ______________________________ DATE: ______________

7-15 Was bedeutet *seit?* Complete the sentences with the correct endings and indicate with a check mark whether the English equivalent of **seit** is *since* or *for*. (☞ Strukturen 11, p. 132)

	since	for
1. Jessica ist seit d_____ 15. September in Deutschland.	____	____
2. Zieglers leben seit über 20 Jahre_____ in Göttingen.	____	____
3. Mein Bruder hat den Scanner erst seit drei Tage_____.	____	____
4. Seit wann fährt Kathrin denn einen Audi?	____	____
5. Moritz arbeitet seit ein_____ halb_____ Jahr bei IBM.	____	____
6. Seit d_____ Party bei Eva ruft Thomas mich jeden Tag an.	____	____
7. Stephanie wohnt schon seit ein_____ Monat nicht mehr im Studentenheim.	____	____
8. Seit ihr_____ Jahr in Deutschland spricht Stephanie fast perfekt Deutsch.	____	____

7-16 Mein bester Freund. Supply adjective endings. (Strukturen 12, p. 133)

> Von wem hast du den toll______ Pulli?

< Von meinem best______ Freund.

> Wie heißt dein best______ Freund?

< Er heißt Omar. Wir kennen einander seit viel______ Jahren.

> Omar ist kein deutsch______ Name (m). Ist er Deutsch______?

< Ja, er ist Deutsch______. Sein Vater ist aus der Türkei, aber er ist mit einer Deutsch______ verheiratet und er und seine Kinder sind jetzt auch Deutsch______.

7-17 Wer ist das? Supply adjective endings. (Strukturen 12, p. 133)

> Wer ist die schick______ Frau dort mit dem groß______ langhaarig______ Hund?

< Das ist unsere neu______ Nachbarin. Sie heißt Beverly Harper und ist aus den Vereinigt______ Staaten, aber sie spricht akzentfrei______ Deutsch (n). Sie ist Journalistin und schreibt interessant______ Artikel für eine groß______ amerikanisch______ Zeitung. Bei schön______ Wetter geht sie oft mit ihrem groß______ Hund spazieren. Beverly und meine Mutter sind sehr gut______ Freundinnen.

7-18 Mein Geburtstag. Supply adjective endings. (Strukturen 12, p. 133)

In unserer Stadt gibt es ein sehr gut______ französisch______ Restaurant (n). Dort habe ich mit meiner ganz______ Familie und mit meinen best______ Freunden zusammen meinen einundzwanzigst______ Geburtstag gefeiert. Nur mein ältest______ Bruder konnte nicht kommen, denn er arbeitet seit einem halb______ Jahr bei einer deutsch______ Firma in South Carolina. Wir haben mit echt______ französisch______ Champagner (m) begonnen. Dann hatten wir ganz delikat______ Hors d'oeuvres (pl), einen fein______ Salat, und nach einem toll______ Hauptgericht noch einen wunderbar______ Nachtisch. Auch der Wein war natürlich vom best______ und es hat mir so Leid getan, dass mein Bruder zu diesem schön______ Fest nicht kommen konnte.

NAME: ______________________ DATE: ______________

Zum Verstehen

7-19 Drei Schilder. Study the three signs in the photo and answer the following questions.

1. In was für ein Gebäude[1] fährt man hier?

   Hier fährt man in ein ______________________________.

2. Wie hoch darf mein Fahrzeug sein, wenn ich in dieses Gebäude hineinfahren will?

   Es darf nur ______________________________.

3. Was darf man im Parkhaus nicht tun?

   Man darf hier nicht ______________________________.

   ______________________________.

4. Welche zwei Wörter zeigen, dass Kinder hier nicht spielen dürfen?

   Die Wörter ______________________________.

[1] *building*

7-20 Sylvia hat Geburtstag. Read Sylvia's account of her 21st birthday and then answer the questions below.

Gestern Nacht um drei hat bei uns das Telefon geklingelt.[1] Ulrike, meine Mitbewohnerin, ist zuerst aufgewacht und ist schnell aufgestanden und zum Telefon gerannt. Der Anruf war aber nicht für sie, sondern für mich, von meiner Mutter zu Hause in Minnesota. „Vor einundzwanzig Jahren bist du Punkt drei Uhr morgens auf die Welt gekommen", hat sie gesagt und gelacht. „Damals habe ich die ganze Nacht nicht geschlafen, und deshalb will ich mich jetzt ein bisschen revanchieren[2]. Dein Vater und ich waren damals so glücklich, denn du warst unsere Erstgeborene, und wir waren so stolz[3] auf dich. Jetzt gratulieren wir dir herzlichst zum Geburtstag und wünschen dir alles Gute für dein neues Lebensjahr." Ich habe dann noch schnell mit meinem Vater und meinen Geschwistern gesprochen. Meine Schwester Lori möchte auch mal ein Jahr in Heidelberg studieren und sie wollte natürlich ganz genau wissen, wie es hier ist. Und zum Schluss[4] hat dann mein kleiner Bruder Dougie noch gesagt, wie sehr er mich vermisst.

Nach diesem Anruf konnte ich nicht gleich einschlafen. Ich musste an meine Kindheit[5] und an meine Familie denken, und wie hier in Heidelberg alles so anders ist als zu Hause in Duluth, und später habe ich dann noch von meiner Familie geträumt. Dann hat Ulrike mich geweckt und mich in die Küche geschickt. Dort stand mitten auf dem Tisch eine große, leckere Torte mit einundzwanzig Kerzen! „Du darfst sie aber jetzt nicht anschneiden[6]", hat sie mir erklärt, „denn für heute Abend habe ich alle unsere Freunde zu einer kleinen Geburtstagsfeier eingeladen." Dann hat es geklopft. Es war mein Freund Michael mit drei wunderbaren roten Rosen!

Die Party am Abend war ganz toll. Meine Freunde haben mir einen Bildband[7] mit wunderschönen Farbfotos aus allen deutschen Ländern geschenkt. „Hoffentlich gefällt er dir", hat Michael gesagt. „Genau das habe ich mir gewünscht", habe ich ihm geantwortet, und dann habe ich die Kerzen ausgeblasen[8] und die Torte aufgeschnitten[9].

[1]*rang* [2]*take revenge* [3]*proud* [4]*at the end* [5]*childhood* [6]*cut into* [7]*coffee-table book* [8]*blew out* [9]*cut up*

Write **R** in the appropriate spaces to indicate which of the two responses is **richtig.**

1. Bei wem war es drei Uhr nachts?
   _____ a. Bei Sylvias Eltern in Duluth.
   _____ b. Bei Sylvia und Ulrike in Heidelberg.
2. Wer wollte ganz genau wissen, wie es in Heidelberg ist?
   _____ a. Sylvias Schwester.
   _____ b. Sylvias Bruder.
3. Wer ist älter, Sylvia oder ihre Schwester?
   _____ a. Sylvia.
   _____ b. Sylvias Schwester.
4. Mit wem hat Sylvia zuletzt gesprochen?
   _____ a. Mit ihrer Schwester.
   _____ b. Mit ihrem Bruder.
5. Warum konnte Sylvia nach dem Anruf nicht gleich einschlafen?
   _____ a. Sie hat von ihrer Familie geträumt.
   _____ b. Sie musste an ihre Kindheit und an ihre Familie denken.
6. Wer hat Sylvia das zweite Mal geweckt?
   _____ a. Ulrike.
   _____ b. Lori.
7. Warum hat Ulrike Sylvia in die Küche geschickt?
   _____ a. Dort war Sylvias Freund Michael mit drei wunderbaren roten Rosen.
   _____ b. Dort war eine große, leckere Torte.
8. Von wem hat Sylvia den Bildband bekommen?
   _____ a. Von ihrem Freund Michael.
   _____ b. Von allen ihren Freunden.

NAME: ______________________ DATE: ______________

Zum Übersetzen

7-21 Eine Postkarte aus Berlin.

Dear Cindy,

Greetings from the new (and old) capital city of Germany. We have been *(present tense!)* here for a week and have already seen a lot. The museums are wonderful and the night life *(neuter, one word)* is really fantastic! The city center *(neuter, one word)* actually never sleeps. Last night I partied **(feiern)** with my friends until three o'clock in the morning. Next time I'll write you from Dresden.

Love,
Yvonne

7-22 Ein Geburtstagsbrief.

Dear Tom,

I have been wanting to write you for months, but at the **(im)** moment my life is so stressful that I simply haven't had time. But I haven't forgotten that you're going to be twenty-two tomorrow. Happy birthday! Yesterday I sent you a CD of my favorite band. I hope you like it.
How and where are you celebrating your twenty-second birthday? Whom have you invited to your party? I'm sorry that I can't celebrate with you and your friends, but from Hamburg to Seattle it is so far and the flight is too expensive! Perhaps we'll see each other in spring. My company is going to send me to Vancouver after Easter. From there it's *(plural verb)* only a few kilometers to your house.

See you then!
Helene

KAPITEL 8

Strukturen

Talking about destination and location

1. *Wohin* and *wo:* a review (☞ Übung 8-1, p. 161)

wohin?	*where (to what place?)*	**Wohin** geht Martin? **Wohin** geht die Schulstraße? **Wohin** soll ich meine Jacke hängen?
wo?	*where (in what place?)*	**Wo** ist Martin? **Wo** ist die Schulstraße? **Wo** ist meine Jacke?

2. Two-case prepositions (☞ Übung 8-2, p. 162)

		wohin? TOWARD A DESTINATION PREPOSITION + ACCUSATIVE	wo? FIXED LOCATION PREPOSITION + DATIVE
an	on *(a vertical surface)* to at	Lisa hängt das Bild **an die** Wand. Kurt geht **an die** Tür.	Das Bild hängt **an der** Wand. Kurt steht **an der** Tür.
auf	on *(a horizontal surface)* to at	Lisa legt das Buch **auf den** Tisch. Kurt geht **auf den** Markt.	Das Buch liegt **auf dem** Tisch. Kurt ist **auf dem** Markt.
hinter	behind	Die Kinder laufen **hinter das** Haus.	Die Kinder sind **hinter dem** Haus.
in	in, into, to	Kurt geht **in die** Küche.	Kurt ist **in der** Küche.
neben	beside	Kurt stellt den Sessel **neben die** Couch.	Der Sessel steht **neben der** Couch.
über	over, above	Kurt hängt die Lampe **über den** Tisch.	Die Lampe hängt **über dem** Tisch.
unter	under, below	Lisa stellt die Hausschuhe **unter das** Bett.	Die Hausschuhe stehen **unter dem** Bett.
vor	in front of	Kurt stellt den Wagen **vor die** Garage.	Der Wagen steht **vor der** Garage.
zwischen	between	Lisa stellt die Stehlampe **zwischen die** Couch und **den** Sessel.	Die Stehlampe steht **zwischen der** Couch und **dem** Sessel.

wohin?	verb signaling movement toward a destination	+	two-case preposition	+	accusative
wo?	verb signaling a fixed location	+	two-case preposition	+	dative

3. Contractions (☞ Übung 8-3, p. 163)

The prepositions **an** and **in** normally contract with the articles **das** and **dem.**

an + das	=	**ans**	Hast du unser Poster **ans** schwarze Brett gehängt?
an + dem	=	**am**	Hängt unser Poster **am** schwarzen Brett?
in + das	=	**ins**	Heute Abend gehen wir **ins** Konzert.
in + dem	=	**im**	Gestern Abend waren wir **im** Kino.

 In colloquial German the article **das** also contracts with other two-case prepositions: **aufs, hinters, übers, unters, vors.**

4. The verbs *stellen/stehen, legen/liegen,* and *hängen* (☞ Übung 8-4, p. 164 and Übung 8-8 p. 168)

German uses three different verbs to describe the different actions conveyed by the English *to put.*

stellen	*to put in an upright position*	**Stell** die Weingläser auf **den** Tisch!
legen	*to put in a horizontal position, to lay (down)*	**Legt** eure Mäntel **aufs** Bett!
hängen	*to hang (up)*	**Häng** deine Jacke in **die** Garderobe!

 When these verbs are followed by a two-case preposition, the object of the preposition appears in the *accusative case.*

German tends to be more exact than English when describing the location of things.

stehen	*to be standing*	Die Weingläser **stehen** auf **dem** Tisch.
liegen	*to be lying*	Eure Mäntel **liegen** auf **dem** Bett.
hängen	*to be hanging*	Deine Jacke **hängt** in **der** Garderobe.

 When these verbs are followed by one of the two-case prepositions, the object of the preposition appears in the *dative case.*

5. More on *da*-compounds (☞ Übung 8-5, p. 165)

Personal pronouns that are objects of prepositions can only refer to people. For things or ideas, **da**-compounds are used.

der Student **neben Martin**	→	der Student **neben ihm**
der Wagen **neben meinem VW**	→	der Wagen **daneben**

If the preposition begins with a vowel, an **r** is added to **da: da*r*an, da*r*auf, da*r*in, da*r*über, da*r*unter.**

6. German *an, auf, in,* and English *to* (☞ Übung 8-6, p. 166, but also read *Strukturen 3* before doing this exercise.)

When the two-case prepositions **an, auf,** and **in** mean *to,* they are followed by the accusative case.

to (next to something)	**an die** Tür; **ans** Telefon; **ans** Meer
to (within a place)	**in die** Küche; **ins** Konzert; **in die** Berge
to (a country that is masculine, feminine, or plural)	**in den** Iran; **in die** Schweiz; **in die** USA
to (a building or institution to do business)	**auf den** Markt; **aufs** Rathaus

Saying when something occurs

7. The two-case prepositions *an, in, vor,* and *zwischen* in time phrases (☞ Übung 8-7, p. 167)

When the prepositions **an, in, vor,** and **zwischen** are used in time expressions, they are followed by the dative case.

am ersten April	***on*** *the first of April*
im September	***in*** *September*
vor der Vorlesung	***before*** *the lecture*
vor einer halben Stunde	*half an hour* ***ago***
zwischen dem dritten und **dem** achten Mai	***between*** *the third and eighth of May*

Vor has two English equivalents: *before* and *ago.*

Word Order

8. Infinitive phrases (☞ Übung 8-9, p. 170)

Common verbs or expressions that introduce infinitive phrases are **anfangen, vergessen, versprechen, versuchen, vorhaben, Zeit haben, Lust haben, es satt haben, es macht Spaß.**

Paul hat vor, **morgen in der Klausur eine Eins** ***zu bekommen.***

 • **Zu** and the infinitive stand at the end of the phrase.

• An infinitive phrase is often marked off by a comma.

With a separable-prefix verb, **zu** is inserted between the prefix and the verb.

Paul hat versprochen, **heute Abend mit Anna** ***auszugehen.***

If there is more than one infinitive in the phrase, **zu** precedes the last infinitive.

Paul hat keine Zeit, **mit Anna** ***tanzen zu gehen.***

Sometimes the English equivalent of the **zu**-infinitive is the *-ing* form of the verb.

Anna hat keine Lust, **ohne Paul** ***tanzen zu gehen.***
Anna doesn't feel like ***going dancing without Paul.***

9. Infinitive phrases introduced by *um* (☞ Übung 8-10, p. 171)

An infinitive phrase introduced by **um** expresses purpose or intention.

Ich brauche ein paar Nägel, **um** meine Bilder **aufzuhängen.**	*I need a few nails* ***(in order) to hang up*** *my pictures.*

English often uses only *to* instead of *in order to.*

Indicating possession or relationships

10. The genitive case (☞ Übung 8-11, p. 172)

The genitive case is used to express the idea of possession or belonging together.

For proper names, add **-s** to the name: Claudia**s** Schreibtisch, Frau Meyer**s** Kinder.

For nouns other than proper names, the genitive form follows the noun it modifies: das Büro **des** Professor**s;** das Zimmer mein**er** Schwester; das Dach dies**es** Haus**es;** die Wohnung unser**er** Eltern.

	masculine		neuter		feminine		plural	
NOMINATIVE	der mein	Vater	das mein	Kind	die meine	Mutter	die meine	Kinder
ACCUSATIVE	den meinen	Vater	das mein	Kind	die meine	Mutter	die meine	Kinder
DATIVE	dem meinem	Vater	dem meinem	Kind	der meiner	Mutter	den meinen	Kindern
GENITIVE	**des** **meines**	Vaters	**des** **meines**	Kindes	**der** **meiner**	Mutter	**der** **meiner**	Kinder

- Most one-syllable masculine and neuter nouns add **-es** in the genitive singular **(Kind*es*).**
- Masculine and neuter nouns with more than one syllable add **-s** in the genitive singular **(Vater*s*).**
- Feminine nouns and the plural forms of all nouns have no genitive ending.

The genitive form of the interrogative pronoun is **wessen.**

Wessen Jacke ist das? *Whose jacket is that?*

Describing people, places, and things

11. Genitive endings of preceded adjectives (☞ Übung 8-12, p. 173)

Adjectives that are preceded by a **der**-word or an **ein**-word in the genitive case always take the ending **-en**.

	masculine		neuter		feminine		plural	
GENITIVE	des eines	jung**en** Mannes	des eines	klein**en** Kindes	der einer	jung**en** Frau	der meiner	klein**en** Kinder

NAME: ______________________________ DATE: ______________

Anwendung

Übungen

8-1 Was passt? Using the question words **wohin** and **wo** as cues, complete sentences *a.* and *b.* with the appropriate verbs. Note that the verbs are given in their correct forms. (☞ Strukturen 1, p. 155)

gehängt / gekauft

1. a. Wo hast du den Mantel __gekauft__?
   b. Wohin hast du den Mantel __gehängt__?

abgeholt / gefahren

2. a. Wo hast du Sabine __abgeholt__?
   b. Wohin bist du mit Sabine __gefahren__?

studiert / fliegt

3. a. Wohin __fliegt__ deine Schwester nächstes Jahr?
   b. Wo __studiert__ deine Schwester nächstes Jahr?

gefunden / geschickt

4. a. Wo haben Sie das Geld __gefunden__?
   b. Wohin haben Sie das Geld __geschicht__?

gehst / bist

5. a. Wo __bist__ du heute Abend?
   b. Wohin __gehst__ du heute Abend?

parken / fahren

6. a. Wo soll ich __parken__?
   b. Wohin soll ich __fahren__?

wohnen / reisen

7. a. Wo __wohnen__ deine Eltern?
   b. Wohin __reisen__ deine Eltern?

8-2 ***Wohin* oder *wo?*** Complete the questions with **wohin** or **wo** and the responses with the proper case endings. (Strukturen 2, pp. 155–156)

1. > ____________ soll ich den Brief schicken?

   < Schick ihn nach Ulm, an dies____ Adresse (f) hier.

2. > ____________ ist Ulm?

   < Ulm liegt an d____ Donau (f).

3. > ____________ ist die Postkarte von Bettina?

   < Ich glaube, sie liegt unter dein____ Bücher____.

4. > ____________ gehst du nach dem Joggen?

   < Unter d____ Dusche (f) natürlich.

5. > ____________ ist Günter?

   < Ich glaube, er sitzt mal wieder vor d____ Fernseher (m).

6. > ____________ soll ich meine nassen Schuhe stellen?

   < Stell sie doch vor d____ Tür (f).

7. > ____________ steht dein Wagen?

   < Auf d____ Parkplatz (m) hinter d____ Bibliothek (f).

8. > ____________ hast du mein Fahrrad gestellt? In d____ Garage (f)?

   < Nein, hinter d____ Garage.

9. > ____________ geht diese Tür?

   < Auf d____ Balkon (m).

10. > ____________ ist die Buchhandlung? Neben d____ Apotheke (f)?

    < Ja, zwischen d____ Apotheke und d____ Blumenhaus (n) Dieterich.

11. > ____________ wohnst du jetzt?

    < In d____ Schillerstraße (f) über d____ Bäckerei (f) Schaufler.

12. > ____________ fährt dieser Bus?

    < Über d____ Rhein (m) nach Bonn.

NAME: ______________________ **DATE:** ______________

8-3 Kontraktionen. Supply **am, im, ans, ins,** or **aufs.** (Strukturen 3, p. 156)

1. > Warum hängt unser Poster denn nicht ____________ schwarzen Brett?

   < Weil Frank vergessen hat, es ____________ schwarze Brett zu hängen.

2. > Ist Beate wieder so spät ____________ Bett gegangen?

   < Ja, und jetzt sitzt sie schon wieder ____________ Computer und arbeitet.

3. > Was sollen wir mit unseren Mänteln machen?

   < Geht bitte ____________ Schlafzimmer und legt sie dort ____________ Bett.

4. > Warum stehen die Leute denn alle ____________ Fenster?

   < Geh auch ____________ Fenster, dann siehst du, warum sie dort stehen.

5. > Essen deine Eltern oft ____________ Gasthaus?

   < Nein, sie essen lieber zu Hause und gehen nur selten ____________ Gasthaus.

6. > Warum ist Stefan denn ____________ Krankenhaus?

   < Weil er beim Hockeyspielen ____________ Gesicht gefallen ist und ein paar Zähne verloren hat.

8-4 Finden Sie die richtigen Verben! Complete the following exchanges with the appropriate forms of **stellen, stehen, legen, liegen,** and **hängen.** Supply the proper case endings where necessary. (Strukturen 4, p. 156)

1. > Wo ist denn mein Mantel? Ich weiß ganz genau, dass ich ihn auf mein_____ Bett (n)
   ___gelegt___________ habe.

   < Ich habe ihn in d_____ Garderobe (f) ____________________. Du weißt doch, dass ich es nicht mag, wenn immer alles auf dein_____ Bett ____________________.

2. > Sollen wir unsere Mäntel in d_____ Garderobe ____________________, Kathrin?

   < Vielleicht ____________________ ihr sie lieber auf mein_____ Bett. Ich glaube nicht, dass in d_____ Garderobe noch viel Platz ist.

3. > ____________________ doch die Zeitung nicht immer auf d_____ Couch (f), Kurt!

   < Ich habe die Zeitung nicht auf d_____ Couch ____________________.

   > Aber du sitzt doch immer auf d_____ Couch, wenn du die Zeitung liest.

   < Ja, aber wenn ich fertig bin, ____________________ ich sie immer ganz ordentlich auf d_____ Couchtisch (m).

4. > Wo ist denn der Papierkorb?

   < ____________________ er nicht neben dein_____ Schreibtisch (m)?

   > Nein, und auch nicht unter d_____ Schreibtisch. Und ich weiß ganz genau, dass ich ihn neben d_____ Schreibtisch ____________________ habe.

   < Dann geh doch mal in d_____ Flur (m) und schau dort. Vielleicht hat die Putzfrau ihn in d_____ Flur ____________________.

5. > Wo ist denn mein Fahrrad? Ich habe es doch gestern Abend auf d_____ Balkon (m) ____________________.

   < Es ____________________ unten vor d_____ Haus (n). Matthias ist heute früh schnell mit deinem Fahrrad weggefahren und hat es dann vor_____ Haus ____________________.

Da with objects, not people

NAME: ______________________________ DATE: ____________________

8-5 ***Präposition + Pronomen oder da-Form?*** Complete the sentences with the prepositions given in parentheses. Use the prepositions with pronouns or in **da**-forms as appropriate. (☞ Strukturen 5, p. 157)

1. Das ist mein Schreibtisch, aber die Bücher ___darauf___ sind alle aus der Bibliothek. (auf)
2. Mitten im Zimmer hängt eine schöne Lampe und ___darunter___ steht ein großer Tisch. (unter)
3. Unter mir wohnen zwei Studenten und ___über mir___ wohnt eine alte Frau. (über)
4. Wohnen Zieglers in dem neuen Haus oder in dem alten Haus ___daneben___? (neben)
5. An dem Tisch dort sitzt Günter und die Studentin ___neben ihm___ ist seine Freundin Tina. (neben)
6. Lehmanns haben eine Bäckerei und ihre Wohnung ist direkt ___darüber___. (über)
7. Vor unserem Haus ist nur wenig Platz, aber ___dahinter___ ist ein großer Garten. (hinter)
8. Ich konnte im Kino nur schlecht sehen, weil die Frau ___vor mir___ einen großen Hut aufhatte. (vor)
9. Die zwei großen Bilder sind von Emil Nolde und das kleine Bild ___dazwischen___ ist von Paul Klee. (zwischen)

N der die das die
A den die das die
D dem der dem den

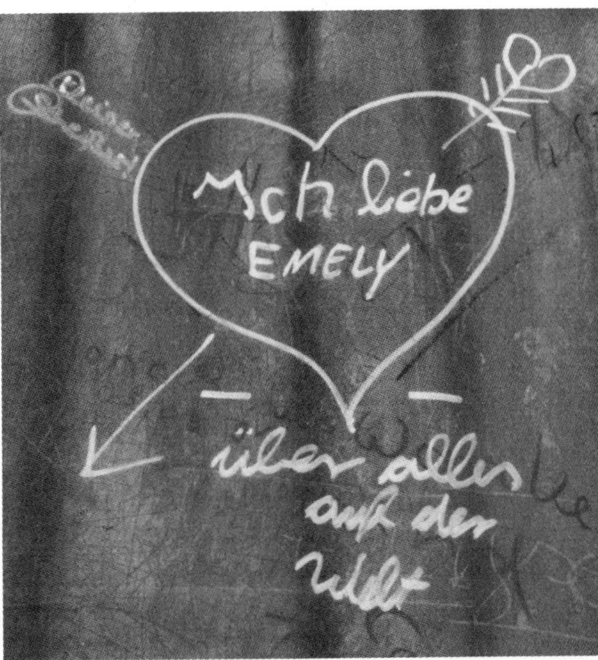

an - on
auf - on
in - in
hinter - behind
neben - next to
über - over
unter - under
vor - in front of

daran darüber
darauf darunter
darin davor
dahinter
daneben

8-6 ***An, auf* oder *in?*** Supply the appropriate prepositions and endings and use contractions wherever possible. (Strukturen 6, p. 157)

1\. > Wart ihr schon oft __________ d_____ Nordsee (f)?

< Schon so oft, dass wir dieses Jahr mal nicht __________ d_____ Nordsee fahren, sondern __________ Schwarze Meer (n).

2\. > Wer ist denn __________ Telefon (n)?

< Deine Freundin Tina. Sie will bestimmt wissen, mit wem du gestern Abend __________ Kino (n) warst.

3\. > Geh bitte __________ Telefon!

< Warum denn?

> Michael möchte wissen, ob du heute Abend mit ihm __________ Kino gehst.

4\. > Was hast du denn __________ d_____ Stadt (f) gemacht, Brigitte?

< Zuerst war ich __________ d_____ Markt (m) und dann __________ d_____ Post (f) und beim Schuhmacher.

> Nicht __________ d_____ Bank (f)? Du weißt doch, dass wir Geld brauchen!

< Nein, ich hatte keine Zeit mehr. Aber ich gehe heute Nachmittag noch mal __________ d_____ Stadt und dann gehe ich auch __________ d_____ Bank.

5\. > Waren Sie letzten Winter wieder __________ d_____ Alpen (pl), Frau Schaller?

< Nein, Frau Lange, wir fahren jetzt nicht mehr __________ d_____ Alpen, sondern fliegen __________ d_____ Rockies (pl).

6\. > Ich muss jetzt __________ Rathaus (n), Irene.

< Was willst du denn __________ d_____ Rathaus?

> Ich muss unsere Grundsteuer[1] bezahlen.

[1]*property tax*

NAME: ______________________________ DATE: ______________

8-7 Kleine Gespräche. Complete the following questions with the question words **wann, wo,** or **wohin,** and the responses with the prepositions **an, in, vor,** or **zwischen,** and the proper case endings. Use contractions wherever possible. (☞ Strukturen 7, p. 157)

1. FRAU HALLER: Wann fliegen Sie denn nach Europa, Frau Bender?

   Im Juli (m)?

   FRAU BENDER: Nein, schon am ersten Juni.

   FRAU HALLER: Und wohin fliegen Sie? Nur zu Ihrer Schwester

   in München?

   FRAU BENDER: Nein, Ende Juni fahre ich dann in die Schweiz (f). Meine

   Tante lebt in der Schweiz, wissen Sie.

   FRAU HALLER: Und wann kommen Sie wieder zurück?

   FRAU BENDER: Zwischen dem zehnten und dem fünfzehnten August.

2. HERR HALLER: Wo ist Ihre Frau jetzt, Herr Bender?

   HERR BENDER: Im Moment ist sie bei Ihrer Tante in der Schweiz.

   HERR HALLER: Und wann kommt sie wieder nach Hause?

   HERR BENDER: Am Montag (m) in einer Woche (f).

3. BETTINA: Warum rennst du denn so, Brigitte?

   BRIGITTE: Ich muss vor der Vorlesung (f) noch schnell

   in die Bibliothek (f).

4. STEPHANIE: __________ kann ich mit Professor Meyer sprechen, Frau Herz?

   FRAU HERZ: Am besten kurz __________ neun, __________ sein_____

   ersten Vorlesung, oder dann __________ sein_____ ersten und

   sein_____ zweiten Vorlesung.

   STEPHANIE: Und __________ ist das?

   FRAU HERZ: Das ist dann __________ zehn und elf.

5. PETER: __________ ist Martin weggefahren?

   CLAUDIA: __________ ein_____ halben Stunde (f).

8-8 Wie gut kennen Sie Schönbach? Look at the drawing on the facing page and complete the responses below with the appropriate prepositions, endings, or contractions. (☞ Strukturen 1 through 4, pp. 155–156)

NEUE VOKABELN

die Drogerie	*drug store*	**der Brunnen**	*fountain*
Schreibwaren	*stationery*	**die Tanne**	*fir tree*
im Freien	*outdoors*	**die Kirche**	*church*
die Bank	*bench*	**die Eiche**	*oak tree*

1. > Wo ist die Bäckerei Biehlmaier?

   < ________________ d____ Blumenhaus (n) Vogel und d____ Drogerie (f) Schulz.

2. > Wo ist das Schreibwarengeschäft Maier?

   < ________________ d____ Markt-Café (n).

3. > Wo kann man im Freien essen?

   < ________________ d____ Gasthaus (n) Lamm.

4. > Wo ist das Krankenhaus?

   < ________________ d____ Silcherstraße (f).

5. > Wohin hat Tanja ihr Fahrrad gestellt?

   < ________________ d____ Marktbrunnen (m).

6. > Was macht Tanja?

   < Sie steht ________________ d____ Marktbrunnen und spricht mit einer Freundin.

7. > Wo ist Tanjas Wohnung?

   < ________________ d____ Wohnung (f) von Müllers.

8. > Was macht Frau Müller gerade?

   < Sie ist ________________ Stadtpark (m) und sitzt ________________ d____ Bank (f) ________________ d____ alten, toten Tanne (f) ________________ Feuersee (m).

9. > Wo ist die Johanneskirche?

   < ________________ d____ Kirchstraße.

10. > Wo ist die große, alte Eiche?

    < ________________ d____ Johanneskirche.

NAME: ______________________ DATE: ______________

Schönbach
1 Marktplatz
2 Rathaus
3 Stadtpark
4 Feuersee
5 Post
6 Bank
7 Silcherstr.
8 Kirchstr.
9 Städtisches Krankenhaus
10 Johanneskirche
11 Buchhandlung Moser
12 Schuhgeschäft Roth
13 Fleischerei Fischer
14 Gasthaus Lamm
15 Markt-Café
16 Schreibwarengeschäft Maier
17 Schuh-Scholler
18 Waschsalon Huber
19 Drogerie Schulz
20 Bäckerei Biehlmaier
21 Blumenhaus Vogel
22 Stadt-Apotheke
23 Tanjas Wohnung
24 Müllers Wohnung

8-9 Kürzer gesagt. Use **zu**-infinitives to combine the two sentences into one. Always use the second sentence to introduce the infinitive phrase. Omit the words in parentheses. (Strukturen 8, p. 158)

1. Du gehst von jetzt ab zu Fuß zur Uni?! Hast du (das) wirklich vor?

   Hast du wirklich vor, von jetzt ab zu Fuß zur Uni zu gehen?

2. Du musst bei diesem schönen Wetter in der Bibliothek sitzen. Nervt es dich nicht?

3. Du gehst jeden Morgen joggen?! Macht es dir wirklich Spaß?

4. Hast du deine Koffer gepackt? Wann fängst du denn endlich an?

5. Ich habe Ferien und muss keine Referate mehr schreiben! Ich finde es toll!

6. Ruf mich heute Abend an! Vergiss (es) nicht!

7. Iss bei uns zu Abend! Hast du Lust?

8. Gehst du heute Nachmittag mit uns schwimmen? Hast du Zeit?

9. Hast du Ingrid angerufen? Hoffentlich hast du (es) nicht vergessen.

10. Du musst jeden Samstag arbeiten?! Nervt es dich nicht?

NAME: ______________________ DATE: ______________

8-10 ***Zu oder um ... zu?*** Complete the sentences with **zu** or **um ... zu** and the appropriate phrases. (Strukturen 8 & 9, p. 158)

1. nicht nass werden / nicht einschlafen / mit uns tanzen gehen

   a. Hast du Lust, mit uns tanzen zu gehen?

   b. Ich habe meinen Regenmantel angezogen, um nicht nass zu werden.

   c. Ich brauche beim Lernen viel Kaffee, ______________________.

2. sein Surfbrett ausprobieren / Milch und Brot kaufen / mein Referat durchlesen

   a. Ich fahre jetzt zum Supermarkt, ______________________.

   b. Kurt fährt heute an den Bodensee, ______________________.

   c. Hast du heute Abend Zeit, ______________________?

3. dort ihre Oma besuchen / seinen Wagen verkaufen / mir bei meinem Referat helfen

   a. Florian versucht seit einem Monat, ______________________.

   b. Maria fährt morgen nach Wien, ______________________.

   c. Heute Abend kommt Lisa, ______________________.

4. Frau Wilds Möbel nicht umstellen / im Studentenheim wohnen / dort ihren Sohn besuchen

   a. Stephanie hat es satt, ______________________.

   b. Frau Wild ist nach Texas geflogen, ______________________.

   c. Martin und Peter haben versprochen, ______________________

   ______________________.

8-11 Der Genitiv. Using the appropriate noun in the genitive case, write questions or statements in the present tense. (☞ Strukturen 10, p. 159)

1. kriegen / du / der Wagen / dein Vater / ?

   Kriegst du den Wagen deines Vaters?

2. sein / der Motor / dieser Wagen / sehr gut / .

3. sein / Frau Meyer / Kinder / immer / so wild / ?

4. gefallen / wie / dir / Jacke / Monika / ?

5. sein / der Freund / meine Schwester / Amerikaner / .

6. dürfen / umstellen / wir / Möbel / Frau Wild / nicht / .

7. finden / ich / der Monitor / dein Computer / viel zu klein / .

8. sein / das Ende / dieser Film / sehr dramatisch / .

9. kennen / du / Freundin / Bernd / ?

10. sein / wo / das neue Haus / deine Eltern / ?

11. lesen / ich / die Bücher / diese Autorin / sehr gern / .

12. finden / wie / du / neue Wohnung / Kathrin / ?

8-12 Ergänzen Sie! Supply genitive endings. (Strukturen 11, p. 159)

1. Der neue Freund mein____ jünger____ Schwester ist Österreicher.
2. Der Motor dies____ neu____ Automodell____ (n) soll sehr gut sein.
3. Wie heißt der Autor dies____ interessant____ Artikel____ (m)?
4. Wo ist das Sommerhaus dein____ deutsch____ Freunde?
5. Wie gefällt dir die Freundin mein____ klein____ Bruder____?
6. Der Sattel dein____ teur____, neu____ Fahrrad____ (n) ist mir zu hart.
7. Die Kapazität dies____ neu____ Computer (pl) ist fantastisch.
8. Am Ende unser____ fabelhaft____ Reise (f) durch Portugal waren wir noch ein paar Tage in der Algarve.
9. Am Abend mein____ einundzwanzigst____ Geburtstag____ waren wir alle bis nach Mitternacht in meiner Lieblingskneipe.
10. Die Farbe dein____ neu____ Wagen____ gefällt mir gar nicht.

Zum Verstehen

8-13 Kombinationen. Indicate the English equivalents of the German compound nouns by writing the appropriate numbers in the spaces provided.

1. die Straßenbahn	___ main street
2. die Milchstraße	___ one-way street
3. das Straßencafé	___ expressway
4. die Seitenstraße	___ milky way
5. der Straßenmusikant	_1_ streetcar
6. die Durchgangsstraße	___ detour
7. die Straßenbahnhaltestelle	___ road map
8. die Umgehungsstraße	___ side street
9. die Passstraße	___ street musician
10. das Straßenrennen	___ outdoor restaurant
11. die Schnellstraße	___ through street
12. die Hauptstraße	___ mountain pass
13. die Straßenkarte	___ road race
14. die Einbahnstraße	___ streetcar stop

8-14 Ein Minikrimi. Read the following story and then decide whether the statements below are **richtig** or **falsch.**

Vor dem Juweliergeschäft[1] Hürlimann in der Züricher Bahnhofstraße hält ein großer, schwarzer Mercedes. Der uniformierte Chauffeur macht die Wagentür auf und ein General und ein Generalleutnant der Schweizer Armee steigen aus[2]. Vor dem Geschäft steht ein Polizist und grüßt die beiden Offiziere mit großem Respekt. Herr Hürlimann hat die beiden Herren auch gesehen. Er geht zur Tür, grüßt höflich und läßt die Offiziere herein.

Der Generalleutnant möchte eine Perlenkette für seine Frau. Er versteht erstaunlich[3] viel von Perlen, und er hat bald eine ganz wunderbare Kette gefunden. Weil sie aber 50 000 Schweizer Franken kostet und weil er ganz sicher sein will, dass sie seiner Frau auch gefällt, sagt er: „Wenn Sie nichts dagegen[4] haben, Herr Hürlimann, fahre ich mit der Perlenkette schnell zu meiner Frau. Der General bleibt solange bei Ihnen im Geschäft."

Der Juwelier hat natürlich nichts dagegen. Eine Verkäuferin bringt eine Flasche Kognak und der General und der Juwelier trinken auf das Wohl[5] der Schweizer Armee. Dann sprechen die beiden über militärische Probleme, und der General staunt[6], wie gut Herr Hürlimann informiert ist. Nach einer halben Stunde steht der General aber plötzlich auf und will gehen. Als[7] der Juwelier ein bisschen nervös zu sagen beginnt: „Aber Herr General ...", unterbricht[8] ihn der General und sagt: „Ich kann leider nicht länger warten, und übrigens sind mein Kollege und ich gar keine Offiziere, sondern Schwindler." Weil der Juwelier sieht, dass der Polizist noch vor seinem Geschäft steht, rennt er zur Tür und ruft: „Kommen Sie schnell, Herr Wachtmeister[9]! Der Mann hier ist ein Schwindler." Der Polizist kommt und legt dem General Handschellen[10] an. Dann hält er ein Taxi an und fährt mit dem falschen General weg.

Herr Hürlimann ist erleichtert[11], trinkt noch ein paar Gläser Kognak und ruft dann die Züricher Kriminalpolizei an. Aber dort ist kein Polizist mit einem falschen General angekommen, denn der Polizist war natürlich auch ein Schwindler.

[1]*jewelry store* [2]*get out* [3]*surprisingly* [4]*against it* [5]*health* [6]*is astonished* [7]*when* [8]*interrupts* [9]*officer* [10]*handcuffs* [11]*relieved*

Decide whether the following statements are **richtig** or **falsch.** Base your responses on what is *actually* happening in this story.

_____ 1. Der Chauffeur der beiden Offiziere gehört auch zur Schweizer Armee.

_____ 2. Weil der Polizist sieht, dass die beiden Herren hohe Offiziere sind, grüßt er sie mit großem Respekt.

_____ 3. Weil der Juwelier denkt, dass die beiden Herren hohe Offiziere der Schweizer Armee sind, grüßt er sie sehr höflich.

_____ 4. Bevor der Generalleutnant die Perlenkette kauft, zeigt er sie seiner Frau.

_____ 5. Der Juwelier lässt den Generalleutnant mit der unbezahlten Perlenkette wegfahren, weil der General solange bei ihm im Geschäft bleibt.

_____ 6. Herr Hürlimann ist sehr nervös, als der Generalleutnant mit der unbezahlten Perlenkette wegfährt.

_____ 7. Als der General aufsteht und weggehen will, wird der Juwelier ein bisschen nervös.

_____ 8. Weil Herr Hürlimann sieht, dass der Polizist noch vor seinem Geschäft steht, läuft er schnell zur Tür.

_____ 9. Der Polizist kommt sofort, um dem Juwelier zu helfen.

_____ 10. Der Juwelier ist sehr erleichtert, als der Polizist dem General Handschellen anlegt und mit ihm wegfährt.

_____ 11. Der Polizist fährt mit dem falschen General direkt zur Züricher Kriminalpolizei.

_____ 12. Der Chauffeur der beiden falschen Offiziere war auch ein Schwindler.

Zum Übersetzen

8-15 Holgers Zimmer.

Mother comes into Holger's room. Holger is sitting in front of his TV. Mother says: „Holger, I don't understand you. How can you live in such **(so)** a pigsty? Your clothes are lying on the floor. Why can't you hang them in the closet? Your books are lying on the bed. Please put them in your bookcase. And on the dresser are five cola cans *(one word).* Didn't I tell you you're not supposed to put your cola cans on the dresser?!"

8-16 Kleine Gespräche.

1. ANJA: Where does you brother's girlfriend live?

   NICOLE: She has a beautiful furnished apartment near the university.

2. TOM: Why do you want to move out of this fantastic apartment?

   LUKAS: The students in the apartment next door are much too loud.

3. DANIEL: What do you need my vacuum cleaner for?

   PETER: I'm sick of living in a dirty apartment.

4. SOPHIA: Where are you *(familiar plural)* going?

   LAURA: We're going to Maria's (in order) to listen to her CDs. She just bought a new stereo.

5. ANNA: You promised to buy me a dishwasher as soon as we have a condominium.

   FLORIAN: We don't have enough money for a dishwasher. But perhaps I can buy you a microwave.

KAPITEL 9

Strukturen

Describing people, places, and things

1. Relative clauses and relative pronouns (☞ Übungen 9-1, 9-2, 9-3, pp. 181–183)

ANTECEDENT	REL. PRON.	RELATIVE CLAUSE	
Der Wein,	**der**	**dich so viel gekostet hat,**	ist nicht sehr gut.
Der Wein,	**den**	**du gekauft hast,**	ist nicht sehr gut.
Der Freund,	**dem**	**du ihn schenken willst,**	ist ein Weinkenner.
Die Freunde,	**die**	**uns eingeladen haben,**	sind Weinkenner.

- Relative clauses are introduced by relative pronouns.
- The noun to which a relative pronoun refers is called its *antecedent.*
- Most forms of the German relative pronoun are identical to those of the definite article.

Determining the gender, number, and case of the relative pronoun

Der Wein, **den** du gekauft hast, ist nicht sehr gut. — *The wine* ***that*** *you bought is not very good.*
The wine you bought is not very good.

- The relative pronoun **den,** like its antecedent **Wein,** is masculine and singular. It is in the accusative case because it is the direct object of the verb within the relative clause.
- Because relative clauses are dependent clauses, they are marked off by commas, and the conjugated verb appears at the end of the clause.
- In contrast to English, the German relative pronoun can never be omitted.

forms of the relative pronoun

	MASCULINE	NEUTER	FEMININE	PLURAL
NOMINATIVE	der	das	die	die
ACCUSATIVE	den	das	die	die
DATIVE	dem	dem	der	**denen**

N-nouns

2. *N*-nouns (☞ Übung 9-4, p. 185)

	singular		plural	
NOMINATIVE	der	Student	die	Studenten
ACCUSATIVE	den	Studenten	die	Studenten
DATIVE	dem	Studenten	den	Studenten
GENITIVE	des	Studenten	der	Studenten

 In German dictionaries, entries show the nominative singular of a noun followed by the changes (if any) that occur in the genitive singular and in the plural. This convention clearly identifies **n**-nouns.

nominative singular	genitive singular	plural
der Mann	-es	¨er
die Frau	-	-en
der Student	-en	-en
der Kunde	-n	-n

Talking about actions one does to or for oneself

3. Reflexive pronouns in the accusative case (☞ Übung 9-5, p. 186)

The accusative reflexive pronoun expresses the idea that one does an action to oneself.

Ich habe **mich** geschnitten. *I cut **myself**.*

personal pronouns		reflexive pronouns
NOMINATIVE	ACCUSATIVE	ACCUSATIVE
ich	mich	**mich**
du	dich	**dich**
er	ihn	
es	es	***sich***
sie	sie	
wir	uns	**uns**
ihr	euch	**euch**
sie	sie	***sich***
Sie	Sie	***sich***

- The accusative reflexive pronoun is identical to the personal pronoun except in the 3rd person singular and plural and in the **Sie**-form.
- In the **Sie**-form, **sich** is not capitalized.

Position of the reflexive pronoun

Kurt hat **sich** heute nicht rasiert.	*Kurt hasn't shaved today.*
Warum hat **sich Kurt** heute nicht rasiert?	*Why hasn't Kurt shaved today?*
Ich verstehe nicht, warum **er sich** heute nicht rasiert hat.	*I don't understand why he hasn't shaved today.*

- Reflexive pronouns are used much more frequently in German than in English.
- In sentences that begin with the subject, the reflexive pronoun follows the conjugated verb directly.
- In sentences that do not begin with the subject, the reflexive pronoun usually precedes noun subjects.
- In sentences that do not begin with the subject, the reflexive pronoun always follows pronoun subjects.

4. Reflexive pronouns in the dative case (☞ Übungen 9-6, 9-7, p. 187)

The dative reflexive pronoun expresses the idea that one does something for oneself or in one's own interest.

Ich kaufe **mir** einen schnelleren Computer.

personal pronouns		reflexive pronouns
NOMINATIVE	DATIVE	DATIVE
ich	mir	**mir**
du	dir	**dir**
er	ihm	
es	ihm	***sich***
sie	ihr	
wir	uns	**uns**
ihr	euch	**euch**
sie	ihnen	***sich***
Sie	Ihnen	***sich***

- The dative reflexive pronoun is identical to the personal pronoun except in the 3rd person singular and plural and in the **Sie**-form.
- In the **Sie**-form, **sich** is not capitalized.

Note the difference in the way German and English refer to actions that involve one's own body.

Oliver wäscht **sich** jeden Tag **die** Haare. ***Oliver*** *washes **his** hair every day.*

Where English uses the possessive adjective *(**his** hair),* German uses the dative reflexive pronoun and the definite article ***(sich die* Haare).**

5. Reflexive pronouns used to express *each other* (☞ Übung 9-8, p. 189)

German commonly uses the plural reflexive pronoun as a reciprocal pronoun corresponding to English *each other.* Note that the pronoun is not always expressed in English.

Wie habt ihr **euch** kennen gelernt?	*How did you get to know* ***each other?***
Wo sollen wir **uns** treffen?	*Where should we meet?*

6. Reflexive verbs (☞ Übungen, 9-9, 9-10, 9-11, pp. 190–191)

Many German verbs are always or almost always accompanied by a reflexive pronoun even though their English equivalents are rarely reflexive. Here are some important ones.

sich auf·regen	*to get excited; to get upset*	**sich erkälten**	*to catch a cold*
sich beeilen	*to hurry (up)*	**sich setzen**	*to sit down*
sich benehmen	*to behave*	**sich verspäten**	*to be late*
sich entschuldigen	*to apologize*	**sich wohl fühlen**	*to feel well*

 In the expression **sich wohl fühlen** the adverb **wohl** (or **krank, besser,** etc.) is used like a separable prefix.

NAME: ______________________ DATE: ______________

Anwendung

Übungen

9-1 Was passst zusammen? Complete the sentences with the appropriate relative clauses by writing the correct letter in the space provided. Note that some clauses complete more than one sentence. (☞Strukturen 1, p. 177)

1. Wer ist denn der Mann, __b__?

   Wer ist denn die Frau, _____?

   a. der du immer Blumen schickst?
   b. der dir immer Blumen schickt?

2. Die Schülerin, _____, hat angerufen und gesagt, dass sie heute nicht kommen kann.

   Der Schüler, _____, hat angerufen und gesagt, dass er heute nicht kommen kann.

   Die Schüler, _____, haben angerufen und gesagt, dass sie heute nicht kommen können.

   a. dem du immer bei den Hausaufgaben hilfst
   b. denen du immer bei den Hausaufgaben hilfst
   c. der du immer bei den Hausaufgaben hilfst

3. Ich glaube, die Bücher gehören der Studentin, _____.

   Ich glaube, die Bücher gehören dem Studenten, _____.

   Ich glaube, die Bücher gehören den Studenten, _____.

   a. die dich nach Hause gebracht hat
   b. die dich nach Hause gebracht haben
   c. der dich nach Hause gebracht hat

4. Der Professor, _____, ist gerade angekommen.

   Die Professorin, _____, ist gerade angekommen.

   Die Professoren, _____, sind gerade angekommen.

   a. denen wir unsere Bibliothek zeigen sollen
   b. dem wir unsere Bibliothek zeigen sollen
   c. der wir unsere Bibliothek zeigen sollen

5. Wer waren denn die Kinder, _____?
   Wer war denn das Kind, _____?
   Wer waren denn die Leute, _____?
   Wer war denn die Schülerin, _____?

   a. denen Kurt sein Video gezeigt hat (2x)
   b. der Kurt sein Video gezeigt hat
   c. dem Kurt sein Video gezeigt hat

6. Wer sind denn die Leute, _____?
   Wer ist denn die Frau, _____?
   Wer ist denn das Kind, _____?
   Wer ist denn der Mann, _____?

   a. die dich immer anruft
   b. der dich immer anruft
   c. die dich immer anrufen
   d. das dich immer anruft

7. Wie viel haben wir noch von dem Wein, _____?
   Wie viel haben wir noch von dem Bier, _____?
   Wie viele haben wir noch von den Bananen, _____?
   Wie viel haben wir noch von der Milch, _____?

   a. den wir gestern gekauft haben
   b. die wir gestern gekauft haben (2x)
   c. das wir gestern gekauft haben

8. Der Wagen, _____, hat bestimmt viel Geld gekostet.
   Das Haus, _____, hat bestimmt viel Geld gekostet.
   Der CD-Spieler, _____, hat bestimmt viel Geld gekostet.
   Die Bilder, _____, haben bestimmt viel Geld gekostet.

   a. das Müllers gekauft haben
   b. die Müllers gekauft haben
   c. den Müllers gekauft haben (2x)

NAME: ______________________________ DATE: ______________

9-2 Das Loch im Pulli. Supply appropriate relative pronouns. (☞Strukturen 1, p. 177)

1. Der Pulli, ___den___ Claudia gestern bei Karstadt gekauft hat, hat leider ein Loch.
2. Claudia braucht den Pulli zu dem schwarzen Rock, __________ sie heute Abend zu Helgas Party anziehen will.
3. Die Verkäuferin, __________ Claudia den Pulli verkauft hat, hat heute einen freien Tag.
4. Die Verkäuferin, __________ Claudia das Loch zeigt, hat den Pulli leider nicht noch mal.
5. Der Pulli, __________ Claudia gestern bei Karstadt gekauft hat, hat sechzig Euro gekostet.
6. Für einen Pulli, __________ schon im Kaufhaus ein Loch hat, will Claudia natürlich nicht den vollen Preis bezahlen.
7. Claudia soll das Loch, __________ sie im Pulli gefunden hat, selbst flicken.
8. Claudia bekommt den Pulli, __________ sie selbst flicken muss, zwanzig Euro billiger.
9. Das Loch, __________ in Claudias Pullover war, kann jetzt kein Mensch mehr sehen.

9-3 Ergänzen Sie. Complete the sentences in each set by choosing the appropriate statements from the choices given and changing them into relative clauses. (☞Strukturen 1, p. 177)

Es liegt hier. / Er hängt dort. / Sie steht dort.

1. Wem gehört denn der Mantel, ___der dort hängt___________________?

   Wem gehört denn das Buch, ______________________________?

   Wem gehört denn die Weinflasche, ______________________________?

Mein Bruder heiratet sie. / Ich habe es gekauft. / Brigitte heiratet ihn.

2. Wie gefällt dir der Mann, ______________________________?

   Wie gefällt dir die Frau, ______________________________?

   Wie gefällt dir das Fahrrad, ______________________________?

Du schickst ihr die Rosen. / Du mähst ihnen immer den Rasen. / Du hilfst ihm beim Lernen.

3. Wer ist denn die Frau, ______________________________?

   Wer ist denn das Kind, ______________________________?

   Wer sind denn die Leute, ______________________________?

Kurt hat sie gekauft. / Claudia hat ihn gekauft. / Claudia hat ihr das Loch gezeigt.

4. Wie gefällt dir der Pulli, ______________________________?

   Was hat die Verkäuferin, ______________________________, zu Claudia gesagt?

   Was machen wir mit den vielen Äpfeln, ______________________________?

Ihr schaut ihn euch heute Abend an. / Ich habe es mir letztes Jahr gekauft. / Er hat dich gestern Abend abgeholt.

5. Woher kennst du den Typ, ______________________________?

   Ist das ein deutscher Film, ______________________________

   ______________________________?

   Mit dem Fahrrad, ______________________________, bin ich schon viele tausend Kilometer gefahren.

Ich schreibe ihnen diese E-Mail. / Du hast sie mir zum Geburtstag geschenkt. / Ich habe ihn gestern verkauft.

6. Mit der Kamera, ______________________________

   ______________________________, habe ich schon viele hundert Fotos gemacht.

   Mit den beiden deutschen Studenten, ______________________________

   ______________________________, bin ich letzten Sommer durch ganz Europa gereist.

   Ich habe den Wagen, ______________________________, fast zehn Jahre lang gefahren.

9-4 Ergänzen Sie! Use the appropriate **n**-nouns in the proper case to complete the sentences below. (☞ Strukturen 2, p. 178)

der Junge, -n, -n (2x)	der Tourist, -en, -en	der Mensch, -en, -en
der Pilot, -en, -en	der Nachbar, -n, -n	der Patient, -en, -en
der Kollege, -n, -n	der Athlet, -en, -en	der Präsident, -en, -en
der Assistent, -en, -en	der Student, -en, -en	der Kunde, -n, -n

1. Dieser Mann wohnt im Weißen Haus. Man nennt ihn den _Präsidenten_ der USA.
2. Dieser Mann wohnt im Haus neben unserem Haus. Er ist unser ______________.
3. Dieser Mann sitzt im Cockpit des Flugzeugs und fliegt die Maschine. Man nennt ihn den ______________.
4. Frau Koch, Frau Berger und Herr Kurz arbeiten alle bei Karstadt. Heute hat Herr Kurz Geburtstag und die beiden Frauen gratulieren ihrem ______________.
5. Die Leute, die in unserer Bäckerei ihr Brot kaufen, sind unsere ______________.
6. Bei jeder Olympiade gibt es ein Olympisches Dorf. Im Olympischen Dorf wohnen die ______________.
7. Zieglers haben zwei Kinder, ein Mädchen und einen ______________. Das Mädchen heißt Nina und der ______________ heißt Robert.
8. Wenn ein Mensch krank ist und im Krankenhaus liegt, ist er ein ______________.
9. Wenn ein ______________ für einen Professor arbeitet, nennt man ihn einen ______________.

9-5 Kleine Gespräche. Supply the appropriate verbs and accusative reflexive pronouns. (☞Strukturen 3, p. 178)

sich kämmen / sich schminken / sich rasieren / sich schneiden / sich anziehen / sich umziehen / sich ausziehen

1. > Bist du aufgestanden, Mieke? Der Schulbus kommt in zehn Minuten!

   < Ja, ich __ziehe__ __mich__ gerade __an__.

2. > Warum hast du ____________ denn nicht ____________, Stefan?

   < Weil mein Rasierapparat kaputt ist.

3. > Seid ihr jetzt endlich im Bett, Kinder?

   < Nein, aber wir ____________ ____________ gerade ____________.

4. > Warum hast du ____________ denn so toll ____________?

   < Ich muss doch gut aussehen, wenn ich mit dir tanzen gehe.

5. > Willst du wirklich in diesen alten Jeans auf Claudias Party?

   < Aber nein, ich ____________ ____________ gleich ____________.

6. > Ist das Messer scharf?

   < Ja, sehr. Passen Sie auf, dass Sie ____________ nicht ____________!

7. > Warum brauchst du denn meinen Kamm?

   < Weil ich keine Zeit mehr hatte, ____________ zu ____________.

NAME: ______________________________ DATE: ______________

9-6 Ergänzen Sie! Supply the appropriate verbs and dative reflexive pronouns. (Strukturen 4, p. 179)

waschen / mieten / putzen / anschauen / machen

1. ____Mach____ ____dir____ doch eine Tasse Kaffee, wenn du so müde bist.
2. ______________ ______________ ja die Zähne, bevor ihr ins Bett geht.
3. Morgen ______________ wir ______________ mal einen Wagen und fahren zum Starnberger See.
4. Vergesst nicht, ______________ die Hände zu ______________, bevor ihr zum Mittagessen kommt.
5. Diesen Film müssen Sie ______________ ______________, Frau Schaufler.

suchen / aufwärmen / machen / kaufen / anhören

6. Darf ich ______________ deine neue CD ______________, Tina?
7. Was für einen Wagen hat ______________ Kathrin ______________?
8. Nächstes Semester ______________ wir ______________ eine viel größere Wohnung.
9. Wenn ihr Hunger habt, könnt ihr ______________ das Gulasch von gestern ______________.
10. Warum ______________ du ______________ denn nicht ein paar Brote, statt immer in der Cafeteria zu essen?

9-7 Was Maria gestern alles gemacht hat. Supply the appropriate verbs and reflexive pronouns in the accusative or dative case. (Strukturen 3 & 4, pp. 178–179)

machen / duschen / waschen / putzen / anziehen

Gestern bin ich sehr früh aufgestanden, habe ____mich____ schnell ____geduscht____ und ____mir____ die Haare ____gewaschen____. Weil es sehr kalt werden sollte, habe ich ______________ dann ganz warm ______________. Zum Frühstück habe ich ______________ eine Tasse Kaffee und zwei Scheiben Toast ______________. Nach dem Frühstück habe ich ______________ noch schnell die Zähne ______________ und bin dann zum Bus gerannt.

aufwärmen / machen (2x) / holen

In der Uni bin ich gleich in die Bibliothek gegangen und habe ____________ für mein Referat über die industrielle Revolution ein paar gute Bücher ____________________. Bis zum Mittagessen habe ich dann viel gelesen und ____________ Notizen ____________________. Weil ich am Morgen keine Zeit hatte, ____________ ein paar Brote zu ____________________ und weil ich das Essen in der Mensa nicht mag, bin ich um halb eins nach Hause gefahren und habe ____________ dort den Rest der Pizza von gestern ____________________.

anziehen / anhören / anschauen / kochen

Nach dem Essen habe ich angefangen, das Referat zu schreiben. Und weil ich mit Musik besser denken kann, habe ich ____________ auch ein paar schöne CDs ____________________. Um sechs war ich dann so müde, dass ich aufhören musste. Ich habe ____________ einen starken Kaffee ____________________ und ein Stück Apfelstrudel dazu gegessen. Dann habe ich ____________ schön ____________________, denn um sieben ist mein Freund Markus gekommen und wir sind zusammen ins Kino gegangen und haben ____________ einen tollen Film ____________________.

NAME: ______________________________ DATE: ______________

9-8 Fragen und Anworten. Supply the appropriate verbs and express the German equivalent of *each other* with reflexive pronouns. (☞ Strukturen 5, p. 180)

schreiben / anrufen

1. > Warum schreibt ihr euch denn nicht mehr?

   < Weil wir jetzt genug Geld haben, ____________ einmal pro Woche ____________.

kennen lernen / kennen

2. > ____________ Sie ____________?

   < Ja, wir haben ____________ auf Professor Bergers Party ____________.

zeigen / treffen

3. > Warum ____________ ihr ____________ heute Abend?

   < Weil wir ____________ die Videos von unseren Ferienreisen ____________ wollen.

schreiben / wiedersehen

4. > ____________ ihr ____________ immer noch fast jeden Tag?

   < Ja, und im Januar ____________ wir ____________ dann endlich ____________.

mögen / grüßen

5. > Warum denkst du, dass ____________ Susanne und Tobias nicht mehr ____________?

   < Weil sie ____________ nicht mehr ____________.

küssen / lieben

6. > Warum denkst du, dass ____________ Tina und Günter ____________?

   < Weil sie ____________ auf Nicoles Party so oft ____________ haben.

9-9 Was passt zusammen? Match the questions and responses by writing the appropriate numbers in the spaces provided. (☞Strukturen 6, p. 180)

1. Wo sollen wir uns hinsetzen?	_____ Weil wir den ganzen Morgen gesessen haben.
2. Wie hat sich Günter gestern Abend benommen?	_____ Er ist vorgestern stundenlang im Regen spazieren gegangen.
3. Warum setzt ihr euch denn nicht hin?	_____ Setzt euch dort in die Ecke.
4. Wo ist Brigitte?	_____ Ich glaube, es geht ihr schon viel besser.
5. Wie fühlt sich Brigitte jetzt?	_____ Er war wieder mal viel zu laut.
6. Wie hat sich Martin denn so erkältet?	_____ Sie ist in ihr Zimmer gegangen und hat sich hingelegt.

9-10 Was passt zusammen? Match the questions and responses by writing the appropriate numbers in the spaces provided. (☞Strukturen 6, p. 180)

1. Warum war Helga heute nicht in der Vorlesung?	_____ Weil die Studenten in seiner Vorlesung so laut waren.
2. Warum lädst du Günter nicht ein?	_____ Gleich nach dieser Vorlesung.
3. Warum regt ihr euch denn so auf?	_____ Weil er sich immer so schlecht benimmt.
4. Wann entschuldigst du dich bei Professor Kuhl?	_____ Weil sie sich gestern beim Schwimmen so erkältet hat.
5. Warum darf ich denn meinen Kaffee nicht austrinken?	_____ Weil du wieder so schlechte Zensuren nach Hause gebracht hast.
6. Warum hat sich Professor Braun denn so aufgeregt?	_____ Weil wir uns beeilen müssen.

NAME: ______________________________ DATE: ______________

9-11 Warum denn? Use the components provided to complete the questions and responses. Write the verbs in the *present tense* unless otherwise indicated. (Strukturen 6, p. 180)

1. > sich anziehen / du / denn so warm
   < sich erkälten / wollen / ich / nicht
   > Warum ziehst du dich denn so warm an?
   < Weil ______________________________.

2. > sich verspäten (perfect) / Sie / denn so
   < starten / wollen (simple past) / mein Wagen / nicht
   > Warum ______________________________?
   < Weil ______________________________.

3. > sich aufregen / du / denn so
   < helfen / wollen / du / mir / nicht
   > Warum ______________________________?
   < Weil ______________________________.

4. > sich setzen / Sie / denn nicht
   < haben / ich / nur ein paar Minuten / Zeit
   > Warum ______________________________?
   < Weil ______________________________.

5. > sich beeilen / du / denn nicht / ein bisschen
   < abfahren / mein Zug / erst / in einer halben Stunde
   > Warum ______________________________?
   < Weil ______________________________
   ______________________________.

6. > mitkommen (perfect) / Brigitte / denn nicht
   < sich wohl fühlen / sie / nicht
   > Warum ______________________________?
   < Weil ______________________________.

7. > sich entschuldigen / wollen / du / bei Frau Meyer / nicht

< sich benehmen (perfect) / ich / gar nicht / schlecht

> Warum ____

____?

< Weil ____.

8. > sich krank fühlen / ich / denn so

< essen (perfect) / du / wieder mal / viel zu viel

> Warum ____?

< Weil ____.

Zum Verstehen

9-12 Im Restaurant. Use the menu on the facing page to answer the following questions. Listed below are some words from the menu which you may not know.

NEUE VOKABELN

die Bohne	*bean*	**Forelle blau**	*poached trout*
die Zwiebel	*onion*	**der Schinken**	*ham*
das Kraut	*cabbage*	**empfehlen**	*to recommend*
Kräuter	*herbs*	**enthalten**	*to contain*
das Kartoffelpüree	*mashed potatoes*	**der Farbstoff**	*coloring agent*

1. Eva isst gern Wurst, ist aber allergisch gegen Farbstoffe. Was kann sie bestellen?

____

2. David hat großen Hunger und möchte gern ein Fleischgericht essen. Er mag aber keinen Salat. Was bestellt er?

____

3. Karin ist sehr hungrig und möchte ein Essen mit Suppe, Fleisch, Kartoffeln und Gemüse oder Salat. Zum Nachtisch möchte sie gern Apfelstrudel und Kaffee. Und zum Essen möchte sie natürlich auch ein Glas Bier. Leider hat sie nur 30 Euro. Was bestellt sie?

____

____

4. Bernd ist Vegetarier, isst aber Eier und Fisch. Er möchte gern ein warmes Essen. Welche zwei Gerichte kann er bestellen?

____

____

5. Maria möchte ein Fleischgericht mit wenig Kalorien. Was bestellt sie?

____

NAME: ______________________ DATE: ______________

Speisekarte

Aus dem Suppentopf

Mexikanische Bohnensuppe	€ 2,50
* Ungarische Gulaschsuppe	€ 3,00
Französische Zwiebelsuppe	€ 2,60
* Bouillon, klar	€ 2,00

Aus der Wurstküche

• Ein Paar Weißwürste mit Bauernbrot	€ 5,50
* Ein Paar Wienerwürste mit Kartoffelsalat	€ 6,50
* Ein Paar Schweinswürste mit Sauerkraut	€ 6,00
* Ein Paar Knackwürste mit Kraut und Kartoffelpüree	€ 7,00

Für den kleinen Appetit

Heringssalat mit Bauernbrot und frischer Butter	€ 5,00
Fleischsalat „italienisch" mit Toast und Butter	€ 6,50
Russische Eier auf Gemüsesalat	€ 5,50
Käseteller mit Brot, Butter und Radieschen	€ 7.00
• Omelette Champignon mit gemischtem Salat	€ 8,00
Toast mit Schinken „Hawaii"	€ 6,00
Kleines Filetsteak auf Toast mit Kräuterbutter	€ 10,50

Der Küchenchef empfiehlt

Cordon bleu natur vom Grill mit Champignons, Kartoffelkroketten und grünem Salat	€ 19,50
• Kalbsschnitzel mit buntem Salatteller	€ 13,50
Filetsteak „amerikanisch" mit Pommes frites und jungen Karotten	€ 20,00
• Forelle blau mit Salzkartoffeln, brauner Butter und grünem Salat	€ 22,00

Zum guten Schluss

Orangensorbet in Orangenfrucht	€ 3,90
Bananensplit	€ 4,00
Apfelstrudel mit Vanille-Eis	€ 4,50
Gemischtes Eis mit Schlagsahne	€ 3,50
Dreifrüchte-Eis	€ 4,00
Fruchteisbecher „Hawaii"	€ 6,50

Für den Durst

Cola, Apfelsaft 0,25 l	€ 1,60
Mineralwasser 0,25 l	€ 1,60
Tasse Kaffee	€ 1,80
Kännchen Kaffee	€ 3,50
Exportbier 0,3 l	€ 1,50
Weißwein (Riesling) 0,2 l	€ 4,00

Die mit • markierten Gerichte sind besonders kalorienarm.
Die mit * markierten Gerichte enthalten Farbstoffe.

9-13 Das billige Mittagessen. Read the following story and then unscramble the statements below.

Ins Gasthaus Krone kommt ein feiner Herr und fragt den Wirt[1]: „Kann ich hier für mein Geld eine gute Suppe bekommen?" „Aber natürlich", antwortet der Wirt und bringt ihm seine feinste Suppe. Als der Herr die Suppe gegessen hat, sagt er zum Wirt: „Die Suppe hat so gut geschmeckt, dass ich richtig hungrig geworden bin. Können Sie mir für mein Geld auch noch ein gutes Schnitzel mit Kartoffeln und Gemüse bringen?" „Wir haben das beste Schnitzel und das feinste Gemüse in der ganzen Stadt", antwortet der Wirt. „Darf ich Ihnen auch eine Flasche Wein bringen und zum Schluss[2] einen guten Nachtisch?" „Aber natürlich," sagt der Herr. „Wenn Sie mir das alles für mein Geld bringen können, dann empfehle[3] ich Ihr Gasthaus allen meinen Freunden."

Als der Herr all die guten Dinge gegessen und den Wein getrunken hat, steht er auf und sagt: „Ich bin sehr zufrieden[4] mit Ihrer ausgezeichneten Küche[5], und auch der Wein war erstklassig. Hoffentlich sind Sie nun auch zufrieden mit meinem Geld." Und mit diesen Worten gibt er dem Wirt ein Zehncentstück.

„Aber mein Herr", ruft der Wirt da ganz schockiert, „Sie haben Suppe, Schnitzel, Kartoffeln, Gemüse und Nachtisch bestellt und eine teure Flasche Wein dazu getrunken. Das kostet keine lächerlichen[6] zehn Cent, sondern fünfzig Euro!" „Mein lieber Herr Wirt", antwortet der Gast ganz ruhig, „Sie haben doch sicher gehört, dass ich alles, was ich gegessen und getrunken habe, für ‚mein Geld' bestellt habe. Diese zehn Cent sind mein ganzes Geld und mehr habe ich leider nicht." Da überlegt[7] der Wirt einen Moment und sagt: „Eigentlich gehören sie ja ins Gefängnis[8]. Wenn Sie mir aber einen Wunsch erfüllen[9], lasse ich Sie laufen." „Und was ist dieser Wunsch?" fragt der Gast. „Der Wirt vom Goldenen Adler ist mein Feind[10]", antwortet der Wirt, „und wenn er hört, was Sie hier gemacht haben, lacht er sich tot. Gehen Sie also morgen in den Goldenen Adler, und machen Sie dort dasselbe, was Sie hier getan haben. Dann bin ich wenigstens nicht allein der Dumme. Hier, nehmen Sie diese zwanzig Euro, und machen Sie Ihre Sache gut."

Der kluge[11] Gast nimmt die zwanzig Euro, dankt dem Wirt und geht zur Tür hinaus. Als er aber auf der anderen Seite der Straße ist, ruft er: „Sie sind übrigens auf keinen Fall[12] allein der Dumme. Ich war nämlich gestern schon im Goldenen Adler, und der Wirt dort hat mich für zwanzig Euro zu Ihnen geschickt."

[1]*innkeeper* [2]**zum ... :** *to top it off* [3]*will recommend* [4]*satisfied* [5]*cuisine* [6]*ridiculous* [7]*thinks* [8]*jail*
[9]**einen ... :** *fulfil a wish* [10]*enemy* [11]*clever* [12]*by no means*

NAME: ______________________________ DATE: ______________

Now put the statements below in the proper sequence by writing the numbers 2 to 6 in the appropriate spaces in Part I and the numbers 8 to 12 in Part II.

PART I

_____ Weil das Geld des Gastes aber nur ein Zehncentstück ist, ist der Wirt ganz schockiert und sagt, dass dieses Essen nicht zehn Cent kostet, sondern fünfzig Euro.

_____ Er trinkt „für sein Geld" auch eine Flasche Wein zum Essen und isst zum Schluss noch einen guten Nachtisch.

_____ Der Gast bleibt aber ganz ruhig und antwortet, dass diese zehn Cent sein ganzes Geld sind.

__1__ In einem deutschen Gasthaus bestellt ein Mann „für sein Geld" einen Teller Suppe.

_____ Nach dem Essen gibt der Gast dem Wirt dann „sein Geld".

_____ Nach der Suppe möchte er „für sein Geld" ein Schnitzel mit Kartoffeln und Gemüse.

PART II

_____ Der Wunsch des Wirtes ist, dass der Gast morgen im Goldenen Adler dasselbe macht, was er heute hier in der Krone getan hat.

_____ Er will aber nicht, dass sein Kollege im Goldenen Adler herausfindet, was hier passiert ist.

_____ Dann geht der Gast zur Tür hinaus, und als er weit genug weg ist, ruft er, dass er gestern schon im Goldenen Adler für „sein Geld" gegessen und auch dort zwanzig Euro bekommen hat.

_____ Deshalb ruft er nicht die Polizei, sondern will den Gast laufen lassen, wenn er ihm einen Wunsch erfüllt.

_____ Und damit er seine Sache im Goldenen Adler auch wirklich gut macht, gibt der Wirt ihm sogar noch zwanzig Euro.

__7__ Der Wirt denkt, dass der Gast eigentlich ins Gefängnis gehört.

Zum Übersetzen

9-14 Kleine Gespräche.

1. SHAUNA: Why do you go to the supermarket with shopping bags?
   NINA: Because each plastic bag that you (*use* **man**) get there costs ten cents.

2. ANNA: Did you try out the recipe that I gave you?
   MARIA: Of course! The dumplings were really delicious.

3. DANIEL: Why don't we eat in the restaurant (*Don't use* **Restaurant!**) that your brother finds so good?
   JULIA: Because the only really good main course there costs over twenty euros.

4. VERKÄUFER: Sometimes it's almost impossible to be friendly to the tourists that shop here.
   CHEF: You are right (*Begin with* **Da haben ...**). But please don't forget to be polite anyway.

5. POLIZIST: Do you know this boy, Mrs. Koch?
   FRAU KOCH: Yes, he's the son of our new neighbors.

9-15 Kleine Gespräche.

1. TOBIAS: Why are you changing? Are you going dancing with Maria?
   FLORIAN: No, we want to see (*use* **sich anschauen**) the newest film by Steven Spielberg.

2. BERND: Why don't you get dressed, Stefan?
   STEFAN: Because I have to wash and shave first.

3. OLIVER: May I make myself a sandwich, Mom?
   MUTTI: Yes, but first you have to wash your hands.

4. ALEX: How did your brother and his wife get to know each other?
   EVA: David was a salesman in a computer store, and Lisa bought her first computer there.

5. TOM: Why don't you hurry? You know that we can't (*use* **dürfen**) be late.
   MARIA: I'm going (*use* **machen**) as fast as possible, but my earring just fell behind the dresser.

6. VATI: Why didn't you tell me that your grades are so bad?
   ANNE: So that you don't get upset.

KAPITEL 10

Strukturen

Narrating past events

1. The simple past tense: regular verbs (☞ Übung 10-1, p. 203)

The simple past or narrative past is used mainly in written German to describe a series of connected events in the past.

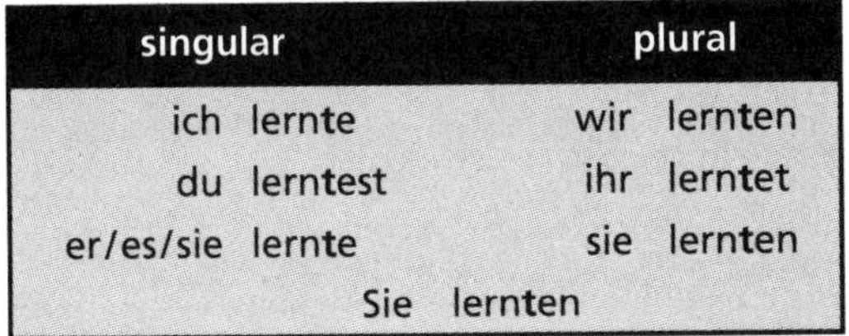

singular		plural	
ich	lernte	wir	lernten
du	lerntest	ihr	lerntet
er/es/sie	lernte	sie	lernten
	Sie lernten		

 The simple past of regular verbs is formed by inserting the past tense marker **-t-** between the verb stem and the personal endings.

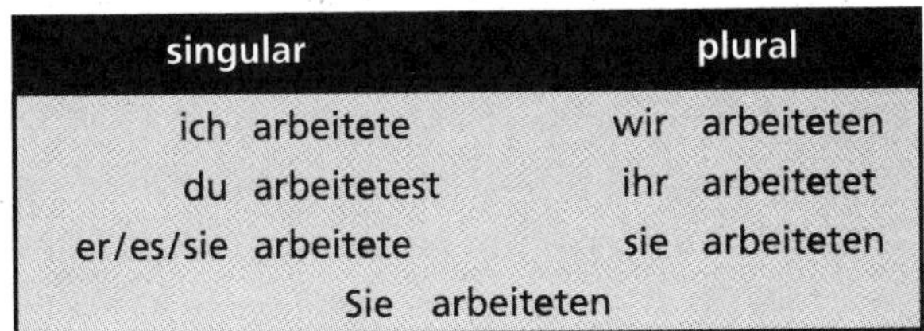

singular		plural	
ich	arbeitete	wir	arbeiteten
du	arbeitetest	ihr	arbeitetet
er/es/sie	arbeitete	sie	arbeiteten
	Sie arbeiteten		

 Verb stems that end in **-d, -t, (land-en, arbeit-en)**, or certain consonant combinations **(reg*n*-en)** add an **-e-** before the past tense marker **-t-**.

2. The simple past tense: irregular verbs (☞ Übungen 10-2, 10-3, 10-4, pp. 204–205)

singular		plural	
ich	kam	wir	kamen
du	kamst	ihr	kamt
er/es/sie	kam	sie	kamen
Sie	kamen		

- The simple past of irregular verbs is always signaled by a stem change.
- There is no personal ending in the 1st and 3rd person singular.

3. The simple past tense: separable-prefix verbs (☞ Übung 10-5, p. 205)

INDEPENDENT CLAUSE: Mein Zug **kam** Punkt eins in Berlin **an.**
DEPENDENT CLAUSE: Als mein Zug in Berlin **ankam,** regnete es wie verrückt.

- In an independent clause, the prefix is separated and appears at the end of the clause.
- In a dependent clause, the unseparated verb appears at the end of the clause.

4. The simple past tense: mixed verbs (☞ Übung 10-6, p. 206)

bringen	**brachte**	nennen	**nannte**
denken	**dachte**	rennen	**rannte**
kennen	**kannte**	wissen	**wusste**

Mixed verbs have the stem change of the irregular verbs, but the past tense marker **-t-** and personal endings of the regular verbs.

Expressing action in different time frames

5. The principal parts of irregular verbs (☞ Übung 10-7, p. 207)

All tenses of regular verbs are derived from the stem of the infinitive. They are completely predictable.

infinitive	tenses		
	PRESENT	SIMPLE PAST	PERFECT
*lern*en	er *lern*t	er *lern*te	er hat ge*lern*t
to learn	*he learns*	*he learned*	*he has learned*

All tenses of irregular and mixed verbs are derived from a set of *principal parts.* These principal parts are not derived from the infinitive and sometimes look quite different from the infinitive.

	infinitive	simple past	past participle
PRINCIPAL PARTS	gehen *to go*	ging *went*	gegangen *gone*
	present	**simple past**	**perfect**
TENSES	er geht *he goes*	er ging *he went*	er ist gegangen *he has gone*

Verbs that are irregular in the present tense have an additional principal part that reflects this irregularity.

infinitive	present tense irregularity	simple past	past participle
geben	er gibt	gab	gegeben
fahren	er fährt	fuhr	gefahren

Mixed verbs show the **-t-** marker of regular verbs and the stem change of irregular verbs.

infinitive	simple past	past participle
bringen	brachte	gebracht

The verb **werden** has characteristics of a mixed verb and an irregular verb.

infinitive	present tense irregularity	simple past	past participle
werden	er wird	wurde	geworden

Expressing *when* in German

6. *Wann, als,* and *wenn* (☞ Übungen 10-8, 10-9, pp. 208–209)

Although **wann, als,** and **wenn** are all equivalents of English *when,* they are not interchangeable.

wann?	als	wenn
• questions	• single event in the past	• events in the present or future
	• block of time in the past	• repeated events (all time frames)

Wann macht Nina ihren Führerschein?
Weißt du, **wann** Nina ihren Führerschein macht?

Als ich zur Tür hereinkam, klingelte das Telefon.
Als ich sieben war, machte meine Familie eine Reise nach Kalifornien.

Ruf uns bitte gleich an, **wenn** du in Frankfurt ankommst.
Wenn Tante Emma uns besuchte, brachte sie immer einen Kuchen mit.

Giving information about people, places, and things

7. The relative pronoun as object of a preposition (☞ Übungen 10-10, 10-11, pp. 210–211)

forms of the relative pronoun				
	MASCULINE	NEUTER	FEMININE	PLURAL
NOMINATIVE	der	das	die	die
ACCUSATIVE	den	das	die	die
DATIVE	dem	dem	der	denen

If a relative pronoun is the object of a preposition, its case is determined by that preposition.

Kennst du den Typ, **mit dem** Monika morgen zum Starnberger See fährt?
Ist das der CD-Spieler, **für den** du nur 150 Euro bezahlt hast?

Relative pronouns never contract with prepositions.

Preposition + definite article	**Preposition + relative pronoun**
Meine Oma wohnt **im** Seniorenheim.	Das ist das Seniorenheim, **in dem** meine Oma wohnt.

A review of adjective endings

8. Adjectives preceded by *der*-words (☞ Übung 10-12, p. 212 and Übung 10-14, p. 214)

	masculine	neuter	feminine	plural
NOMINATIVE	der junge Mann	das kleine Kind	die junge Frau	die kleinen Kinder
ACCUSATIVE	den jungen Mann	das kleine Kind	die junge Frau	die kleinen Kinder
DATIVE	dem jungen Mann	dem kleinen Kind	der jungen Frau	den kleinen Kindern
GENITIVE	des jungen Mannes	des kleinen Kindes	der jungen Frau	der kleinen Kinder

 Adjectives preceded by **der**-words (such as **der, dieser, jeder, welcher**) end in **-e** or **-en.**

9. Adjectives preceded by *ein*-words (☞ Übung 10-12, p. 212 and Übung 10-14, p. 214)

	masculine	neuter	feminine	plural
NOMINATIVE	ein junger Mann	ein kleines Kind	eine junge Frau	meine kleinen Kinder
ACCUSATIVE	einen jungen Mann	ein kleines Kind	eine junge Frau	meine kleinen Kinder
DATIVE	einem jungen Mann	einem kleinen Kind	einer jungen Frau	meinen kleinen Kindern
GENITIVE	eines jungen Mannes	eines kleinen Kindes	einer jungen Frau	meiner kleinen Kinder

 An adjective preceded by an **ein**-word without an ending shows the gender, number, and case of the noun by taking the appropriate **der**-word ending: **ein jung*er* Mann, ein klein*es* Kind.**

10. Unpreceded adjectives (☞ Übung 10-13, p. 213)

	masculine	neuter	feminine	plural
NOMINATIVE	guter Kaffee	gutes Bier	gute Salami	gute Äpfel
ACCUSATIVE	guten Kaffee	gutes Bier	gute Salami	gute Äpfel
DATIVE	gutem Kaffee	gutem Bier	guter Salami	guten Äpfeln

 Adjectives that are not preceded by a **der**-word or an **ein**-word show the gender, number, and case of the noun by taking the appropriate **der**-word endings.

NAME: ______________________ DATE: ______________

Anwendung

Übungen

10-1 Stephanie bekommt Besuch von Freunden aus Amerika. Supply the appropriate regular verbs in the simple past tense. (Strukturen 1, p. 197)

besuchen / erzählen / landen / reisen

Unser Flugzeug ___landete___ morgens um acht auf dem Frankfurter Flughafen. Von Frankfurt ______________ wir dann mit dem Zug nach München. Dort ______________ wir Stephanie Braun, und Stephanie ______________ uns viel von ihrem Leben in dieser schönen Stadt.

übernachten / bestellen / baden / bezahlen / machen

Wir ______________ in Stephanies WG. Am nächsten Morgen ______________ wir einen Spaziergang durch den Englischen Garten. Weil es sehr heiß war, ______________ wir im Eisbach. Später ______________ Stephanies Freund Peter in einem Biergarten für uns alle Bier und Weißwürste und er ______________ dann auch alles.

öffnen / kochen / diskutieren / spielen / regnen / hören

Am Nachmittag ______________ es und wir waren dann bei Peter und seinem Freund Martin. Stephanie ______________ Kaffee und später ______________ Martin noch ein paar Flaschen Wein. Wir ______________ Karten, ______________ CDs und ______________ über wichtige Probleme.

reisen / bestellen / packen

Am Abend ______________ wir bei Stephanie unsere Rucksäcke, ______________ ein Taxi zum Bahnhof und ______________ zu meinem Onkel nach Hannover.

10-2 Fremdsprachen muss man können! The following anecdote demonstrates the importance of knowing foreign languages. Supply the appropriate irregular verbs in the simple past tense. (Strukturen 2, p. 198)

NEUE VOKABELN

Lieder	*songs*	**riesig**	*huge*
Beeren	*berries*	**erschrocken**	*startled*
Nüsse	*nuts*	**zittern**	*to tremble*

singen / gehen / laufen / fressen / tragen

Eine Mäusemama ___ging___ einmal mit ihren vier kleinen Kindern durch den Wald. Das Baby __________ sie auf dem Arm und die älteren Kinder __________ um die Bäume und durch die Büsche, __________ lustige Lieder oder __________ auch Beeren und Nüsse.

rufen / sprechen / stehen / beginnen / springen

Plötzlich __________ mitten auf dem Weg eine riesige Katze. Die Kinder hatten große Angst und __________ zu zittern und zu weinen. Die Mäusemama aber __________ wie ein Hund ganz laut: „Wau wau!" und die Katze __________ erschrocken auf den nächsten Baum. Da __________ die Mäusemama zu ihren Kindern: „Seht ihr jetzt, wie wichtig es ist, Fremdsprachen zu können?"

10-3 Gestern Abend. Supply the appropriate regular or irregular verbs in the simple past tense. Irregular verbs are marked with (I). (Strukturen 1 & 2, pp. 197–198)

stellen / trinken (I) / kommen (I) / essen (I) / holen

Als ich gestern Abend nach Hause ___kam___, ___stellte___ ich gleich Brot auf den Tisch und __________ Butter, Wurst und Bier aus dem Kühlschrank. Weil ich sehr hungrig und sehr durstig war, __________ ich drei Scheiben Brot mit viel Butter und Wurst und __________ zwei Flaschen Bier dazu.

telefonieren / schreiben (I) / gehen (I) / reden / lernen

Nach dem Abendessen __________ ich mit Brigitte und wir __________ über eine Stunde miteinander. Dann __________ ich meinen Eltern eine lange E-Mail, __________ schnell noch meine französischen Vokabeln, und um zwölf __________ ich endlich ins Bett.

NAME: ______________________________ DATE: ______________

10-4 Ein warmer Tag. Supply the appropriate regular or irregular verbs in the simple past tense. Irregular verbs are marked with (I). (☞ Strukturen 1 & 2, pp. 197–198)

sitzen (I) / fahren (I) / lesen (I) / baden / treffen (I)

Weil es gestern so warm war, ______________ Stephanie und Peter gleich nach den Vorlesungen zum Englischen Garten. Beim Eisbach ______________ sie Martin und Claudia. Claudia ______________ im Gras und ______________ ein Buch, und Martin ______________ in dem eiskalten Wasser.

essen (I) / tanzen / gehen (I) / trinken (I) / nehmen (I)

Peter und Stephanie ______________ dann in ein kleines Gartenrestaurant, wo sie ein Stück Kuchen ______________ und eine Tasse Kaffee dazu ______________. Dann ______________ sie den Bus nach Schwabing, wo sie in einer tollen Disco bis spät in die Nacht hinein ______________.

10-5 Austauschstudentinnen. Lisa and Susan, two American exchange students, are on their way to the **Technische Universität** in Berlin. Using the appropriate separable-prefix verbs in the simple past tense, complete Lisa's account of their trip. (☞ Strukturen 3, p. 198)

einschlafen / ausziehen / abfliegen / anschauen

Unser Lufthansa-Jet ___flog___ am ersten Oktober kurz nach neunzehn Uhr von New York ___ab___. Es war ein kühler Herbsttag, aber im Flugzeug war es so warm, dass wir gleich unsere Jacken ___auszogen___. Nach dem Abendessen ______________ Susan den Film ______________ und ich las ein bisschen und ______________ dann bald ______________.

abholen / hineinfahren / abfahren / aufwachen

Als ich wieder ______________, waren wir schon über der Bundesrepublik. Eine Stunde später landeten wir auf dem Rhein-Main-Flughafen, ______________ unsere Rucksäcke ______________ und ______________ dann mit der S-Bahn nach Frankfurt ______________. Dort mussten wir fast eine Stunde warten, weil der ICE nach Berlin erst um elf ______________.

aufhören / anfangen / abfahren / hineinfahren

Kurz bevor der Zug ____________________, ____________________ es zu regnen ____________________. Es regnete auf dem ganzen Weg nach Berlin und es ____________________ erst ____________________, als wir fünf Stunden später nach Berlin ____________________.

umziehen / ankommen / zusammensitzen

Als wir auf dem Bahnhof Zoologischer Garten ____________________, wartete dort ein Typ auf uns und sagte: „Ich bin Michael Körner. Seid ihr vielleicht Lisa Hunt und Susan Perry aus Kansas?" Er fuhr uns zu unserem Studentenheim, wo wir uns schnell ____________________. Dann gingen wir mit Michael in eine Kneipe, ____________________ dort lange mit ein paar von seinen Freunden ____________________ und erzählten.

10-6 Vetter David aus Amerika. Supply mixed verbs appropriately in the simple past or as a past participle. (Strukturen 4, p. 198)

erkennen[1] / kennen / wissen / rennen / mitbringen / denken

Als ich letztes Jahr in Deutschland war, besuchte ich meine Verwandten in Köln. Sie ___wussten___, dass ich komme, aber nicht genau wann. Als ich zu ihrem Haus kam, spielte meine kleine Kusine Andrea im Garten vor dem Haus. Weil sie mich nur von Fotos ____________________, ____________________ sie mich nicht und ____________________ wohl: „Wer ist denn dieser Mann?" Als ich ihr sagte, wer ich bin, fragte sie gleich: „Was hast du mir ____________________?" Erst dann ____________________ sie ins Haus und schrie: „Vetter David aus Amerika ist hier!"

[1] *to recognize*

NAME: ______________________ DATE: ______________

10-7 Was fehlt hier? Supply the missing principal parts. Write the present tense only if it is irregular. (☞ Strukturen 5, p. 199)

INFINITIVE	IRR. PRESENT	SIMPLE PAST	PAST PARTICIPLE
halten	hält	hielt	hat gehalten
______	______	schrieb	______
______	______	______	hat gefunden
______	hilft	______	______
______	______	______	hat gewaschen
bleiben	______	______	______
fliegen	______	______	______
______	______	______	hat gelesen
______	weiß	______	______
______	______	brachte	______
______	isst	______	______
______	______	______	ist gegangen
fahren	______	______	______
______	______	gab	______
______	______	______	hat geheißen
nehmen	______	______	______
______	______	______	hat gekannt
______	______	vergaß	______
______	______	trug	______
______	______	______	hat geschlafen
trinken	______	______	______
______	wird	______	______
______	______	log	______
verstehen	______	______	______
sprechen	______	______	______
______	______	kam	______

10-8 *Wann, als* oder *wenn?* In each group supply **wann, als,** or **wenn.** (☞ Strukturen 6, p. 200)

1. a. Könnten Sie mir bitte sagen, ____________ dieser Zug in Hamburg ankommt?

   b. ____________ mein Zug gestern Abend in Hamburg ankam, regnete es wie verrückt.

   c. ____________ ich in Hamburg bin, regnet es fast immer.

2. a. ____________ der Regen aufhört, gehen wir spazieren.

   b. ____________ hört dieser Regen denn endlich auf?

   c. ____________ der Regen endlich aufhörte, gingen wir spazieren.

3. a. Jedes Mal ____________ wir spazieren gehen wollten, fing es an zu regnen.

   b. ____________ wir gestern Nachmittag spazieren gehen wollten, fing es an zu regnen.

   c. Weißt du vielleicht, ____________ es aufhören soll zu regnen?

4. a. ____________ Maria morgens wegfährt, ist es immer noch ganz dunkel.

   b. ____________ Maria heute früh wegfuhr, war es noch ganz dunkel.

   c. Weißt du, ____________ Maria weggefahren ist?

5. a. ____________ Eva morgens wegfährt, ist Ralf meistens noch im Bett.

   b. ____________ Eva heute früh wegfuhr, war Ralf noch im Bett.

   c. ____________ fährt Eva morgens weg?

6. a. ____________ bist du denn in Köln, am Montag oder am Dienstag?

   b. Besucht du mich, ____________ du nach Köln kommst?

   c. Hast du Julia besucht, ____________ du letzten Montag in Köln warst?

NAME: ______________________ DATE: ______________

10-9 Ist das fair? Supply **wann, wenn,** or **als.** (Strukturen 6, p. 200)

___Wenn___ Ingrid und ich miteinander ausgehen wollen, gibt es oft Probleme. So kam sie zum Beispiel gestern Abend, __________ ich gerade im Sessel saß und die Zeitung las, zur Tür herein und rief: „__________ bist du denn endlich fertig mit deiner Zeitung? Du weißt doch, dass wir tanzen gehen wollen." Ich sagte: „__________ ich diesen Artikel fertig gelesen habe, können wir gehen." Ich las den Artikel dann so schnell wie möglich zu Ende, aber ich dachte: „__________ Ingrid tanzen gehen will, muss ich alles liegen und stehen lassen. Aber __________ ich mal ausgehen will und sie gerade im Sessel sitzt und einen von ihren Kriminalromanen liest, muss ich warten, bis sie fertig ist." So zum Beispiel letzte Woche, __________ ich mit ihr ins Kino wollte. __________ ich ihr sagte, um wieviel Uhr der Film anfängt und __________ wir wegfahren müssen, antwortete sie: „Wir gehen erst, __________ ich diesen Krimi fertig gelesen habe." Und __________ sie dann endlich fertig war, hatte der Film längst angefangen und wir blieben zu Hause. Deshalb saß ich, __________ Ingrid ein paar Minuten später wieder hereinkam, noch immer im Sessel und las meine Zeitung. Und __________ Ingrid sagte: „Aber David, wie kannst du denn einfach weiterlesen, __________ du ganz genau weißt, dass ich mit dir tanzen gehen will?", da antwortete ich ganz ruhig: „__________ ich letzte Woche mit dir ins Kino wollte, da hast du deinen Krimi gelesen, bis es zu spät war. Aber __________ du tanzen gehen willst, soll ich mitten in einem interessanten Artikel die Zeitung weglegen. Denkst du wirklich, dass das fair ist?"

10-10 Ein Ferienjob in der Schweiz (I). The following sentence pairs mean essentially the same thing. Read sentence *a.* and then complete sentence *b.* by replacing the phrase in bold in sentence *a.* with the appropriate preposition and relative pronoun. (☞ Strukturen 7, p. 200)

1. a. Ich bekam den Ferienjob **durch einen Mann,** der ein guter Freund meines Vaters war.

   b. Der Mann, durch_______ den_______ ich den Ferienjob bekam, war ein guter Freund meines Vaters.

2. a. Ich wohnte **bei einer Familie,** die zwei Söhne hatte.

   b. Die Familie, ____________ ____________ ich wohnte, hatte zwei Söhne.

3. a. Ich arbeitete **für eine Firma,** die Roboter machte.

   b. Die Firma, ____________ ____________ ich arbeitete, machte Roboter.

4. a. Ich arbeitete **unter einem Meister,** von dem ich sehr viel lernte.

   b. Von dem Meister, ____________ ____________ ich arbeitete, lernte ich sehr viel.

5. a. **Für das Fahrrad,** das ich mir kaufte, musste ich nur hundert Schweizer Franken bezahlen.

   b. Ich kaufte mir ein Fahrrad, ____________ ____________ ich nur hundert Schweizer Franken bezahlen musste.

6. a. Im August machte ich **mit einem Arbeitskollegen,** der auch aus Amerika war, eine Radtour durch die ganze Schweiz.

   b. Der Arbeitskollege, ____________ ____________ ich im August eine Radtour durch die ganze Schweiz machte, war auch aus Amerika.

7. a. Wir übernachteten **in Jugendherbergen** und trafen dort junge Leute aus aller Welt.

   b. In den Jugendherbergen, ____________ ____________ wir übernachteten, trafen wir junge Leute aus aller Welt.

8. a. **In dieser Zeit** in der Schweiz habe ich viel gelernt und gesehen und viele nette Menschen kennen gelernt.

   b. Dieser Sommer in der Schweiz war eine Zeit, ____________ ____________ ich viel gelernt und gesehen und viele nette Menschen kennen gelernt habe.

10-11 Ein Ferienjob in der Schweiz (II). Supply relative pronouns. (☞ Strukturen 7, p. 200)

1. Der Tag, an ___dem___ ich in Zürich landete, war sonnig und warm.
2. Der Freund meines Vaters, durch __________ ich meinen Ferienjob bekommen habe, holte mich vom Flughafen ab und brachte mich zu den Leuten, bei __________ ich wohnen sollte.
3. Das Zimmer, in __________ ich wohnte, war klein, aber sehr hell und sehr schön möbliert.
4. Die Leute, bei __________ ich wohnte, hatten zwei nette kleine Söhne, mit __________ ich später an Tagen, an __________ ich nicht arbeiten musste, oft im Zürichersee schwimmen ging.
5. Die Firma, für __________ ich arbeitete, machte Roboter (pl), für __________ sie in der ganzen Welt viele Kunden hatte.
6. Der Meister, unter __________ ich arbeitete, war ein sehr netter Mann, von __________ ich viel lernte.
7. Durch diesen Meister bekam ich ein tolles Fahrrad, für __________ ich nur hundert Schweizer Franken bezahlen musste und mit __________ ich dann im August mit einem Arbeitskollegen zusammen eine Radtour durch die ganze Schweiz machte.
8. Der höchste Pass, über __________ wir fuhren, war der St. Bernhard.
9. Natürlich besuchten wir hier auch das Kloster[1] St. Bernhard, aus __________ die berühmten Bernhardinerhunde stammen[2].
10. In den Jugendherbergen, in __________ wir übernachteten, trafen wir junge Leute aus aller Welt.
11. Dieser Sommer in der Schweiz war eine Zeit, in __________ ich viel gelernt und gesehen und viele nette Menschen kennen gelernt habe.

[1] *monastery* [2] *originate*

10-12 Das Geburtstagsgeschenk. Supply adjective endings. (Strukturen 8 & 9, p. 201)

Nicoles Bruder David wird morgen dreizehn und Nicole möchte ihm ein schön_____ Geburtstagsgeschenk kaufen. Weil sie aber nicht weiß, was sie ihm kaufen soll, fragt sie ihre Freundin Maria, denn Maria hat immer die tollst_____ Ideen.

„Kauf ihm doch eine lustig_____ Swatch", sagt Maria, „oder die neuest_____ CD von seiner liebst_____ Rockgruppe. Oder noch besser! Kauf ihm ein interessant_____ Computerspiel (n), denn ein dreizehnjährig_____ Junge mag heutzutage nichts lieber als Computerspiele." Ein gut_____ Computerspiel ist Nicole aber viel zu teuer, eine Swatch hat David schon zu seinem zwölft_____ Geburtstag bekommen, und eine CD mag sie ihm nicht kaufen, weil sie den musikalisch_____ Geschmack[1] ihres klein_____ Bruders ganz schrecklich[2] findet. Die beid_____ Freundinnen gehen deshalb zum KaDeWe, dem größt_____ Kaufhaus in Berlin, denn dort fällt ihnen bestimmt etwas ein.

Im KaDeWe hat heute der groß_____ Winterschlussverkauf begonnen und in den meist_____ Abteilungen sind die Preise stark reduziert. Maria kauft sich eine schick_____, warm_____ Winterjacke und Nicole gibt fast ihr ganz_____ Geld für einen elegant_____, schwarz_____ Pulli aus. Dann schaut sie ein bisschen beschämt in ihre fast leer_____ Geldtasche, denn mit den paar lächerlich_____ Cent kann sie David kein Geburtstagsgeschenk kaufen.

Zum Glück hat Maria aber auch diesmal eine gut_____ Lösung. „Kauf deinem klein_____ Bruder doch eine lustig_____ Geburtstagskarte", sagt sie, „und mit dieser Karte zusammen schickst du ihm einen Schuldschein mit den folgend_____ Worten: ‚Mein lieb_____ David, ich schulde dir zu deinem dreizehnt_____ Geburtstag ein schön_____ Geschenk. Wenn ich im nächst_____ Monat wieder mehr Geld habe, bekommst du es ganz bestimmt.'"

[1]*taste* [2]*terrible*

10-13 Ergänzen Sie! Supply the appropriate adjectives and endings. (Strukturen 10, p. 201)

blond / klein / interessant / reich / stark

1. Der Mercedes 600 ist ein Wagen für sehr reiche ______________ Leute.
2. Mit ______________ Haar hat Sabine mir viel besser gefallen.
3. So ______________ Kaffee kann nicht gesund sein!
4. Dieser Journalist schreibt sehr ______________ Artikel.
5. Das ist kein Film für ______________ Kinder.

viel / gelb / regnerisch / rot / schwer

6. Ich mag ______________ Rosen viel lieber als ______________.
7. Wir hatten während dieser Reise fast immer ______________ Wetter!
8. ______________ Einwanderer sind durch ______________ Arbeit sehr reich geworden.

kalt / schön / wollen / nett / heiß / groß

9. Bei ______________ Wetter gehen die Leute gern spazieren.
10. So ______________ Winter wie in Kanada gibt es in Deutschland nicht.
11. Tina hat ______________Glück (n) gehabt. Sie hat bei sehr ______________ Leuten ein ______________ Zimmer mit Küchenbenutzung gefunden.
12. ______________ Pullis darf man nicht in ______________ Wasser waschen.

10-14 Immobilien. The following real estate ad for a vacation home in Spain shows some of the typical abbreviations found in German newspapers. Using the glossary and adding the appropriate adjective endings, complete the full-sentence version. (☞Strukturen 8 & 9, p. 201)

> SPANIEN EXKLUSIV
>
> Schick. Bungalow, dir. am geplant. Golfplatz, Nähe wunderb. Sandstrand, 2 Schlafzi., gr. Wohnzi., mod. Küche, gr. schatt. Gartenterr., brandn. Pergola-Gar. f. 2 PKWs. Nur €195 700,-
>
> Tel. 0761/407355 Fax 0761/407356

dir.	direkt	schatt.	schattig
wunderb.	wunderbar	brandn.	brandneu
gr.	groß	f.	für
mod.	modern		

Der Bungalow liegt ___direkt___ am ___geplanten___ Golfplatz.

Es ist ein ______________ Bungalow (m) und er ist nicht weit weg von einem ______________ Sandstrand. Der Bungalow hat zwei Schlafzimmer, ein ______________ Wohnzimmer, eine ______________ Küche, eine ______________, ______________ Gartenterrasse und eine ______________ Pergola-Garage ______________ zwei PKWs.

NAME: ______________________________ **DATE:** ____________________

Zum Verstehen

10-15 Raubüberfall in Wien. Read the following story about a robbery in Vienna and then decide whether the statements below are **richtig** or **falsch.**

Franz Mark, der bekannte Autor vieler interessanter Krimis, hatte den ganzen Tag an seinem neuesten Roman gearbeitet. Er hatte genug für heute, und weil man auf der Wiener Donauinsel[1] auch am Abend spazieren gehen kann, ohne Angst vor einem Raubüberfall zu haben, fuhr er gleich nach dem Abendessen dorthin. Es war ein regnerischer Tag, und weil es im Moment schon wieder nach Regen aussah, waren nur wenige Menschen auf den Wegen. An einer besonders einsamen[2] Stelle[3] sprang plötzlich ein maskierter Mann hinter einem Busch hervor, hielt Franz Mark eine Pistole auf die Brust und rief: „Geld oder Leben!"

Weil Franz Mark in seinen Krimis solche Situationen oft beschrieb, regte er sich gar nicht auf, sondern sagte ganz ruhig: „Mein lieber Mann, Sie bekommen mein Geld sofort. Aber wissen Sie auch, vor wem ich viel mehr Angst habe, als vor Ihnen und Ihrer Pistole?" „Vor wem denn?" fragte der Mann verblüfft[4]. „Vor meiner Frau, wenn ich ohne Geld nach Hause komme. Sie glaubt mir die Geschichte von dem Überfall bestimmt nicht und denkt, dass ich das Geld für eine Geliebte[5] ausgegeben habe."

Der Räuber wusste nicht recht, was er von der seltsamen[6] Reaktion seines Opfers[7] denken sollte. Aber weil auch er eine Frau *und* eine Geliebte hatte, konnte er verstehen, dass ein Mann vor seiner Frau solche Angst haben konnte, und sagte: „Sie tun mir Leid, mein Herr, aber ihr Geld brauche ich trotzdem. Und eine Quittung[8] kann ich Ihnen natürlich nicht geben." „Das kann ich verstehen", antwortete Franz Mark, „aber schießen[9] Sie mir doch bitte ein paar Löcher durch meinen Mantel und meinen Hut, dann glaubt mir meine Frau bestimmt." Dem Räuber gefiel diese originelle Idee. Franz Mark zog seinen Mantel aus und hängte ihn über einen Busch und der Räuber schoss fünf schöne Löcher hindurch. Dann nahm Franz Mark seinen Hut vom Kopf und auch der Hut bekam ein schönes Loch. Als der Räuber dann aber das Geld verlangte[10], fühlte er plötzlich eine schwere Hand auf seiner Schulter: ein patrouillierender Polizist hatte die Schüsse[11] gehört und war schnell herbeigeeilt[12].

[1]name of a park on an island in the Danube [2]*lonely* [3]*place* [4]*perplexed* [5]*mistress* [6]*strange* [7]*victim* [8]*receipt* [9]*shoot* [10]*demanded* [11]*shots* [12]**schnell ... :** *rushed to the scene*

Now write **R** or **F** in the spaces provided.

_____ 1. Die Krimis von Franz Mark waren sehr bekannt.
_____ 2. Als Franz Mark seinen neuesten Roman fertig geschrieben hatte, fuhr er zur Donauinsel.
_____ 3. Auf der Wiener Donauinsel gibt es viele Räuber.
_____ 4. Weil es heute immer wieder regnete, ging außer Franz Mark fast niemand spazieren.

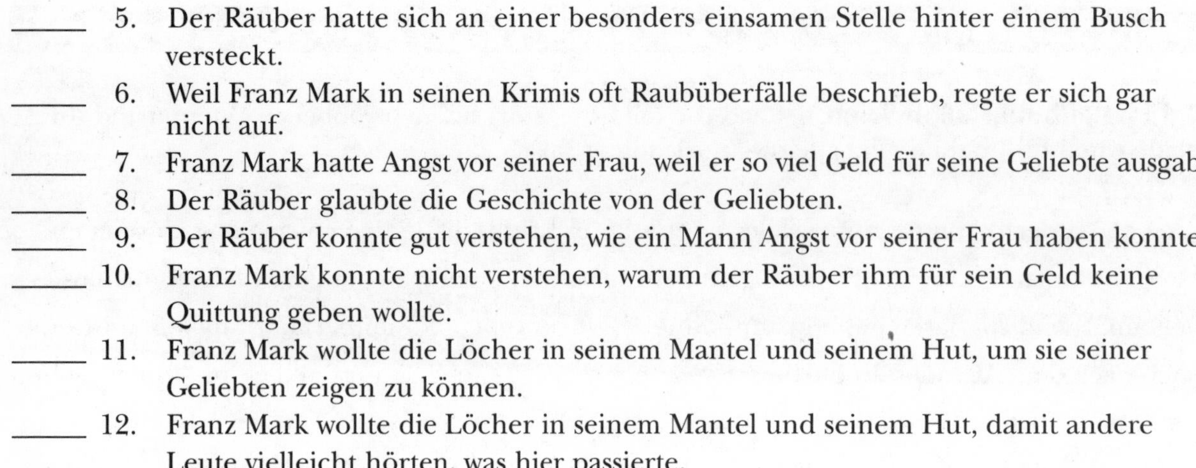

_____ 5. Der Räuber hatte sich an einer besonders einsamen Stelle hinter einem Busch versteckt.

_____ 6. Weil Franz Mark in seinen Krimis oft Raubüberfälle beschrieb, regte er sich gar nicht auf.

_____ 7. Franz Mark hatte Angst vor seiner Frau, weil er so viel Geld für seine Geliebte ausgab.

_____ 8. Der Räuber glaubte die Geschichte von der Geliebten.

_____ 9. Der Räuber konnte gut verstehen, wie ein Mann Angst vor seiner Frau haben konnte.

_____ 10. Franz Mark konnte nicht verstehen, warum der Räuber ihm für sein Geld keine Quittung geben wollte.

_____ 11. Franz Mark wollte die Löcher in seinem Mantel und seinem Hut, um sie seiner Geliebten zeigen zu können.

_____ 12. Franz Mark wollte die Löcher in seinem Mantel und seinem Hut, damit andere Leute vielleicht hörten, was hier passierte.

Zum Übersetzen

10-16 Mein Ferienjob. Use the simple past tense.

Last year I was in Germany the whole summer. I lived with an uncle who has a bakery and for whom I also worked. It was hard work, because (*use* **denn**) I had to get up at four, so that the people in the village had fresh rolls for breakfast. But the pay was good and after a few weeks I bought myself an old, but good car. On the weekends I then went on (*use* **machen**) many interesting trips.

10-17 Kleine Gespräche.

1. DANIEL: When are you flying to Switzerland?

   SOPHIA: When the flights are a bit cheaper.

2. FLORIAN: Is this **(das)** the house in which you lived as a child?

   ANNA: Yes. When I was little, I always thought: „What a big house!" And now it looks so small.

3. MARIA: Can you recommend a good restaurant to me?

   PHILIPP: Why don't you go to the „Green Garden"? There you **(man)** always get big, juicy steaks, fresh vegetables *(sing!)*, and a delicious dessert.

4. LUKAS: How big is your new apartment, Kirsten?

   KIRSTEN: I have a big, bright living room with a balcony, a small bedroom, and a tiny kitchen.

5. LAURA: What should I put on? My gray sweater or my blue jacket?

   SYLVIA: I like (*use* **gefallen**) your gray sweater better.

KAPITEL 11

Strukturen

Focusing on the receiver of an action

1. The passive voice (☞ Übungen 11-1, 11-2, 11-3, 11-4, pp. 219–222)

active voice	passive voice
The *doer* of the action is the subject.	The *receiver* of the action is the subject.
Peter *holt* mich um acht *ab*.	**Ich** *werde* um acht *abgeholt*.

In the passive voice

- the receiver of the action appears in the nominative case;
- the verb appears as a past participle with a form of **werden** as auxiliary.

The most commonly used tenses in the passive are the present and simple past.

PRESENT	ich **werde** abgeholt	*I'm being picked up*
SIMPLE PAST	ich **wurde** abgeholt	*I was picked up*

2. Mentioning the agent in a passive sentence (☞ Übung 11-5, p. 223)

If the agent is mentioned in a passive sentence, it appears in the dative case after the preposition **von.**

Dieses Buch wurde mir **von einem Freund** empfohlen. — *This book was recommended to me* ***by a friend.***

Describing people, places, and things

3. The past participle used as an adjective (☞ Übungen 11-6, 11-7, pp. 224–225)

Past participles are frequently used as adjectives. Before a noun, the past participle takes the same endings as other adjectives.

ein frisch **gewaschener** Pullover — *a freshly* ***washed*** *sweater*
ein **aufgeräumtes** Zimmer — *a* ***cleaned up*** *room*
eine **möblierte** Wohnung — *a* ***furnished*** *apartment*

Expanding the meaning of some verbs

4. Special verb-preposition combinations (☞ Übungen 11-8, 11-9, 11-10, pp. 226–227)

Commonly used verb-preposition combinations:

Angst haben vor *(+ dative)*	*to be afraid of*
arbeiten an *(+ dative)*	*to work on*
denken an *(+ accusative)*	*to think of, about*
erzählen von	*to tell about*
warten auf *(+ accusative)*	*to wait for*
wissen von	*to know about*

For the two-case prepositions, the test of **wohin/wo** does not apply. The correct case is therefore given in parentheses.

Commonly used verb-preposition combinations with reflexive verbs:

sich ärgern über *(+ accusative)*	*to be annoyed with*
sich aufregen über *(+ accusative)*	*to get upset about*
sich freuen auf *(+ accusative)*	*to look forward to*
sich freuen über *(+ accusative)*	*to be happy about; to be pleased with*
sich interessieren für	*to be interested in*
sich verlieben in *(+ accusative)*	*to fall in love with*

Asking questions about people or things

5. *Wo*-compounds (☞ Übungen 11-11, 11-12, pp. 229–230)

The question words **wem** and **wen** refer to persons. If a preposition is involved, it precedes the question word.

Vor wem hast du Angst?	***Who*** *are you afraid* ***of?***
An wen denkst du?	***Who*** *are you thinking* ***of?***

The question word **was** refers to things or ideas. If a preposition is involved, a **wo-**compound is used.

Wovor hast du Angst?	***What*** *are you afraid* ***of?***
Woran denkst du?	***What*** *are you thinking* ***of?***

An **r** is added to **wo** if the preposition begins with a vowel: **wo*r*an, wo*r*auf, wo*r*über,** etc.

NAME: ______________________________ DATE: ______________

Anwendung

Übungen

11-1 Fragen und Antworten. Complete the responses in the present passive, using the appropriate components. (☞ Strukturen 1, p. 217)

er / dort gut / bezahlen — mein Wagen / gerade / reparieren

1. > Warum bist du mit dem Bus zur Uni gekommen?

   < Weil mein Wagen gerade repariert wird.

2. > Warum arbeitet Martin jeden Sommer für dieselbe Firma?

   < Weil ______________________________

sie / gerade / renovieren — die Geschäfte / erst um halb zehn / öffnen

3. > Warum darf man denn nicht in diese schöne, alte Kirche?

   < Weil ______________________________

4. > Warum fahrt ihr erst um neun in die Stadt?

   < Weil ______________________________

ihr Büro / frisch / streichen — sein neuestes Buch / so viel / kaufen

5. > Warum hat Herr Merk denn plötzlich so viel Geld?

   < Weil ______________________________

6. > Warum ist unsere Direktorin heute nicht hier?

   < Weil ______________________________

ich / in einer Minute / abholen — immer mehr Fabriken / automatisieren

7. > Warum liest du denn in Mantel und Handschuhen die Zeitung?

   < Weil ______________________________

8. > Warum gibt es eigentlich so viele Arbeitslose?

   < Weil ______________________________

11-2 Ein bisschen kompakter, bitte! Focus on the receiver of the action by omitting the doer and by expressing the rest of the sentence in the passive voice. Note that in almost every instance the resulting passive sentence is more natural than its active counterpart. (☞ Strukturen 1, p. 217)

1. Wann operieren die Ärzte deinen Großvater?

   Wann wird dein Großvater operiert?

2. Der Automechaniker repariert gerade Ihren Wagen, Frau Schmidt.

3. Warum putzt die Putzfrau mein Zimmer nie?

4. Bezahlt deine Firma dich gut?

5. Warum laden deine Freunde mich nie ein?

6. Lesen die Leute diese Zeitung viel?

7. Die Leute kaufen diesen Computer viel.

8. Hoffentlich findet bald jemand deinen Pass.

9. Wann holt dein Freund dich ab?

NAME: ______________________ DATE: ______________

11-3 Fragen und Antworten. Complete the responses in the simple past passive, using the appropriate components. (Strukturen 1, p. 217)

das Haus / verkaufen — ich / nicht / einladen

1. > Gehst du auf Monikas Party, Günter?

   < Nein, ich wurde nicht eingeladen.

2. > Warum sind Meyers denn aus dem schönen Haus ausgezogen, in dem sie so lange in Miete gewohnt haben?

   < Ich glaube, ______________________

sie / für dich / bringen — das arme Tier / überfahren *(inseparable!)*

3. > Für wen sind denn die tollen Rosen hier?

   < ______________________

4. > Habt ihr euren Hund noch?

   < Nein, ______________________

sie / nie / gießen — sein Fahrrad / stehlen (o)

5. > Warum ist Thomas denn so aufgeregt?

   < Ich glaube, ______________________

6. > Warum ist die Geranie denn kaputtgegangen?

   < ______________________

Amerika / entdecken *(to discover)* — ich / so schlecht / bezahlen

7. > Warum arbeitest du denn nicht mehr auf dem Golfplatz?

   < Weil ______________________

8. > Was ist im Jahr 1492 passiert?

   < Da ______________________

11-4 Ein bisschen kompakter, bitte! Focus on the receiver of the action by omitting the doer and by expressing the rest of the sentence in the passive voice. Use the simple past tense. Note that in almost every instance the resulting passive sentence is more natural than its active counterpart. (Strukturen 1, p. 217)

1. Die Ärzte haben meinen Großvater gestern Nachmittag operiert.

   Mein Großvater wurde gestern Nachmittag operiert.

2. Gestern hat ein Lastwagen unseren Hund überfahren.

   ____

3. Warum haben die Polizisten diesen Mann verhaftet?

   ____

4. Weißt du schon, dass jemand Peters Fahrrad gestohlen hat?

   ____

5. Hat jemand deine Geldtasche gefunden?

   ____

6. Warum haben Müllers uns nicht eingeladen?

   ____

7. Warum hat die Lehrerin euch denn gleich wieder nach Hause geschickt?

   ____

   ____

8. Wann hat Kolumbus Amerika entdeckt?

   ____

9. Über die Entdeckung Amerikas haben Autoren viele Bücher geschrieben.

   ____

10. Viele Übersetzer haben die Märchen der Brüder Grimm in über 140 Sprachen übersetzt.

    ____

    ____

NAME: ______________________________ DATE: ______________

11-5 Aus zwei alten Märchen. The following statements describe what happened to the characters in two well-known fairy tales. Rewrite them in the simple past tense of the passive voice and mention the agent. (☞ Strukturen 2, p. 217)

NEUE VOKABELN

böse	*bad*	**schlachten**	*to butcher*
der Jäger	*hunter*	**retten**	*to save*
die Hexe	*witch*		

1. a. Die Mutter schickte Rotkäppchen zur Großmutter.

   Rotkäppchen wurde von der Mutter zur Großmutter geschickt.

   b. Ein böser Wolf fraß die Großmutter und Rotkäppchen auf.

   ____

   ____

   c. Ein Jäger holte die Großmutter und Rotkäppchen wieder aus dem Bauch des Wolfs heraus.

   ____

   ____

2. a. Die Eltern ließen Hänsel und Gretel ganz allein im Wald.

   ____

   ____

   b. Dort hat eine böse Hexe sie gefangen.

   ____

   c. Die Hexe steckte Hänsel in einen kleinen Stall.

   ____

   d. In diesem Stall machte sie ihn schön fett.

   ____

   e. Die Hexe hat Hänsel dann fast geschlachtet und gefressen.

   ____

   ____

   f. Gott sei Dank hat seine Schwester ihn im letzten Moment gerettet.

   ____

   ____

11-6 Ergänzen Sie! Write the English equivalents of the verbs below. Try to guess those that you do not already know. Then write the past participles (all verbs are regular except **backen**). Use the past participles appropriately as adjectives. (Strukturen 3, p. 217)

a. Was möchten Sie essen und trinken?

räuchern ___geräuchert___ ___smoked___ pressen ________ ________

mischen ________ ________ rösten ________ ________

grillen ________ ________ backen ________ ________

Ich möchte ...

eine Scheibe Brot mit Käse und ___geräuchert___em Lachs.

einen Teller ________en Salat.

ein frisch ________es Brötchen mit Butter und Marmelade.

ein Glas frisch ________en Orangensaft.

eine Tasse frisch ________en Kaffee.

ein großes ________es Steak.

b. Ingrid macht alles selbst.

nähen ___genäht___ ___sewn___ backen ________ ________

pflanzen ________ ________ malen ________ ________

brauen ________ ________ bauen ________ ________

Ingrid isst nur selbst ________es Brot und selbst ________es Gemüse. Sie trinkt nur selbst ________es Bier und sie trägt auch nur selbst ________e Kleider. In ihrer Wohnung stehen nur selbst ________e Möbel und an den Wänden hängen überall selbst ________e Bilder.

NAME: ______________________________ DATE: ______________

11-7 Was passt wo? In each set, supply past participles of the appropriate verbs. (☞ Strukturen 3, p. 217)

pressen / packen / versprechen / leihen / backen

1. Maiers haben ihren neuen BMW bestimmt wieder mit ________geliehen em Geld gekauft.
2. Möchtest du ein Stück von meinem frisch ____________en Kuchen?
3. Ich möchte gern ein Glas frisch ____________en Orangensaft.
4. Gestern kam endlich dein lang ____________er Brief.
5. Stellen Sie die ____________en Koffer bitte vor die Tür!

anfangen / bauen / verdienen / waschen / möblieren

6. Das ist ja wunderbar! Soße auf dem frisch ____________en Hemd!
7. Wann schreibst du den ____________n Brief denn endlich fertig?
8. Soll ich diese ____________e Wohnung mieten oder nicht?
9. Peter ist ein sehr gut ____________er junger Mann.
10. Diese hundert Euro sind schwer ____________es Geld.

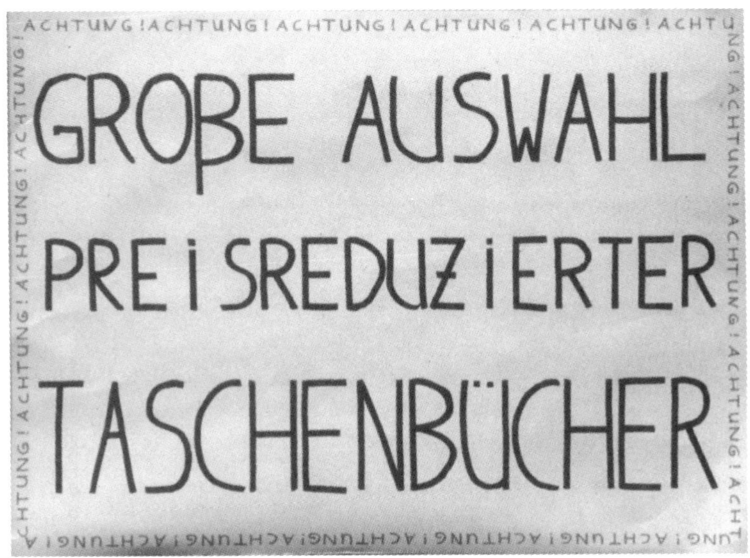

11-8 Was passt zusammen? Match the questions and responses by writing the appropriate numbers in the spaces provided. (Strukturen 4, p. 218)

1. Warum gehst du denn so oft ins Deutsche Museum, Claudia?
2. Warum freust du dich denn nicht auf Sylvias Party?
3. Warum arbeitet Peter denn nicht an seinem Referat?
4. Warum laden Sie Fischers nie mehr ein?
5. Warum regst du dich über meine schlechten Zensuren so auf, Vati?
6. Warum geht ihr nicht mit uns Kaffee trinken?
7. Warum denkst du, dass Holger sich in Anna verliebt hat?

___ Weil sie immer nur von ihren Reisen erzählen wollen.

___ Weil ich Angst habe, dass du dein Schuljahr wiederholen musst.

___ Weil ich mich für Technik interessiere.

___ Weil wir auf Martina warten müssen.

___ Weil Günter auch dort sein wird.

___ Weil er von morgens bis abends von ihr erzählt.

___ Weil er es erst nächste Woche abgeben muss.

Ladendiebstahl

Denken Sie an die Folgen!

NAME: ______________________________ DATE: ______________

11-9 Was passt zusammen? Match the questions and responses by writing the appropriate numbers in the spaces provided. (Strukturen 4, p. 218)

1. Warum kommt die Katze denn nie zu mir?	___ Weil er immer von dir spricht.
2. Was wissen Sie von Christoph Kolumbus?	___ Weil ich nicht genug gelernt habe.
3. Warum hast du dich über Frank so geärgert?	___ Sie hat es mir gesagt.
4. Warum freust du dich denn nicht auf die Ferien?	___ Weil ich den ganzen Sommer arbeiten und Geld verdienen muss.
5. Woher weißt du, dass Nicole sich über meine Rosen so gefreut hat?	___ Weil er nicht auf mich gewartet hat.
6. Woher weißt du, dass Moritz so viel an mich denkt?	___ Dass er Amerika entdeckt hat.
7. Warum hast du denn solche Angst vor dieser Klausur?	___ Ich glaube, sie hat Angst vor dir.

11-10 Meinungen (I). Complete the opinions expressed in this survey on flying by supplying the appropriate verb forms, prepositions, and case endings. (Strukturen 4, p. 218)

1. Angst haben vor (+ dat)

   Ich _habe_ immer noch _Angst vor_ d_em_ Fliegen. Heutzutage sind einfach zu viele Flugzeuge in der Luft. *(Hans Krause, Cottbus)*

2. sich verlieben in (+ acc)

   Was ich vom Fliegen denke? Ich finde es toll! Ich habe ___________ bei einem Flug nach New York ___________ mein____ zweite Frau ___________, und ein halbes Jahr später haben wir dann geheiratet. *(Karl-Heinz Petsch, Baden-Baden)*

3. sich ärgern über (+ acc)

Ich __________________ ____________ immer wieder ____________ d____ langen Wartezeiten auf dem Flughafen. Und bis man erst zum Flughafen kommt! Das braucht alles viel zu viel Zeit! *(Helga Neumann, Plön)*

4. sich aufregen über (+ acc)

Ich muss ____________ immer ____________ d____ schlechte Essen __________________. Das letzte Mal war alles so versalzen, dass ich nachher stundenlang Mineralwasser trinken musste. *(Ilse Motz, Kassel)*

5. sich freuen auf (+ acc)

Also ich muss sagen, ich __________________ ____________ ____________ jed____ Flug und ich fliege so oft ich kann. *(Markus Huber, Dresden)*

6. denken an (+ acc)

Der Service wird immer schlechter. Wenn ich ____________ d____ Versprechungen der Chartergesellschaften __________________, kann ich nur lachen. Sie versprechen den tollsten Luxus, und in Wirklichkeit sitzt man in diesen Maschinen wie Sardinen in der Dose. *(Suse Wittmer, Oldenburg)*

7. sich interessieren für (+ acc)

Meine Frau und ich reisen sehr viel, weil wir ____________ ____________ andere Kulturen __________________. Mit dem Flugzeug sind wir in wenigen Stunden in exotischen Ländern. Fliegen ist wunderbar! *(Holger und Bettina Zeuner, Flensburg)*

8. erzählen von (+ dat)

Ich fliege sehr viel und ich kann Ihnen die tollsten Geschichten ____________ mein____ Flugerlebnissen __________________. Leider sind es oft richtige Horrorgeschichten. *(Maria Vogt, Bad Hersfeld)*

NAME: ______________________________ **DATE:** ______________

11-11 Kleine Gespräche. Supply **wo**-compounds or prepositional phrases with **wem** or **wen,** and endings. (Strukturen 5, p. 218)

1. > Worüber ______________ hast du dich denn so geärgert?

   < Über die____ schlechte Zensur, die ich für mein Referat bekommen habe.

2. > Über wen ______________ hast du dich denn so geärgert?

   < Über meinen____ Bruder.

3. > ____________________ hat sich Stephanie in München verliebt?

   < In ein____ sehr netten jungen Mann namens Peter Ackermann.

4. > ____________________ arbeitet Professor Müller zur Zeit?

   < An ein____ Buch über die Geschichte der DDR.

5. > ____________________ weißt du, dass Professor Rieger krank ist?

   < Von ihr____ Sekretärin.

6. > ____________________ wartest du denn?

   < Auf ein____ Anruf von meinen Eltern.

7. > ____________________ wartest du?

   < Auf mein____ Freund.

8. > ____________________ hat sich dein Vater denn so aufgeregt?

   < Über mein____ neue Frisur.

9. > ____________________ hat deine kleine Schwester denn so Angst?

   < Vor d____ beiden bösen Nachbarsjungen.

10. > ____________________ musst du denken, wenn du diese Melodie hörst?

    < An unser____ letzten Abend in Heidelberg.

11. > ____________________ musst du denken, wenn du diese Melodie hörst?

    < An mein____ Freund in Heidelberg.

12. > ____________________ interessiert sich deine neue Mitbewohnerin?

    < Für Sport und für klassisch____ Musik.

11-12 Was halten Sie vom Fliegen? (II) Complete the following opinions about flying with appropriate prepositions and endings. Then complete the exchanges that follow with verbs, **wo-**compounds, or prepositions and pronouns. (Strukturen 5, p. 218)

1. Am meisten ärgert _sich_ Frau Neumann _über_ d_ie_ langen Wartezeiten auf dem Flughafen.

   > Wissen Sie, _worüber_ _sich_ Frau Neumann am meisten _ärgert_?

   < _Worüber_ denn?

   > _Über die langen Wartezeiten auf dem Flughafen._

2. Ich rege ________ oft ________ d___ schlechte Essen auf.

   > Wissen Sie, ________ ich ________ oft ________?

   < ________ denn?

   > ________________

3. Herr Petsch hat ________ bei einem Flug nach New York ________ sein___ zweite Frau verliebt.

   > Wissen Sie, ________ ________ Herr Petsch bei einem Flug nach New York ________ ________?

   < ________ denn?

   > ________________

4. Herr Krause hat ________ d___ Landung am meisten Angst.

   > Wissen Sie, ________ Herr Krause am meisten ________ ________?

   < ________ denn?

   > ________________

5. Zeuners interessieren ________ ________ die Kulturen exotischer Länder.

   > Wissen Sie, ________ ________ Zeuners ________?

   < ________ denn?

   > ________________

6. Diese Horrorgeschichten über das Fliegen kenne ich alle ________ Frau Vogt.

   > Wissen Sie, ________ ich alle diese Horrorgeschichten über das Fliegen ________?

   < ________ denn?

   > ________________

NAME: ______________________________ DATE: ______________

Zum Verstehen

11-13 Der alte Großvater und der Enkel. Read this fairy tale by the Grimm brothers and then match the clauses below.

Es war einmal ein uralter Mann, dem waren die Augen trüb[1] geworden, die Ohren taub[2], und die Knie zitterten[3] ihm. Wenn er nun bei Tisch saß und den Löffel kaum halten konnte, schüttete[4] er Suppe auf das Tischtuch[5], und es floss[6] ihm auch etwas wieder aus dem Mund. Sein Sohn und seine Schwiegertochter[7] ekelten sich davor[8], und deshalb musste sich der alte Großvater endlich hinter den Ofen[9] in die Ecke setzen und sie gaben ihm sein Essen in ein irdenes[10] Schüsselchen; da sah er betrübt[11] nach dem Tisch und die Augen wurden ihm nass.

Einmal konnten seine zitterigen Hände das Schüsselchen nicht festhalten[12], und es fiel auf den Fußboden und zerbrach[13]. Die junge Frau schalt[14], er sagte aber nichts und seufzte[15] nur. Da kaufte sie ihm ein hölzernes[16] Schüsselchen für ein paar Pfennige, daraus musste er nun essen.

Wie sie da so sitzen, so trägt der kleine Enkel von vier Jahren auf dem Fußboden kleine Brettlein[17] zusammen. „Was machst du da?" fragte der Vater. „Ich mache ein Tröglein[18]", antwortete das Kind, „daraus sollen Vater und Mutter essen, wenn ich groß bin."

Da schauten sich Vater und Mutter eine Weile an, fingen endlich an zu weinen, holten den alten Großvater an den Tisch und ließen ihn von nun an immer mitessen, sagten auch nichts, wenn er ein wenig verschüttete.

[1]*dim* [2]*deaf* [3]*trembled* [4]*spilled* [5]*tablecloth* [6]*dribbled* [7]*daughter-in-law* [8]**ekelten ... :** *found this disgusting* [9]*woodstove* [10]*earthenware* [11]*sadly* [12]*hold on to* [13]*broke* [14]*scolded* [15]*sighed* [16]*wooden* [17]*boards* [18]*little trough*

Match the clauses below by writing the appropriate numbers in the spaces provided.

1. Weil der Großvater den Löffel kaum halten konnte,	_____	kaufte ihm die junge Frau ein hölzernes Schüsselchen.
2. Weil dem Großvater beim Essen oft ein bisschen Suppe wieder aus dem Mund floss,	_____	begann er, ein hölzernes Tröglein für sie zu bauen.
3. Weil der Großvater in der Ecke hinter dem Ofen essen musste,	_____	ekelten sich sein Sohn und seine Schwiegertochter.
4. Weil der Großvater das irdene Schüsselchen fallen ließ und zerbrach,	_____	mussten sie weinen, und holten Großvater wieder an den Tisch.
5. Weil der Enkel sah, was seine Eltern mit dem Großvater machten,	_____	schüttete er oft ein bisschen Suppe auf das Tischtuch.
6. Weil der Sohn und seine Frau plötzlich verstanden, was sie getan hatten,	_____	sah er oft betrübt nach dem Tisch und weinte ein bisschen.

Zum Übersetzen

11-14 Ein bisschen Geschichte. Use the simple past tense.

In the year 1961 the Berlin Wall was built, a wall which divided the city into East Berlin *(one word!)* and West Berlin. After twenty-eight years, on the 9th of November 1989, the Wall that separated East Germans *(one word!)* and West Germans was opened (*use* **öffnen**) again. For the Berliners and for all Germans it was a historical day.

11-15 Kleine Gespräche.

1. FRAU KUHN: Who is the elegantly dressed woman there?
   FRAU HAHN: That's the wife of the federal chancellor.

2. MARKUS: Are you interested in modern music?
   NICOLE: No, I prefer to listen to classical music. Bach is my favorite composer.

3. ANNE: What are you doing in the holidays?
   EVA: My boyfriend and I are planning a cycling tour to the coast. We're really **(sehr)** looking forward to it.

4. PAUL: Why don't you go into the garden? What are you afraid of?
   MELANIE: I'm afraid of our neighbor's dog.

5. LAURA: Who is the guy that Maria has fallen in love with?
   YVONNE: He's a Canadian exchange student from Ontario.

6. MORITZ: Why are you always annoyed with your girlfriend?
   MICHAEL: Because she's so stubborn. Sometimes I don't understand her at all.

KAPITEL 12

Strukturen

Expressing hypothetical situations

1. Present-time subjunctive (☞ Übungen 12-1, 12-2, pp. 237–238)

By using subjunctive forms a speaker indicates that what she/he says is hypothetical or contrary-to-fact.

FACTUAL	HYPOTHETICAL (contrary-to-fact)
Ich **habe** keinen Wagen.	Wenn ich nur einen Wagen **hätte!**
Peter **ist** nicht hier.	Wenn Peter nur hier **wäre!**
Martin **muss** arbeiten und **kann** uns nicht helfen.	Wenn Martin nicht arbeiten **müsste, könnte** er uns helfen.

infinitive	simple past	subjunctive
haben	hatte	**hätte**
sein	war	**wäre**
werden	wurde	**würde**
dürfen	durfte	**dürfte**
können	konnte	**könnte**
mögen	mochte	**möchte**
müssen	musste	**müsste**
sollen	sollte	**sollte**
wollen	wollte	**wollte**
wissen	wusste	**wüsste**

- Although the forms of the present-time subjunctive are derived from the second principal part, i.e., the simple past, they do not refer to the past, but to present time.
- Except for **sollte** and **wollte,** all the forms above are umlauted.

In the subjunctive all verbs have the following set of personal endings:

singular		plural	
ich	hätte	wir	hätt**en**
du	hätt**est**	ihr	hätt**et**
er/es/sie	hätte	sie	hätt**en**
Sie	hätt**en**		

- The **e** in the personal ending of the **du-** and **ihr-**forms of **sein** is frequently omitted: **du wärst, ihr wärt.**
- English equivalents for these forms often include the auxilary verb *would.*

Ich **wüsste** gern, was du denkst.	*I **would** like to **know** what you are thinking.*
Ich **hätte** gern einen neuen Computer.	*I **would** like to **have** a new computer.*
Das **wäre** toll.	*That **would be** fantastic.*

2. *Würde* + infinitive (☞ Übungen 12-3, 12-4, 12-5, pp. 239–240)

To express present-time hypothetical or contrary-to-fact situations, colloquial German commonly uses the subjunctive forms for **haben, sein, werden,** the modals, and **wissen.** All other verbs tend to appear in a construction that is parallel to English *would + infinitive:* **würde** + *infinitive.*

Was **würdest** du **tun,** wenn dein Freund ständig eifersüchtig wäre?	*What* ***would*** *you* ***do*** *if your boyfriend were constantly jealous?*
Ich **würde** mir einen anderen Freund **suchen.**	***I would look for*** *another boyfriend.*

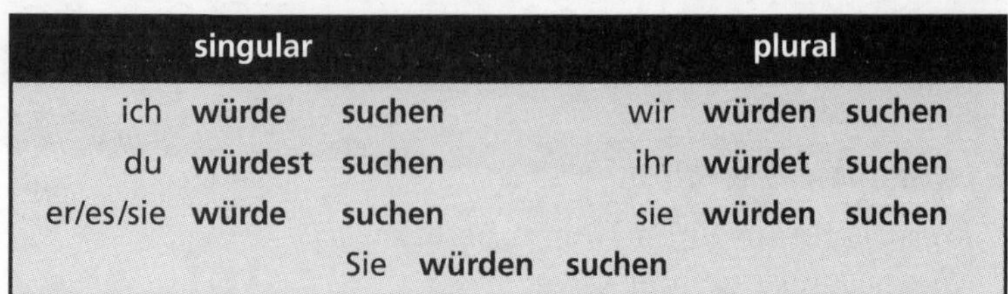

singular			plural		
ich	**würde**	**suchen**	wir	**würden**	**suchen**
du	**würdest**	**suchen**	ihr	**würdet**	**suchen**
er/es/sie	**würde**	**suchen**	sie	**würden**	**suchen**
		Sie **würden suchen**			

3. The subjunctive in polite requests (☞ Übung 12-6, p. 241)

The following expressions are used to express wishes and requests more politely:

Ich **hätte gern** ein Glas Bier.	***I would like*** *a glass of beer.*
Ich **möchte** ein Glas Bier.	***I would like*** *a glass of beer.*
Könnten Sie mir bitte sagen, wo die Apotheke ist?	***Could*** *you please tell me where the pharmacy is?*
Wäre es möglich, statt der Suppe Salat zu bekommen?	***Would*** *it* ***be*** *possible to get salad instead of soup?*

More on expressing hypothetical situations

4. Past-time subjunctive (☞ Übungen 12-7, 12-8, 12-9, pp. 242–244)

In past-time hypothetical situations, the verb appears as a past participle with the auxiliary in the subjunctive **(wäre, hätte).**

FACTUAL	HYPOTHETICAL
Ich **bin** zu schnell **gefahren** und **habe** einen Strafzettel **bekommen.**	Wenn ich nicht zu schnell **gefahren wäre, hätte** ich keinen Strafzettel **bekommen.**
I ***was driving*** *too fast and* ***got*** *a ticket.*	*If I* ***hadn't been driving*** *too fast, I* ***wouldn't have gotten*** *a ticket.*

- In past-time subjunctive, German never uses **würde:**

Meine Freundin **wäre** nicht zu schnell **gefahren.**	*My girlfriend* ***wouldn't have driven*** *too fast.*
Sie **hätte** keinen Strafzettel **bekommen.**	*She* ***wouldn't have gotten*** *a ticket.*

- When **haben** and **sein** are the main verbs in past-time hypothetical situations, they appear as past participles with the auxiliaries in the subjunctive **(hätte gehabt, wäre gewesen).**

FACTUAL	HYPOTHETICAL
Ich **hatte** heute eine Klausur und **war** gestern bis nachts um eins in der Bibliothek.	Wenn ich heute keine Klausur **gehabt hätte, wäre** ich gestern nicht bis nachts um eins in der Bibliothek **gewesen.**

Expressing cause, opposition, alternatives, and simultaneity

5. Genitive prepositions (☞ Übungen 12-10, 12-11, p. 245)

wegen	*because of*	**Wegen des Schneesturms** waren gestern keine Vorlesungen.
trotz	*in spite of*	Lisa ist **trotz des Schneesturms** in die Bibliothek gegangen.
statt	*instead of*	Sie hat aber **statt einer Jacke** einen dicken Wintermantel angezogen.
während	*during*	Lisa war **während des ganzen Sturms** in der Bibliothek.

Giving information about people, places, and things

6. The relative pronoun in the genitive case (☞ Übung 12-12, p. 246)

A relative pronoun in the genitive case expresses a relationship of possession or belonging together between the antecedent and the noun following the relative pronoun.

antecedent	rel. pron.	
Der Student,	**dessen**	Wagen ich gekauft habe, studiert jetzt in den USA.
Die Frau,	**deren**	Bild gestern in der Zeitung war, ist unsere Nachbarin.
Die Jungen,	**deren**	Foto auf meinem Schreibtisch steht, sind meine Neffen.

- The gender and number of the relative pronoun is determined by the antecedent.
- The English equivalent of the genitive relative pronoun is *whose*.

forms of the relative pronoun				
	MASCULINE	NEUTER	FEMININE	PLURAL
NOMINATIVE	der	das	die	die
ACCUSATIVE	den	das	die	die
DATIVE	dem	dem	der	denen
GENITIVE	**dessen**	**dessen**	**deren**	**deren**

The relative pronoun has the same forms as the definite article except in the dative plural and the genitive.

NAME: ______________________ DATE: ______________

Anwendung

Übungen

12-1 Wenn ich nur eine andere Mitbewohnerin hätte! Using present-time subjunctive with **nur** or **nur nicht,** write in what ways you wish that your roommate were different than she is. (Strukturen 1, p. 233)

1. Ich weiß nicht, wo ich ein anderes Zimmer bekommen kann.

   Wenn ich nur wüsste, wo ich ein anderes Zimmer bekommen kann!

2. Sylvia ist so unordentlich.

   ____

3. Sie hat so doofe Freunde.

   ____

4. Sie kann ihre Hausaufgaben nicht ohne meine Hilfe machen.

   ____

   ____

5. Ich muss alle ihre Referate schreiben.

   ____

   ____

6. Sie wird immer so wütend, wenn ich mal keine Zeit für sie habe.

   ____

   ____

7. Sie will immer mein Fahrrad leihen.

   ____

   ____

8. Ich kann nicht nein sagen.

   ____

12-2 Situationen. In the following situations, people wish that things were not as they are. Complete their wishful thinking with appropriate verbs in the subjunctive. (Strukturen 1, p. 233)

1. Holgers Schweizer Verwandte haben ihn eingeladen, sie im Sommer zu besuchen. Holger kann aber leider nicht kommen, denn er hat nicht viel Geld und muss den ganzen Sommer arbeiten, um sein Studium zu finanzieren. Er denkt:

   a. Wenn ich nur mehr Geld hätte!

   b. Wenn ich nur nicht den ganzen Sommer arbeiten ____________________!

   c. Wenn ich nur meine Schweizer Verwandten besuchen ____________________!

2. Günter hat sich in der Cafeteria zu Monika an den Tisch gesetzt und sie eingeladen, mit ihm heute abend tanzen zu gehen. Monika kann ihm nicht direkt sagen, dass sie ihn nicht mag, aber sie hat leider auch keine gute Ausrede. Sie weiß nicht, was sie sagen soll, und sie denkt:

   a. Wenn ich nur eine gute Ausrede ____________________!

   b. Wenn ich ihm nur sagen ____________________, dass ich ihn nicht mag!

   c. Wenn ich nur ____________________, was ich sagen soll!

3. Onkel Alfred ist bei Zieglers zu Besuch. Er ist viel älter als Herr Ziegler und wird abends sehr früh müde. Er geht deshalb schon um halb zehn ins Bett und Nina und Robert dürfen dann keine laute Musik mehr hören. Das gefällt ihnen natürlich gar nicht und sie denken:

   a. Wenn Onkel Alfred nur nicht so alt ____________________!

   b. Wenn er nur nicht immer so früh müde ____________________!

   c. Wenn wir nur endlich auch am Abend wieder laute Musik hören ____________________!

4. Ralf ist sehr faul und hat deshalb ziemlich schlechte Zensuren. Aber Geld will er natürlich viel, und er weiß gar nicht, wie schwer es für seinen Eltern ist, ihm jeden Monat einen fetten Scheck zu schicken. Seine Eltern denken:

   a. Wenn Ralf nur bessere Zensuren ____________________!

   b. Wenn er nur ein bisschen fleißiger ____________________!

   c. Wenn er nur nicht immer so viel Geld ____________________!

   d. Wenn er nur ____________________, wie schwer es uns fällt, ihm so viel Geld zu schicken!

NAME: ______________________ DATE: ____________

12-3 Was passt zusammen? Complete the following contrary-to-fact conditions by writing the appropriate numbers in the spaces provided. (Strukturen 2, p. 234)

1. Wenn Ihr Sohn so schlechte Zensuren hätte wie unserer,	____ würde ich mir einen Ferienjob suchen.
2. Wenn ich so musikalisch wäre wie du,	____ würde ich nicht Auto fahren.
3. Wenn ich so schlecht sehen könnte wie du,	____ würden Sie sich auch aufregen.
4. Wenn ich so wenig Geld hätte wie du,	____ würden Sie sich auch freuen.
5. Wenn Ihre Tochter so einen netten Freund hätte wie unsere,	____ würde ich mir gleich ein Klavier kaufen.

12-4 Was passt zusammen? Complete the following contrary-to-fact conditions by writing the appropriate numbers in the spaces provided. (Strukturen 2, p. 234)

1. Wenn du so schlecht kochen könntest wie ich,	____ würdest du auch so schnell wie möglich Deutsch lernen wollen.
2. Wenn du so viele Referate schreiben müsstest wie ich,	____ würdest du auch im Bett bleiben.
3. Wenn du so hohes Fieber hättest wie ich,	____ würdest du auch immer in der Mensa essen.
4. Wenn du nächstes Jahr in Deutschland studieren dürftest,	____ würdest du auch den ganzen Tag in der Bibliothek sitzen.
5. Wenn du so schlecht rechnen könntest wie ich,	____ würdest du dir auch einen Taschenrechner kaufen.

12-5 Fragen und Antworten. Complete the hypothetical part of each response with appropriate subjunctive forms. (Strukturen 2, p. 234)

1. > Warum kauft sich Helga denn kein Klavier?

   < Weil sie kein Geld hat. Wenn sie Geld hätte ____________,

   würde ____________ sie sich bestimmt ein Klavier kaufen ____________.

2. > Warum darf ich denn nicht aufstehen?

   < Weil du immer noch Fieber hast. Wenn du kein Fieber mehr ____________,

   ____________ du ____________.

3. > Warum ladet ihr Kurt nicht ein?

   < Weil er sich immer so schlecht benimmt. Wenn er sich besser ____________

   ____________, ____________ wir ihn ____________.

4. > Warum rufst du denn Brigitte nicht an?

   < Weil ich ihre Telefonnummer nicht weiß. Wenn ich ihre Telefonnummer

   ____________, ____________ ich sie ____________.

5. > Warum nehmt ihr denn die Wohnung nicht?

   < Weil sie so teuer ist. Wenn sie nicht so teuer ____________,

   ____________ wir sie sofort ____________.

6. > Warum besuchen Sie uns denn so selten, Frau Dollinger?

   < Weil ich so viel zu tun habe. Wenn ich nicht so viel zu tun ____________,

   ____________ ich Sie bestimmt viel öfter ____________.

7. > Warum trinken Sie denn nicht noch einen Sherry, Frau Reimer?

   < Weil ich Auto fahren muss. Wenn ich nicht Auto fahren ____________,

   ____________ ich gern noch einen ____________.

8. > Warum lernen Sie denn nicht Auto fahren, Herr Haag?

   < Weil ich so nervös bin. Wenn ich nicht so nervös ____________,

   ____________ ich gleich Auto fahren ____________.

9. > Warum mieten Sie denn nie einen Wagen, wenn Sie in Europa sind?

   < Weil ich nicht Auto fahren kann. Wenn ich Auto fahren ____________,

   ____________ ich natürlich einen Wagen ____________.

NAME: ______________________________ DATE: ______________

12-6 Ein bisschen höflicher, bitte! Use the subjunctive to express the following requests more politely. (Strukturen 3, p. 234)

1. Ist es möglich, mit Professor Weber zu sprechen?

   Wäre es __________ möglich, mit Professor Weber zu sprechen?

2. Darf ich Sie einen Augenblick stören, Frau Professor?

   ______________________ Sie einen Augenblick stören, Frau Professor?

3. Kannst du diese Briefe für mich zur Post nehmen?

   ______________________ diese Briefe für mich zur Post nehmen?

4. Können Sie mir sagen, wo die Post ist?

   ______________________ mir sagen, wo die Post ist?

5. Ich will zehn Briefmarken zu 56 Cent.

   ______________________ zehn Briefmarken zu 56 Cent.

6. Musst du nicht an deinem Referat arbeiten?

   ______________________ nicht an deinem Referat arbeiten?

7. Hast du Lust, heute Abend mit mir essen zu gehen?

   ______________________ Lust, heute Abend mit mir essen zu gehen?

8. Willst du ein Glas Bier?

   ______________________ ein Glas Bier?

12-7 Wenn das nur alles nicht passiert wäre! Using past-time subjunctive with **nur nicht** or **nur,** express regret about what happened last night and this morning. (☞ Strukturen 4, p. 234)

1. Ich bin zu Holgers Party gegangen.

   Wenn ich nur nicht zu Holgers Party gegangen wäre!

2. Ich bin so lange geblieben.

3. Ich habe so viel Wein getrunken.

4. Ich bin erst um drei Uhr morgens nach Hause gekommen.

5. Ich habe meinen Wecker nicht gehört.

6. Der Achtuhrbus ist mir vor der Nase weggefahren.

7. Ich bin eine Viertelstunde zu spät zu dieser wichtigen Klausur gekommen.

8. Ich habe meine Notizen gestern nicht noch mal durchgelesen.

9. Professor Weber hat so komplizierte Fragen gestellt.

NAME: ______________________ DATE: __________

12-8 Wenn, wenn, wenn. Transform the following statements of fact into contrary-to-fact conditions in past-time subjunctive. (☞ Strukturen 4, p. 234)

1. Ich war so müde. / Ich bin nicht mit euch tanzen gegangen.

   Wenn ich nicht so müde gewesen wäre, wäre ich mit euch tanzen gegangen.

2. Ich hatte Fieber. / Ich bin im Bett geblieben.

   Wenn ich kein Fieber gehabt hätte, wäre ich nicht im Bett geblieben.

3. Ich war so krank. / Ich habe die Klausur nicht geschrieben.

4. Kurt hatte nicht genug Geld. / Er hat keinen Sportwagen gekauft.

5. Ich hatte keinen Hunger. / Ich bin nicht mit euch essen gegangen.

6. Es war so kalt. / Wir sind nicht schwimmen gegangen.

7. Du warst nicht zu Hause. / Ich habe dich nicht besucht.

8. Ich hatte deine Telefonnummer nicht. / Ich habe dich nicht angerufen.

9. Es war so heiß. / Wir haben nicht Tennis gespielt.

10. Ich hatte keine Zeit. / Ich habe dir nicht geholfen.

12-9 Ergänzen Sie! Read the statements of fact under *a.* Then complete the hypothetical statements under *b.* according to the example. (Strukturen 4, p. 234)

1. a. Weil ich so viele Hausaufgaben hatte, bin ich gestern Abend nicht ausgegangen.

   b. Wenn ich nicht so viele Hausaufgaben gehabt hätte, wäre ich gestern Abend

   ausgegangen.

2. a. Weil Anitas Party so langweilig war, sind wir schon nach einer Stunde wieder nach Hause gegangen.

   b. Wenn Anitas Party nicht so langweilig ______________________

   ____

   ____

3. a. Weil Robert so schlechte Zensuren hatte, hat er den Computer nicht bekommen.

   b. Wenn Robert keine so schlechten Zensuren ______________________

   ____

4. a. Weil ich vierzehn Tage lang krank war, habe ich Professor Webers Vorlesung nicht verstanden.

   b. Wenn ich nicht vierzehn Tage lang krank ______________________

   ____

   ____

5. a. Weil Günter so viel getrunken hat, hat er sich schlecht benommen.

   b. Wenn Günter nicht so viel getrunken ______________________

   ____

6. a. Weil Silke nicht genug Geld hatte, hat sie das Fahrrad nicht gekauft.

   b. Wenn Silke genug Geld ______________________

   ____

7. a. Weil es gestern so heiß war, sind wir zum Starnberger See gefahren.

   b. Wenn es gestern nicht so heiß ______________________

   ____

NAME: ______________________________ DATE: ______________

12-10 Ergänzen Sie! Supply genitive endings. (☞ Strukturen 5, p. 235)

1. Könnte ich statt d_____ Pommes frites (pl) vielleicht Reis oder Nudeln bekommen?
2. Frau Keller geht trotz ihr_____ schwer_____ Arthritis (f) und trotz ihr_____ hoh_____ Alter_____ (n) jeden Tag eine Stunde spazieren.
3. Während d_____ lang_____ Trockenzeit (f) ist Südkalifornien braun und golden, aber während d_____ kurz_____ Regenzeit wird dann plötzlich alles grün.
4. In der Nähe von Schulen und Seniorenheimen dürfen Autos wegen d_____ viel_____ Kinder und wegen d_____ alt_____ Leute nur sehr langsam fahren.

12-11 Kleine Gespräche. Complete with **statt, trotz, während,** or **wegen** and genitive endings. (☞ Strukturen 5, p. 235)

1. > Warum rufst du Kathrin nicht an?

   < Weil sie ________________ d_____ Tag_____ nicht zu Hause ist.

2. > Warum gehen Köhlers denn so selten aus?

   < ________________ ihr_____ beiden kleinen Kinder.

3. > Warum hast du denn Salat ________________ d_____ Pommes frites bestellt?

   < Weil ich schlank bleiben will.

4. > Ist Julia tanzen gegangen?

   < Ja, und das ________________ ihr_____ vielen Hausaufgaben.

5. > Warum ist Gerd denn nicht mitgekommen?

   < ________________ sein_____ vielen Hausaufgaben.

6. > Warum ist Sabine nicht mitgekommen?

   < Weil sie ________________ d_____ Woche keine Zeit hat.

7. > Sollen wir unserem Sohn einen Computer zum Geburtstag schenken?

   < Ich glaube, er möchte lieber Geld ________________ ein_____ Computer_____.

8. > Wissen Sie, dass Frau Keller morgen neunzig wird?

   < Ja, und sie geht ________________ ihr_____ Alter_____ jeden Tag eine Stunde spazieren.

12-12 ***Dessen* oder *deren*?** Supply appropriate relative pronouns. (Strukturen 6, p. 235)

1. Der Professor, _____________ Vorlesungen ich am interessantesten finde, wird leider dieses Jahr pensioniert.

2. Barbara Frischmuth ist eine Autorin, _____________ Erzählungen mich immer wieder faszinieren.

3. Mozart ist der Komponist, _____________ Opern ich am liebsten sehe und höre.

4. U2 ist die Rockgruppe, _____________ Musik mir am besten gefällt.

5. Auch Studenten, _____________ Eltern nicht viel Geld haben, sollten ein Jahr im Ausland studieren dürfen.

6. Der Journalist, _____________ Artikel du so toll findest, ist ein guter Bekannter von mir.

7. Kinder, _____________ Eltern beide arbeiten, sitzen oft viel zu lange vor dem Fernseher.

8. Weißt du, dass der Mann, _____________ Tochter Bernd heiratet, Millionär ist?

9. Bernd heiratet eine Frau, _____________ Vater Millionär ist.

10. Die Leute, _____________ Sohn ich immer bei den Hausaufgaben helfe, haben viel Geld.

NAME: ______________________________ DATE: ______________

Zum Verstehen

12-13 Synonyme. Find a synonym for each word or expression and write it in the appropriate space.

überhaupt nicht	ewig	die Kleider
intelligent	verstehen	kaputt
glücklich	die Bezahlung	viel
wunderbar	schauen	nur
die Geschichte	gleich	aufmachen
zwei	das ist richtig	der Ozean
schon	bekommen	kaputtmachen
riesig	endlich	auf einmal

herrlich ______________ defekt ______________

immer ______________ kriegen ______________

sehr groß ______________ bloß ______________

öffnen ______________ klug ______________

eine Menge ______________ sofort ______________

die Klamotten ______________ ein Paar ______________

schließlich ______________ das Meer ______________

begreifen ______________ plötzlich ______________

froh ______________ gucken ______________

die Erzählung ______________ zerstören ______________

bereits ______________ gar nicht ______________

das stimmt ______________ der Lohn ______________

12-14 Der schlaue Soldat. Read the following adaptation of a story by the Swiss writer Johann Peter Hebel (1760-1826), and then match the clauses below.

Im Dreißigjährigen Krieg (1618-1648) waren überall[1] in Deutschland Soldaten, die den Menschen in den Städten und den Bauern auf dem Land das Leben schwer machten. Im Jahr 1630 war bei Regensburg eine große kaiserliche[2] Armee, und als ein Bauer aus einem benachbarten Dorf auf dem Regensburger Wochenmarkt zwei fette Ochsen verkaufte, sah ein Soldat, der in der Nähe stand, dass der Fleischer ihm hundert Taler[3] dafür bezahlte. Als der Bauer dann in sein Dorf zurückwanderte, folgte ihm der Soldat, und bat[4] ihn, ihm doch ein bisschen Geld zu geben. Der Bauer sagte: „Wenn ich Geld bei mir hätte, würde ich dir gern etwas geben. Aber du weißt ja, dass überall Soldaten sind, die uns Bauern alles wegnehmen. Deshalb habe ich nur einen Taler nach Regensburg mitgenommen, und mit diesem Taler habe ich im Gasthaus mein Essen bezahlt."

Der Soldat war kein gewalttätiger[5] Mensch und wollte dem Bauern kein Leid antun[6], aber Geld wollte er natürlich. Und so sagte er: „Was für ein miserables Leben, du hast nichts und ich habe nichts, und wenn ich kein so guter Christ wäre, so würde ich verzweifeln[7]. Doch Gott sei Dank gibt es noch Heilige[8], die uns armen Leuten helfen können. Komm, lass uns zu der kleinen Kapelle[9] dort gehen. Wenn wir den Heiligen Alphonsus ganz demütig[10] bitten, gibt er uns bestimmt etwas, und was er uns gibt, das wollen wir dann brüderlich teilen."

Der Bauer wäre viel lieber nach Hause gegangen, aber der Soldat gab nicht nach[11], und so musste er mit ihm zu der Kapelle. Sie gingen hinein, knieten nieder[12] und sahen wie die frömmsten Menschen aus. Der Bauer betete[13] auch wirklich und dachte: „Oh Heiliger Alphonsus! Wenn du mich von dem Soldaten befreien würdest, würde ich einen ganzen Taler in deinen Opferstock[14] stecken!"

Da sagte der Soldat plötzlich: „Jetzt hat der Heilige mir ein Zeichen[15] gegeben." Er stand auf, ging zur Statue des Alphonsus und legte sein Ohr an Alphonsus' hölzerne Lippen. Dann kam er ganz aufgeregt zurück und sagte: „Zwei Taler hat er mir gegeben, sie sollen schon in meiner Tasche sein." Und er holte wirklich zwei Taler aus der Tasche, die er natürlich schon vorher dort gehabt hatte, und die er nun brüderlich mit dem Bauern teilte.

Das gefiel dem Bauern, und er war jetzt ganz dafür, dass der Soldat den Heiligen noch einmal um Hilfe bitten sollte. Der Soldat ging also ein zweites Mal zu der Statue und hielt sein Ohr wieder an die hölzernen Lippen. Dann rief er ganz glücklich: „Hundert Taler hat uns der gute Alphonsus geschenkt, und diesmal sollen sie in deiner Tasche stecken." Da wurde der arme Bauer totenbleich[16], und ob er wollte oder nicht, er musste die hundert Taler aus der Tasche holen und sie genauso brüderlich mit dem Soldaten teilen, wie der Soldat seine zwei mit ihm geteilt hatte.

[1]*everywhere* [2]*imperial* [3]medieval German currency [4]*asked* [5]*violent* [6]**kein Leid ... :** *not harm* [7]*despair* [8]*saints* [9]*chapel* [10]*humbly* [11]*didn't give in* [12]*knelt down* [13]*prayed* [14]*offertory box* [15]*sign* [16]*pale as a ghost*

NAME: ______________________________ DATE: ______________

In each set, match the clauses by writing the appropriate numbers in the spaces provided.

A.

1.	Wenn im Dreißigjährigen Krieg nicht überall in Deutschland Soldaten gewesen wären,	_____	hätte er dem Bauern die hundert Taler einfach weggenommen.
2.	Wenn der Soldat nicht gesehen hätte, dass der Bauer für seine zwei Ochsen hundert Taler bekam,	_____	dass er seinen letzten Taler in einem Regensburger Gasthaus ausgegeben hätte.
3.	Weil der Bauer dem Soldaten kein Geld geben wollte, sagte er,	_____	der Heilige Alphonsus würde ihnen bestimmt etwas geben.
4.	Wenn der Soldat ein gewalttätiger Mensch gewesen wäre,	_____	wäre er ihm nicht gefolgt.
5.	Weil der Soldat wollte, dass der Bauer mit ihm zu der Kapelle ging, sagte er,	_____	hätten die Bauern ein viel leichteres Leben gehabt.

B.

1.	Wenn die kleine Kapelle nicht da gewesen wäre,	_____	musste er mit dem Soldaten zu der Kapelle.
2.	Obwohl der Bauer lieber nach Hause gegangen wäre,	_____	wäre der Soldat nicht auf die Idee mit dem Heiligen Alphonsus gekommen.
3.	Als die beiden Männer dann vor Altar knieten,	_____	sahen sie wie die frömmsten Menschen aus.
4.	Als der Soldat von der Statue des Alphonsus zurückkam, sagte er,	_____	hätte der Bauer seine hundert Taler nicht mit dem Soldaten teilen müssen.
5.	Wenn der Soldat seine zwei Taler nicht mit dem Bauern geteilt hätte,	_____	der hölzerne Heilige hätte ihm zwei Taler gegeben.

Zum Übersetzen

12-15 Wenn ich nach Berlin fliegen könnte ...

If I had more money, I would fly to Berlin. I would go to Checkpoint Charlie (m), where the Wall stood a few years ago. I would think of Erich Honecker, the *(accusative!)* head of state of the former GDR. Shortly before the reunification of Germany he said: „This Wall will still be standing in a hundred years.“ I would also think of President Kennedy, who in a speech in front of the city hall in Schöneberg said: „I am a Berliner.“

12-16 Kleine Gespräche.

1. GAST: Would it be possible to get a hot soup instead of the salad?
   KELLNER: Of course! And would you also like a roll with **(zu)** your soup?

2. CINDY: Do you know what a widower is?
   KAYLA: Of course! That's a man whose wife has died.

3. FRAU WITT: Did you see the TV program *(one word)* about single mothers?
   FRAU STIHL: Unfortunately not. I watch very little TV during the week.

12-17 Wessen Schuld ist es?

If you hadn't drunk all the **(die ganze)** milk, I wouldn't have driven to the supermarket. If I hadn't driven to the supermarket, I wouldn't have had an accident **(der Unfall).** If I hadn't had an accident, I wouldn't be lying here in the hospital now. So **(also)** everything's your fault **(die Schuld)**!

HÖRVERSTÄNDNIS

Upper Saddle River,
New Jersey 07458

ERSTE KONTAKTE

E-1 Erste Kontakte. Using the cues you see, respond to the questions or statements you hear.

BEISPIEL: Sie hören: *Wie heißt du?*
Sie sehen: Sabine
Sie sagen: Ich heiße Sabine.
Sie hören: *Ich heiße Sabine.*

Fangen wir an!

1. Tom

   ____

2. aus Hamburg

   ____

3. danke / gut

   ____

4. nein / Heike

   ____

5. Ziegler

   ____

E-2 Wir lernen einander kennen. You will hear and see responses. Ask the appropriate questions.

BEISPIEL: Sie hören: *Ja, ich heiße Sabine.*
Sie sehen: Ja, ich heiße Sabine.
Sie sagen: Heißt du Sabine?
Sie hören: *Heißt du Sabine?*

Fangen wir an!

1. Ja, ich bin Asha Singh.

   ______________________?

2. Danke, gut.

   ______________________?

3. Ich komme aus Pittsburgh.

   ______________________?

4. Ich heiße Ziegler.

   ______________________?

5. Ich bin aus Hamburg.

   ______________________?

E-3 Formell oder informell? Choose **Wie heißt du? Wir heißt ihr?** or **Wie heißen Sie?** according to the person mentioned by the speaker.

BEISPIEL: Sie hören: *your professor*
Sie sagen: Wie heißen Sie?
Sie hören: *Wie heißen Sie?*

Fangen wir an!

1. ______________________?
2. ______________________?
3. ______________________?
4. ______________________?
5. ______________________?
6. ______________________?
7. ______________________?
8. ______________________?

E-4 Grußformeln. Of the two greetings you see, choose the one that is appropriate to the information you hear.

BEISPIEL: Sie hören: *your father at 8 p.m.*
Sie sehen: guten Tag! 'n Abend!
Sie sagen: 'n Abend!
Sie hören: *'n Abend!*

Fangen wir an!

1. Tag! Guten Morgen!

______________________!

2. Grüß dich! Guten Tag!

______________________!

3. Morgen! 'n Abend!

______________________!

4. Servus! Guten Tag!

______________________!

5. Guten Tag! Guten Abend!

______________________!

E-5 Wie viel ist das? Respond in complete sentences to the questions you hear.

BEISPIEL:	Sie hören:	*Wie viel ist drei plus drei?*
	Sie sagen:	Drei plus drei ist sechs.
	Sie hören:	*Drei plus drei ist sechs.*

Fangen wir an!

1. ______________________
2. ______________________
3. ______________________
4. ______________________
5. ______________________

E-6 Wer ist Stefan? Listen to and read what Stefan says about himself. You will hear the text twice.

Hallo, ich heiße Stefan. Ich komme aus Hamburg und studiere in München. Meine Adresse hier in München ist Marktstraße 61. Die Postleitzahl ist 81375. Meine Telefonnummer ist 72 21 37 und die Vorwahl ist 089.

Now answer the questions you hear in complete sentences.

1. Stefan kommt aus ...

   ____

2. Stefan studiert in ...

   ____

3. Stefans Straße heißt ...

   ____

4. Stefans Hausnummer ist ...

   ____

5. Die Postleitzahl ist ...

   ____

6. Stefans Telefonnummer ist ...

   ____

7. Die Vorwahl ist ...

   ____

E-7 Wie heißt die Person? Listen to the spellings and then say the names.

BEISPIEL: Sie hören: *P-a-u-l*
Sie sagen: Paul
Sie hören: *Paul*

Fangen wir an!

1. ______________________
2. ______________________
3. ______________________
4. ______________________
5. ______________________
6. ______________________

E-8 Wie schreibt man das? Spell out the names of the European cities you hear and see.

BEISPIEL: Sie hören: *Athen*
Sie sehen: Athen
Sie sagen: A-t-h-e-n
Sie hören: *A-t-h-e-n*

Fangen wir an!

1. Berlin
____
2. London
____
3. Paris
____
4. Rom
____
5. Madrid
____
6. Lissabon
____
7. Helsinki
____
8. Amsterdam
____

NAME: ______________________ DATE ______________

E-9 Zur Aussprache. Repeat the numbers you hear.

1. eins elf einundzwanzig

____

2. zwei zwölf zweiundzwanzig

____

3. drei dreizehn dreiunddreißig

____

4. vier vierzehn vierundvierzig

____

5. fünf fünfzehn fünfundfünfzig

____

6. sechs sechzehn sechsundsechzig

____

7. sieben siebzehn siebenundsiebzig

____

8. acht achtzehn achtundachtzig

____

9. neun neunzehn neunundneunzig

____

KAPITEL 1

1-1 Was für ein Wetter! Listen to the conversation between Stefan and Kathrin. You will hear the conversation twice.

Now listen to the questions and answer in complete sentences, using the cues.

1. Das Wetter ist ...

   ____

2. Es sind ...

   ____

3. Es ist ...

   ____

4. Kathrin geht heute ...

   ____

5. Stefan und Kathrin gehen ...

   ____

1-2 Was machst du? Answer the questions you hear in complete sentences, using the cues you see.

BEISPIEL:	Sie hören:	*Was machst du jetzt?*
	Sie sehen:	jetzt / gehen / in die Vorlesung
	Sie sagen:	Jetzt gehe ich in die Vorlesung.
	Sie hören:	*Jetzt gehe ich in die Vorlesung.*

Fangen wir an!

1. heute Nachmittag / gehen / zum Auslandsamt

   ____

2. morgen / kaufen / zuerst / meine Bücher

   ____

3. morgen Nachmittag / gehen / schwimmen

   ____

4. dann / schreiben / ein paar / E-Mails

   ____

5. morgen Abend / gehen / mit Claudia / ins Kino

   ____

1-3 Was sind die Farben? Repeat what you hear, adding the appropriate colors.

BEISPIEL:	Sie hören:	*Gras ist ...*
	Sie sagen:	Gras ist grün.
	Sie hören:	*Gras ist grün.*

Fangen wir an!

1. ____________________
2. ____________________
3. ____________________
4. ____________________
5. ____________________
6. ____________________

1-4 Nationalitäten. You hear which city various people come from. Indicate their nationalities in complete sentences.

BEISPIEL:	Sie hören:	*Herr Springli kommt aus Zürich.*
	Sie sehen:	Herr Springli ist ...
	Sie sagen:	Herr Springli ist Schweizer.
	Sie hören:	*Herr Springli ist Schweizer.*

Fangen wir an!

1. Herr Jones ist ...

   ____

2. Frau Smith ist ...

   ____

3. Frau Niedermayer ist ...

   ____

4. Herr Lehmann ist ...

   ____

1-5 Plural. Say the sentences you hear in the plural.

BEISPIEL:	Sie hören:	*Die Banane ist gelb.*
	Sie sehen:	die Banane, -n
	Sie sagen:	Die Bananen sind gelb.
	Sie hören:	*Die Bananen sind gelb.*

1. der Ball, ¨e

   ____

2. das Haus, ¨er

   ____

3. der Apfel, ¨

   ____

4. die Blume, -n

   ____

5. die Studentin, -nen

   ____

6. der Freund, -e

   ____

NAME: ______________________________ DATE ______________

1-6 *Ein* und *kein?* Listen to the questions and respond negatively.

BEISPIEL: Sie hören: *Ist das ein Buch?*
Sie sagen: Nein, das ist kein Buch.
Sie hören: *Nein, das ist kein Buch.*

Fangen wir an!

1. ____________________ 5. ____________________
2. ____________________ 6. ____________________
3. ____________________ 7. ____________________
4. ____________________ 8. ____________________

1-7 Fragewörter. You will hear responses. Ask the appropriate questions, using the cues given.

BEISPIEL: Sie hören: *Ich heiße Achim.*
Sie sehen: Wie ...?
Sie sagen: Wie heißt du?
Sie hören: *Wie heißt du?*

Fangen wir an!

1. Woher ...?
____
2. Was ...?
____
3. Wann ...?
____
4. Wo ...?
____
5. Wie ...?
____
6. Wer ...?
____
7. Wie viel ...?
____

1-8 Positive Antworten. Answer the following questions affirmatively. Begin with **Ja** followed by the adverb of time.

BEISPIEL:

Sie hören:	*Ist das Wetter heute schön?*
Sie sehen:	Ja, ...
Sie sagen:	Ja, heute ist das Wetter schön.
Sie hören:	*Ja, heute ist das Wetter schön.*

Fangen wir an!

1. Ja, ... ________________________
2. Ja, ... ________________________
3. Ja, ... ________________________
4. Ja, ... ________________________
5. Ja, ... ________________________
6. Ja, ... ________________________
7. Ja, ... ________________________

1-9 Negative Antworten. Answer the following questions negatively. Begin each response with **Nein.** Remember to add **nicht** or **kein** as appropriate.

BEISPIEL:

Sie hören:	*Ist das Wetter heute schön?*
Sie sehen:	Nein, das Wetter ...
Sie sagen:	Nein, das Wetter ist heute nicht schön.
Sie hören:	*Nein, das Wetter ist heute nicht schön.*
Sie hören:	*Ist das ein Mercedes?*
Sie sehen:	Nein, das ...
Sie sagen:	Nein, das ist kein Mercedes.
Sie hören:	*Nein, das ist kein Mercedes.*

Fangen wir an!

1. Nein, das ... ________________________
2. Nein, das ... ________________________
3. Nein, das ... ________________________
4. Nein, ich ... ________________________
5. Nein, ich ... ________________________
6. Nein, ich ... ________________________
7. Nein, Martin ... ________________________
8. Nein, wir ... ________________________

NAME: ______________________ DATE ______________

1-10 Kein guter Tag. Florian isn't having a good day. Listen to his story. You will hear the story twice.

Now listen to the questions and respond, using the cues and personal pronouns.

BEISPIEL: Sie hören: *Ist Florians Tag gut?*
Sie sehen: Nein, ...
Sie sagen: Nein, er ist nicht gut.
Sie hören: *Nein, er ist nicht gut.*

Fangen wir an!

1. Nein, ...
____
2. Ja, ...
____
3. Ja, ...
____
4. Nein, ...
____
5. Ja, ...
____
6. Nein, ...
____

1-11 Verbformen. Answer the questions you hear, using the cues you see.

BEISPIEL: Sie hören: *Wer bist du?*
Sie sehen: Nina
Sie sagen: Ich bin Nina.
Sie hören: *Ich bin Nina.*

Fangen wir an!

1. Alexander
____
2. aus Köln
____
3. Biologie
____
4. schwimmen gehen
____
5. aus Wien
____
6. Physik
____
7. bei McDonald's arbeiten
____
8. Sabine und Moritz
____

9. aus Hamburg

____

11. in die Mensa gehen

____

10. Musik

____

12. Kaffee trinken

____

1-12 Zur Aussprache. German **ei** and **ie**

Sprechen Sie nach!

Eins, zwei, drei, vier,

____

Dieter trinkt viel Bier,

____

Dieter trinkt viel Wein,

____

Das ist gar nicht fein.

____

Melanie ist aus Stein am Rhein

____

Und fliegt am Freitag nach Wien.

____

In Wien trinkt Melanie zu viel Wein.

____

Oh Melanie, nein, nein, nein!

____

KAPITEL 2

2-1 Ninas toller Freund! Listen to the conversation between Nina and Robert. You will hear the conversation twice.

Now listen to the statements and answer with **richtig** or **falsch.** The speaker will verify your answer. If the answer was **falsch,** you will hear a question to help you correct the statement.

1. ____________________
2. ____________________
3. ____________________
4. ____________________
5. ____________________
6. ____________________
7. ____________________

2-2 Wie viel Uhr ist es? Say the times you see, using official time.

BEISPIEL:	Sie sehen:	15.15
	Sie sagen:	Es ist fünfzehn Uhr fünfzehn.
	Sie hören:	*Es ist fünfzehn Uhr fünfzehn.*

Fangen wir an!

1. 8.30

   ____

2. 22.45

   ____

3. 9.25

   ____

4. 20.35

   ____

2-3 Wie spät ist es? Say the times you see, using colloquial time. Add the appropriate adverb of time to indicate what part of the day it is.

BEISPIEL:	Sie sehen:	15.15
	Sie sagen:	Es ist Viertel nach drei nachmittags.
	Sie hören:	*Es ist Viertel nach drei nachmittags.*

Fangen wir an!

1. 8.30

   ____

2. 19.45

   ____

3. 10.10

   ____

4. 20.50

   ____

2-4 Um wie viel Uhr? Listen as Herr Ziegler and Beverly Harper plan a tennis match. You will hear the conversation twice.

Now answer the questions you hear by choosing a. or b. Read out your choice.

1. a. Sie schreibt einen Artikel über die politische Szene in Deutschland.

   b. Sie schreibt einen Artikel über die politische Szene in Amerika.

   ____

2. a. Er spielt mit Beverly Tennis.

   b. Er kocht das Abendessen für Brigitte und ein paar Freunde.

   ____

3. a. Sie telefoniert mit Amerika.

   b. Sie telefoniert mit Brigitte Ziegler.

   ____

4. a. Beverly Harper und Herr Ziegler spielen am Montagabend Tennis.

   b. Beverly Harper und Frau Ziegler spielen am Montagabend Tennis.

   ____

5. a. Brigitte Ziegler fliegt am Dienstagmorgen schon um halb acht nach New York.

   b. Beverly Harper fliegt am Dienstagmorgen schon um halb acht nach New York.

   ____

NAME: ______________________ DATE ______________

2-5 Wer hat was? Say complete sentences, using the correct form of **haben** and the cues you hear and see.

BEISPIEL:	Sie hören:	*Nina*
	Sie sehen:	einen neuen Computer
	Sie sagen:	Nina hat einen neuen Computer.
	Sie hören:	*Nina hat einen neuen Computer.*

Fangen wir an!

1. keine Zeit
   ____
2. ein interessantes Hobby
   ____
3. eine gute Gitarre
   ____
4. eine nette Freundin
   ____
5. neue Fahrräder
   ____
6. ein schönes Haus
   ____

2-6 Was machst du gern oder nicht gern? Using **gern** and the cues you hear, say what you like or don't like to do.

BEISPIEL:	Sie hören:	*tanzen gehen*
	Sie sagen:	Ich gehe gern tanzen.
	Sie hören:	*Ich gehe gern tanzen.*
	Sie hören:	*nicht in die Disco gehen*
	Sie sagen:	Ich gehe nicht gern in die Disco.
	Sie hören:	*Ich gehe nicht gern in die Disco.*

Fangen wir an!

1. ______________________
2. ______________________
3. ______________________
4. ______________________
5. ______________________
6. ______________________

2-7 Was macht Anna lieber? Listen to what Anna says and then report about her preferences.

BEISPIEL: Sie hören: *Ich trinke gern Bier, aber Wein trinke ich lieber.*
Sie sagen: Anna trinkt lieber Wein.
Sie hören: *Anna trinkt lieber Wein.*

Fangen wir an!

1. ____________________
2. ____________________
3. ____________________
4. ____________________
5. ____________________

2-8 *Dieser* und *welcher.* Transform the following sentences into questions beginning with **Welcher, Welches,** or **Welche.** Then respond to these questions, beginning with **Dieser, Dieses,** or **Diese.**

BEISPIEL: Sie hören: *Das Buch ist interessant.*
Sie sagen: Welches Buch ist interessant?
Sie hören: *Welches Buch ist interessant?*
Sie sagen: Dieses Buch ist interessant.
Sie hören: *Dieses Buch ist interessant.*

Fangen wir an!

1. ____________________?
   ____________________.
2. ____________________?
   ____________________.
3. ____________________?
   ____________________.
4. ____________________?
   ____________________.
5. ____________________?
   ____________________.

NAME: ______________________ DATE ______________

2-9 Mein, dein, sein ... Answer the questions you hear, using the cues you see and appropriate possessive adjectives.

BEISPIEL:

Sie hören:	*Ist das Pauls Porsche?*
Sie sehen:	Ja, das ist ...
Sie sagen:	Ja, das ist sein Porsche.
Sie hören:	*Ja, das ist sein Porsche.*
Sie hören:	*Sind das eure Fahrräder?*
Sie sehen:	Nein, das sind ...
Sie sagen:	Nein, das sind nicht unsere Fahrräder.
Sie hören:	*Nein, das sind nicht unsere Fahrräder.*

Fangen wir an!

1. Nein, das ist ...
   ____
2. Ja, das sind ...
   ____
3. Ja, das ist ...
   ____
4. Ja, das sind ...
   ____
5. Nein, das ist ...
   ____
6. Nein, das ist ...
   ____
7. Nein, das ist ...
   ____

2-10 Adjektive mit *dieser, dieses, diese.* Using the cues you hear and see, ask the appropriate questions.

BEISPIEL:

Sie hören:	*Diese Jacke ist schick.*
Sie sehen:	Was kostet diese ...?
Sie sagen:	Was kostet diese schicke Jacke?
Sie hören:	*Was kostet diese schicke Jacke?*

Fangen wir an!

1. Was kostet dieser ...?
   ____
2. Was kosten diese ...?
   ____
3. Was kostet dieses ...?
   ____
4. Was kostet diese ...?
   ____
5. Was kosten diese ...?
   ____
6. Was kostet dieser ...?
   ____

2-11 Adjektive mit *ein, ein, eine*. Repeat the sentences you hear. Then adapt them to the new subjects you see and hear.

BEISPIEL:	Sie hören:	*Nina ist eine gute Freundin.*
	Sie sagen:	Nina ist eine gute Freundin.
	Sie sehen:	Und Alexander?
	Sie sagen:	Alexander ist ein guter Freund.
	Sie hören:	*Alexander ist ein guter Freund.*

Fangen wir an!

1. ______________________

   Und Tina?

   ____

2. ______________________

   Und Martin?

   ____

3. ______________________

   Und Herr Ziegler?

   ____

4. ______________________

   Und Deutschland?

   ____

2-12 Adjektive ohne Artikel. Repeat the sentences you hear. Then adapt them to the new subjects you see and hear.

BEISPIEL:	Sie hören:	*Das ist gute Pizza.*
	Sie sagen:	Das ist gute Pizza.
	Sie sehen:	Und der Salat?
	Sie sagen:	Das ist guter Salat.
	Sie hören:	*Das ist guter Salat.*

Fangen wir an!

1. ______________________

   Und der Tee?

   ____

2. ______________________

   Und der Wein?

   ____

3. ______________________

   Und das Brot?

   ____

2-13 Mein bester Freund und ich. Listen to what Achim says about himself and his Turkish friend Osman. You will hear the story twice.

Now say whether the statements you see and hear are **richtig** or **falsch.** The speaker will verify your answer. If the statement was **falsch,** you will hear a question to help you correct the statement.

1. Achim ist 22 Jahre alt.

   ____

2. Achim studiert in Bonn.

   ____

3. Er wohnt zu Hause.

   ____

4. Achims Mitbewohner kommt aus der Türkei.

   ____

5. Achims Mitbewohner heißt Mehmet.

   ____

6. Osman lernt in Bonn Englisch.

   ____

7. Achim und Osman spielen zusammen Tennis.

   ____

8. Sie gehen oft in die Disco.

   ____

9. Osman trinkt viel Bier.

   ____

10. Osman kocht besser als ein türkisches Restaurant.

    ____

11. Achim und Osman fliegen nächstes Jahr zusammen in die Türkei.

    ____

2-14 Zur Aussprache. The vowels **a, e, i, o,** and **u**

Sprechen Sie nach!

machen	alle	Stadt	Straße	paar	Jahr
Wetter	elf	Geld	gehen	zehn	Tee
trinken	bis	Winter	fliegen	viel	Bier
Woche	oft	Sommer	doof	Oper	groß
Butter	dumm	Stunde	Schule	Uhr	Natur

KAPITEL 3

3-1 Familie. Listen to what Oma Ziegler says about her family. You will hear her report twice.

Now say whether the statements you see and hear are **richtig** or **falsch.** The speaker will verify your answer. If the statement was **falsch,** you will hear a question to help you correct the statement.

1. Oma Ziegler hat drei Kinder.

   ____

2. Oma Zieglers Tochter heißt Brigitte.

   ____

3. Oma Zieglers zwei Söhne heißen Klaus und Alfred.

   ____

4. Klaus ist noch ledig.

   ____

5. Oma Ziegler hat drei Enkel.

   ____

6. Oma Zieglers Enkel heißen Brigitte und Klaus.

   ____

7. Bettina ist Ninas und Roberts Tante.

   ____

8. Alexander ist Ninas Bruder.

   ____

9. Nina ist Roberts Schwester.

   ____

10. Nina, Robert und Alexander gehen alle noch in die Schule.

    ____

3-2 Was kaufen Sie? Using the cues you hear, form sentences beginning with **Ich kaufe ...**

BEISPIEL: Sie hören: *der Gürtel*
Sie sagen: Ich kaufe den Gürtel.
Sie hören: *Ich kaufe den Gürtel.*

Fangen wir an!

1. ______________________
2. ______________________
3. ______________________
4. ______________________
5. ______________________
6. ______________________
7. ______________________
8. ______________________

3-3 Ja oder nein? Respond to the questions you hear, using the cues you see and hear.

BEISPIEL: Sie hören: *Kaufst du diesen VW?*
Sie sehen: Ja, ...
Sie sagen: Ja, ich kaufe diesen VW.
Sie hören: *Ja, ich kaufe diesen VW.*

Sie hören: *Kaufst du diesen VW?*
Sie sehen: Nein, ...
Sie sagen: Nein, ich kaufe diesen VW nicht.
Sie hören: *Nein, ich kaufe diesen VW nicht.*

Fangen wir an!

1. Nein, ...
____
2. Ja, ...
____
3. Nein, ...
____
4. Ja, ...
____
5. Nein, ...
____
6. Ja, ...
____
7. Ja, ...
____
8. Nein, ...
____

NAME: ______________________ DATE ______________

3-4 Ja oder nein? Respond to the questions you hear, using the cues you see and hear.

BEISPIEL:
Sie hören: *Brauchst du einen Wagen?*
Sie sehen: Ja, ...
Sie sagen: Ja, ich brauche einen Wagen.
Sie hören: *Ja, ich brauche einen Wagen.*

Sie hören: *Brauchst du einen Wagen?*
Sie sehen: Nein, ...
Sie sagen: Nein, ich brauche keinen Wagen.
Sie hören: *Nein, ich brauche keinen Wagen.*

Fangen wir an!

1. Ja, ... ______________________
2. Nein, ... ______________________
3. Nein, ... ______________________
4. Ja, ... ______________________
5. Ja, ... ______________________
6. Nein, ... ______________________
7. Ja, ... ______________________
8. Nein, ... ______________________

3-5 Besuche. Answer the questions you hear, using the cues you see and hear.

BEISPIEL:
Sie hören: *Wen besucht Anna?*
Sie sehen: ihr Bruder
Sie sagen: Sie besucht ihren Bruder.
Sie hören: *Sie besucht ihren Bruder.*

Fangen wir an!

1. ihre Schwester ______________________
2. sein Freund ______________________
3. seine Freundin Nina ______________________
4. ihr Onkel Alfred ______________________
5. ihre Freundin Beverly ______________________
6. unsere Großeltern ______________________
7. mein Vetter Frank ______________________
8. unser Vater ______________________

3-6 Was machen sie alle? Answer the questions you hear, using the cues you see and hear.

BEISPIEL: Sie hören: *Was macht Robert?*
Sie sehen: essen / ein Stück Pizza
Sie sagen: Er isst ein Stück Pizza.
Sie hören: *Er isst ein Stück Pizza*

Fangen wir an!

1. lesen / die Zeitung

____

2. waschen / seinen Wagen

____

3. sprechen / mit Tante Bettina

____

4. backen / einen Kuchen

____

5. nehmen / ein Stück Kuchen

____

6. fahren / Motorrad

____

7. laufen / zum Bus

____

8. schlafen

____

3-7 Adjektive nach *der*-Wörtern. Answer the questions you hear, using the cues you see and hear.

BEISPIEL: Sie hören: *Welchen Drucker kaufst du, den teuren oder den preisgünstigen?*
Sie sehen: preisgünstig
Sie sagen: Ich kaufe den preisgünstigen Drucker.
Sie hören: *Ich kaufe den preisgünstigen Drucker.*

1. digital

____

2. deutsch

____

3. groß

____

4. letzt

____

5. dick

____

6. kurz

____

NAME: ______________________________ DATE ______________

3-8 Adjektive nach *ein*-Wörtern. Answer the questions you hear, using the cues you see and hear.

BEISPIEL: Sie hören: *Was für einen Wagen fährt Herr Ziegler, einen deutschen oder einen japanischen?*
Sie sehen: deutsch
Sie sagen: Er fährt einen deutschen Wagen.
Sie hören: *Er fährt einen deutschen Wagen.*

Fangen wir an!

1. digital

   ____

2. groß

   ____

3. blond

   ____

4. neu

   ____

5. amerikanisch

   ____

6. hell

   ____

3-9 Ein Gourmet. Onkel Alfred has very distinct tastes. Using the cues you hear and see, say what he likes to eat or drink.

BEISPIEL: Sie hören: *norwegisch / Lachs*
Sie sehen: norwegisch / Lachs (m)
Sie sagen: Onkel Alfred isst nur norwegischen Lachs.
Sie hören: *Onkel Alfred isst nur norwegischen Lachs.*

Fangen wir an!

1. ungarisch / Salami (f)

   ____

2. französisch / Käse (m)

   ____

3. deutsch / Weißwein (m)

   ____

4. belgisch / Schokolade (f)

   ____

5. bayerisch / Bier (n)

   ____

6. griechisch / Oliven (pl)

   ____

7. iranisch / Kaviar (m)

   ____

8. italienisch / Mineralwasser (n)

   ____

3-10 Beim Skilift in Innsbruck. Listen to the following dialogue. You will hear it twice.

Sabine is spending her winter vacation skiing in Innsbruck. She is standing at the ski lift waiting her turn when a young man addresses her. You will hear the conversation twice.

Now say whether the statements you see and hear are **richtig** or **falsch.** The speaker will verify your answer. If the statement is **falsch,** you will hear a question to help you correct the statement.

1. Sabines Familienname ist Bosch.

   ____

2. Sabine und Karin sind Freundinnen.

   ____

3. Sabine ist Frank Lehmanns Freundin.

   ____

4. Karin und Frank studieren beide Biologie.

   ____

5. Sabine hat heute Besuch aus Denver.

   ____

6. Karins Besuch heißt Jessica.

   ____

7. Jessica ist Karins Tante.

   ____

8. Jessica ist morgen schon um elf in Innsbruck.

   ____

9. Sabine, Karin und Frank gehen morgen Abend zusammen tanzen.

   ____

NAME: ______________________________ DATE ______________

3-11 Zur Aussprache. The diphthongs **au, ei (ey, ai, ay),** and **eu (äu)**

Sprechen Sie nach!

In Claudias Haus sitzt eine graue Maus,

____

denn auch eine graue Maus braucht ein schönes Haus.

____

Herr Meyer arbeitet für eine bayerische Zeitung.

____

Im Mai hat er dann frei und reist in die Schweiz.

____

Diese freundlichen Leute haben neun neue Häuser

____

und neunundneunzig Mäuse in ihren teuren Häusern.

____

KAPITEL 4

4-1 Ein Telefongespräch. Listen to the telephone conversation between Stephanie and Peter. You will hear the dialogue twice.

Now listen to the statements and answer with **richtig** or **falsch.** The speaker will verify your answer. If the statement is **falsch,** you will hear a question to help you correct the statement.

1. ____________________
2. ____________________
3. ____________________
4. ____________________
5. ____________________
6. ____________________
7. ____________________

4-2 Modalverben. Repeat the sentences you hear, adding the modal verbs you see.

BEISPIEL:	Sie hören:	*Peter isst Schokolade.*
	Sie sehen:	wollen
	Sie sagen:	Peter will Schokolade essen.
	Sie hören:	*Peter will Schokolade essen.*

Fangen wir an!

1. können

   ____

2. müssen

   ____

3. wollen

   ____

4. sollen

   ____

5. dürfen

   ____

6. möcht-

   ____

7. können

   ____

8. wollen

   ____

4-3 *Mögen* und *möcht-*. Answer the questions in complete sentences, using the cues.

BEISPIEL:	Sie hören:	*Magst du Pudding?*
	Sie sehen:	Ja, ...
	Sie sagen:	Ja, ich mag Pudding.
	Sie hören:	*Ja, ich mag Pudding.*
	Sie hören:	*Möchte Eva Kuchen?*
	Sie sehen:	Nein, ...
	Sie sagen:	Nein, sie möchte keinen Kuchen.
	Sie hören:	*Nein, sie möchte keinen Kuchen.*

Fangen wir an!

1. Nein, ... __________________________
2. Ja, ... __________________________
3. Ja, ... __________________________
4. Ja, ... __________________________
5. Nein, ... __________________________
6. Ja, ... __________________________

4-4 Negation und Modalverben. Negate the sentences you hear, using the cues you see.

BEISPIEL:	Sie hören:	*Herr Ziegler muss das Haus putzen.*
	Sie sehen:	nicht wollen
	Sie sagen:	Herr Ziegler will das Haus nicht putzen.
	Sie hören:	*Herr Ziegler will das Haus nicht putzen.*

Fangen wir an!

1. nicht wollen __________________________
2. nicht möchten __________________________
3. nicht können __________________________
4. nicht dürfen __________________________
5. nicht können __________________________
6. nicht dürfen __________________________

NAME: ______________________________ DATE ______________

4-5 Trennbare Verben. Construct sentences, using the verbs you hear and the cues you see.

BEISPIEL:
Sie hören: *aufwachen*
Sie sehen: Sabine um sieben Uhr
Sie sagen: Sabine wacht um sieben Uhr auf.
Sie hören: *Sabine wacht um sieben Uhr auf.*

Fangen wir an!

1. Sabine um halb acht

   ____

2. dann sie Maria

   ____

3. sie um neun

   ____

4. Sabine dreißig Minuten später

   ____

5. Maria und Sabine ihre neuen CDs

   ____

6. dann sie den neuen Kaffee

   ____

7. abends sie schick

   ____

4-6 *Ihr*- und *du*-Imperativ. Read the statements and give advice, using the cues you hear.

BEISPIEL:
Sie sehen: Wir gehen jetzt Rad fahren.
Sie hören: *bitte gut aufpassen*
Sie sagen: Passt bitte gut auf.
Sie hören: *Passt bitte gut auf.*

Fangen wir an!

1. Wir wollen ein Picknick organisieren

   ____

2. Ich bin so gestresst.

   ____

3. Wir gehen heute Abend in die Disco.

   ____

4. Wir haben nichts zu essen und zu trinken.

   ____

5. Ich bin ein bisschen zu dick.

   ____

6. Wir wollen schwimmen gehen.

   ____

7. Ich kann nicht schlafen.

   ____

8. Ich bin gar nicht fit.

   ____

4-7 *Sie*-Imperativ. Mrs. Maier is looking for a gift for five-year-old Tanja. Make suggestions using the cues.

BEISPIEL:	Sie sehen:	einen Hund
	Sie hören:	*doch einen Hund kaufen*
	Sie sagen:	Kaufen Sie Tanja doch einen Hund.
	Sie hören:	*Kaufen Sie Tanja doch einen Hund.*

Fangen wir an!

1. ein Eis

   ____

2. Schokolade

   ____

3. in den Zoo

   ____

4. bei McDonalds

   ____

5. einen Goldfisch

   ____

4-8 Koordinierende Konjunktionen. Repeat the sentence you hear and conclude it appropriately with one of the two choices.

BEISPIEL:	Sie hören:	*Martin hat Geburtstag*
	Sie sehen:	und bäckt einen Kuchen oder bäckt einen Kuchen
	Sie hören:	*Martin hat Geburtstag*
	Sie sagen:	Martin hat Geburtstag und bäckt einen Kuchen.
	Sie hören:	*Martin hat Geburtstag und bäckt einen Kuchen.*

Fangen wir an!

1. denn er hat Geburtstag
   aber er hat Geburtstag

   ____

2. sondern hören CDs an
   und hören CDs an

   ____

3. aber um vier
   sondern um vier

   ____

4. und essen Kuchen
   sondern essen Kuchen

   ____

5. aber gehen tanzen
   oder gehen tanzen

   ____

NAME: ______________________________ DATE ______________

4-9 Subordinierende Konjunktionen. Complete the sentences you hear with the appropriate dependent clause you see.

BEISPIEL:	Sie hören:	*Frau Ziegler nimmt den späten Zug nach Göttingen,*
	Sie sehen:	obwohl sie in Berlin noch einkaufen will
		weil sie in Berlin noch einkaufen will
	Sie hören:	*Frau Ziegler nimmt den späten Zug nach Göttingen,*
	Sie sagen:	weil sie in Berlin noch einkaufen will.
	Sie hören:	*weil sie in Berlin noch einkaufen will.*

Fangen wir an!

1. weil er nicht viel Geld hat
   obwohl er nicht viel Geld hat

   ____

2. bis er zur Uni kommt
   wenn er zur Uni kommt

   ____

3. damit sie frühstückt
   bevor sie frühstückt

   ____

4. weil sie nach Hause kommt
   sobald sie nach Hause kommt

   ____

5. damit er nicht Bus fahren muss
   obwohl er nicht Bus fahren muss

   ____

6. bevor es nicht zu viel kostet
   wenn es nicht zu viel kostet

   ____

4-10 Fragen und Antworten. Answer the questions you hear with the appropriate one of the two responses you see.

BEISPIEL:	Sie hören:	*Warum lädt Peter Stephanie und Claudia ein?*
	Sie sehen:	weil / er / Geburtstag / haben
		wenn / er / Geburtstag / haben
	Sie hören:	*Warum lädt Peter Stephanie und Claudia ein?*
	Sie sagen:	Weil er Geburtstag hat.
	Sie hören:	*Weil er Geburtstag hat.*

Fangen wir an!

1. obwohl / Claudia / ihn / so gern / essen
   weil / Claudia / ihn / so gern / essen

   ____

2. bevor / Claudia und Stephanie / kommen
   sobald / Claudia und Stephanie / kommen

   ____

3. sobald / ihre Vorlesung / zu Ende sein
bis / ihre Vorlesung / zu Ende sein

____

4. ja, / weil / er / kein Geld / haben
ja, / obwohl / er / kein Geld / haben

____

5. bis / seine Eltern / das Geld / senden
sobald / seine Eltern / das Geld / senden

____

6. weil / er / den Wagen / haben
wenn / er / den Wagen / haben

____

4-11 Mein Vormittag. Answer the questions with the help of the cues.

BEISPIEL: Sie hören: *Wann stehst du an Wochentagen auf?*
Sie sehen: an Wochentagen / ich / um acht
Sie sagen: An Wochentagen stehe ich um acht auf.
Sie hören: *An Wochentagen stehe ich um acht auf.*

Fangen wir an!

1. ich / um neun

____

2. zum Frühstück / ich / nur einen Becher Jogurt

____

3. ich / um zehn / weggehen

____

4. ja, ich / meistens / den Bus / zur Uni

____

5. meine Vorlesungen / um halb elf

____

6. ich / in der Cafeteria / zu Mittag

____

4-12 Zur Aussprache. The vowels **ä, ö,** and **ü**

Sprechen Sie nach!

Äpfel	wäscht	bäckt	spät	fährt	erklären
können	möchte	zwölf	hören	mögen	Söhne
müssen	dünn	hübsch	Züge	Bücher	Tür

KAPITEL 5

5-1 Schöne Tage in München. Jürgen brings a travel bag to the lecture. Listen to the conversation between Thomas and Jürgen. You will hear the dialogue twice.

Now listen to the questions. Do not answer in complete sentences.

BEISPIEL:	Sie sehen:	Wohin will Jürgen fahren?
	Sie sagen:	nach München
	Sie hören:	*nach München*

Fangen wir an!

1. Wen besucht Jürgen in München?

   ____

2. Welches Museum wollen Jürgen und seine Freundin anschauen?

   ____

3. In welche Galerie wollen sie gehen?

   ____

4. In welchen Park wollen sie gehen?

   ____

5. Wohin gehen sie abends?

   ____

5-2 Nomen und Pronomen. Respond to the questions you hear, using personal pronouns.

BEISPIEL:	Sie hören:	*Findest du die Jacke schön?*
	Sie sehen:	Ja, ...
	Sie sagen:	Ja, ich finde sie schön.
	Sie hören:	*Ja, ich finde sie schön.*

Fangen wir an!

1. Ja, ...

   ____

2. Ja, ...

   ____

3. Ja, ...

5. Ja, ...

4. Ja, ...

6. Ja, ...

5-3 Fragen und Antworten. Answer the questions you hear, replacing the nouns with personal pronouns.

BEISPIEL:	Sie hören:	*Findet David deinen Mantel elegant?*
	Sie sehen:	Ja, ...
	Sie sagen:	Ja, er findet ihn elegant.
	Sie hören:	*Ja, er findet ihn elegant.*
	Sie hören:	*Findet Lisa deine Brille cool?*
	Sie sehen:	Nein, ...
	Sie sagen:	Nein, sie findet sie nicht cool.
	Sie hören:	*Nein, sie findet sie nicht cool.*

Fangen wir an!

1. Ja, ...

2. Ja, ...

3. Ja, ...

4. Nein, ...

5. Nein, ...

6. Nein, ...

NAME: ____________________ DATE ____________

5-4 *Durch, für, gegen, ohne* oder *um?* With the help of the statements you hear and the questions you see, answer with the prepositional phrase.

BEISPIEL:	Sie hören:	*Ich bekomme durch meinen Onkel billige Theaterkarten.*
	Sie sehen:	Durch wen bekommst du billige Theaterkarten?
	Sie sagen:	Durch meinen Onkel.
	Sie hören:	*Durch meinen Onkel.*

Fangen wir an!

1. Für wen kaufst du ein schönes Bild?

   ____

2. Gegen wen hat sie nichts?

   ____

3. Ohne wen kommt er auf die Party?

   ____

4. Wo ist das Museum?

   ____

5. Durch wen buchst du das Hotel?

   ____

6. Wann kommst du in der Jugendherberge an?

   ____

7. Für wen schreibt er das Referat?

   ____

8. Ohne was macht Frau Ziegler keine Reise?

   ____

5-5 Vergleichen Sie. Using the cues you see and hear, make statements of comparison.

BEISPIEL:	Sie sehen:	Bernds VW ist alt, aber er ist nicht so alt wie Ralfs Ford.
	Sie hören:	*älter als*
	Sie sagen:	Ralfs Ford ist älter als Bernds VW.
	Sie hören:	*Ralfs Ford ist älter als Bernds VW.*

Fangen wir an!

1. Annas Deutsch ist gut, aber es ist nicht so gut wie Marias Deutsch.

   ____

2. Mein Bruder verdient viel, aber er verdient nicht so viel wie meine Schwester.

   ____

3. Das Hotel Kempinski ist teuer, aber es ist nicht so teuer wie das Hotel Adlon.

   ____

4. In Florida ist es heute heiß, aber es ist nicht so heiß wie in Mexiko.

   ____

5. Der Pullover ist warm, aber er ist nicht so warm wie die Jacke.

____

6. Lisas Schuhe sind elegant, aber sie sind nicht so elegant wie Bettinas Schuhe.

____

7. Annas Zimmer ist groß, aber es ist nicht so groß wie mein Zimmer.

____

5-6 Entscheidungen. Answer the questions you hear, using the cues.

BEISPIEL:	Sie hören:	*Welche Bluse kaufst du?*
	Sie sehen:	die teurer_____ Bluse
	Sie sagen:	Ich kaufe die teurere Bluse.
	Sie hören:	*Ich kaufe die teurere Bluse.*

Fangen wir an!

1. das neuer_____ Auto

____

2. den billiger_____ Pullover

____

3. die schöner_____ Jacke

____

4. die besser_____ Schuhe

____

5. das größer_____ Stück Kuchen

____

6. den älter_____ Wein

____

7. die kürzer_____ Wurst

____

8. die kleiner_____ Äpfel

____

NAME: ______________________________ DATE ______________

5-7 Superlative I. Complete the statements you hear, using the superlative.

BEISPIEL: Sie hören: *Sabine findet Physik und Chemie sehr interessant,*
Sie sehen: aber Mathematik findet sie am ______________________.
Sie sagen: aber Mathematik findet sie am interessantesten.
Sie hören: *aber Mathematik findet sie am interessantesten.*

Fangen wir an!

1 aber Deutsch spricht er natürlich am ______________________.

2. aber Jazz hört sie am ______________________.

3. aber Lilli singt am ______________________.

4. aber bei Hertie sind sie am ______________________.

5. aber heute wird es bestimmt am ______________________.

6. aber in München sind sie am ______________________.

5-8 Superlative II. Respond to the questions you hear, using the superlative of the adjective provided.

BEISPIEL: Sie hören: *Welches Stück Kuchen möchtest du?*
Sie sehen: Natürlich d_____ ______________________. (groß)
Sie sagen: Natürlich das größte.
Sie hören: *Natürlich das größte.*

Fangen wir an!

1. Natürlich d_____ ______________________. (warm)

2. Natürlich d_____ ______________________. (cool)

3. Natürlich d_____ ______________________. (elegant)

4. Natürlich d_____ ______________________. (sonnig)

5. Natürlich d_____ ______________________. (preisgünstig)

6. Natürlich d_____ ______________________. (billig)

5-9 Ich weiß, dass ... Express the sentences you hear as dependent clauses by starting with **Ich weiß, dass ...**

BEISPIEL: Sie hören: *Ich muss mein Referat fertig schreiben.*
Sie sagen: Ich weiß, dass ich mein Referat fertig schreiben muss.
Sie hören: *Ich weiß, dass ich mein Referat fertig schreiben muss.*

Fangen wir an!

1. ____________________ 5. ____________________

2. ____________________ 6. ____________________

3. ____________________ 7. ____________________

4. ____________________

5-10 Höfliche Fragen. Ask the questions you hear more politely. Begin with **Könnten Sie mir bitte sagen, ...**

BEISPIEL: Sie hören: *Wo ist die Universität?*
Sie sagen: Könnten Sie mir bitte sagen, wo die Universität ist?
Sie hören: *Könnten Sie mir bitte sagen, wo die Universität ist?*

Sie hören: *Ist die Universität groß?*
Sie sagen: Könnten Sie mir bitte sagen, ob die Universität groß ist?
Sie hören: *Könnten Sie mir bitte sagen, ob die Universität groß ist?*

Fangen wir an!

1. ____________________? 4. ____________________?

2. ____________________? 5. ____________________?

3. ____________________? 6. ____________________?

NAME: ______________________ DATE ______________

5-11 *Wissen* versus *kennen*. Answer the questions you hear with the help of the cues.

BEISPIEL:		
	Sie hören:	*Kennst du die neue Studentin?*
	Sie sehen:	Ja, ...
	Sie sagen:	Ja, ich kenne die neue Studentin.
	Sie hören:	*Ja, ich kenne die neue Studentin.*
	Sie hören:	*Weißt du, wo sie wohnt?*
	Sie sehen:	Nein, ...
	Sie sagen:	Nein, das weiß ich nicht.
	Sie hören:	*Nein, das weiß ich nicht.*

Fangen wir an!

1. Ja, ...

   ____

   Ja, ...

   ____

2. Ja, ...

   ____

   Nein, ...

   ____

3. Ja, ...

   ____

   Ja, ...

   ____

4. Ja, ...

   ____

   Nein, ...

   ____

5. Ja, ...

   ____

   Ja, ...

   ____

5-12 Fragen und Antworten. Respond appropriately to the questions you hear, using the cues in one of the two choices.

BEISPIEL:	Sie hören:	*Warum warst du nicht auf Tanjas Fete?*
	Sie sehen:	weil / ich / keine E-Mails / schreiben / müssen
		weil / ich / E-Mails / schreiben / müssen
	Sie hören:	*Warum warst du nicht auf Tanjas Fete?*
	Sie sagen:	Weil ich E-Mails schreiben musste.
	Sie hören:	*Weil ich E-Mails schreiben musste.*

Fangen wir an!

1. weil / sie / nicht ausgehen / dürfen

   weil / sie / ausgehen / dürfen

   ____

2. weil / wir / lernen / müssen

   weil / wir / nicht lernen / müssen

   ____

3. weil / sie / ihren Freund / nicht besuchen / wollen

   weil / sie / ihren Freund / besuchen / wollen

   ____

4. weil / sie / nicht genug / lernen / können

   weil / sie / genug / lernen / können

   ____

5. weil / er / das Abendessen / mögen

   weil / er / das Abendessen / nicht mögen

   ____

5-13 Zur Aussprache. Listen to the word you hear and find two words that sound similar. Read these two words out loud.

1. Kuchen, acht, Bauch, Milch, Nächte, Nacht

   ______________ ______________

2. windig, Michael, versuchen, kochen, Tochter, Töchter

   ______________ ______________

3. ich, suchen, Tellerchen, mich, Kätzchen, möchte

   ______________ ______________

4. Bauch, Buch, Tochter, Strauch, suchen, Nacht

   ______________ ______________

5. acht, kocht, Kuchen, Woche, versuchen, auch

   ______________ ______________

6. wenig, Nacht, Töchter, Milch, Mächte, rächen

   ______________ ______________

7. mochte, kochen, Köche, Kuchen, Milch, Töchter

   ______________ ______________

KAPITEL 6

6-1 Ein Interview. Listen as Florian Hillebrandt, a German student who is working for the university newspaper, interviews James Stewart, an American exchange student. You will hear the interview twice.

Now answer the questions you hear with the help of the cues.

1. weil / sie / beide / Studenten / sein

   Weil sie beide studenten sind.

2. James / sagen / dass / die Deutschen / sehr formell / sein

   James sagt das die Deutschen sehr formell sind.

3. auf der Autobahn / fahren / die Deutschen / sehr schnell

   Auf der Autobahn fahren die Deutschen sehr schnell

4. die Städte / sein / kleiner und älter / als in Amerika

   die Stadte sind kleiner und älter als in Amerika

5. weil / es / so viele Busse und so schnelle Züge / geben

   Weil es so viele Busse und so schnelle Zuge gibt.

6. Autos, Benzin und Hotels / sein / hier / viel teurer

   Autos, Benzin und Hotels sind hier viel teurer.

7. nein / das Studentenheim und die Mensa / sein / billiger

   Nein das Studentenheim und die Mensa sind billiger

8. er / mögen / die Cafés, die Kneipen und die freundlichen Studenten

   Er mag die Cafés, die Kneipen und die freundlichen Studenten.

9. weil / er / nicht zu spät / zum Abendessen / kommen / dürfen

   Weil er nicht zu spät zum Abendessen kommen darf.

6-2 Wie sehen die zwei Personen aus? Answer the questions of the police about two thieves. Answer in complete sentences.

BEISPIEL:

Sie sehen:	Was für ein Gesicht hat der Mann?
Sie hören:	*lang*
Sie sagen:	Der Mann hat ein langes Gesicht.
Sie hören:	*Der Mann hat ein langes Gesicht*
Sie sehen:	Und die Frau?
Sie hören:	*oval*
Sie sagen:	Die Frau hat ein ovales Gesicht.
Sie hören:	*Die Frau hat ein ovales Gesicht.*

Fangen wir an!

1. Wie groß ist der Mann?

____

2. Und die Frau, ist sie auch groß?

____

3. Hat der Mann grüne, blaue oder braune Augen?

____

4. Und die Frau?

____

5. Hat der Mann eine lange oder eine kurze Nase?

____

6. Und die Frau?

____

7. Hat der Mann einen großen oder einen kleinen Mund?

____

8. Und die Frau?

____

9. Was für Haar hat der Mann?

____

10. Und die Frau?

____

NAME: ____________________ DATE ____________

6-3 Das Perfekt. Convert the sentences you hear into the perfect tense.

BEISPIEL: Sie hören: *Jennifer bucht ihren Flug nach Deutschland.*
Sie sagen: Jennifer hat ihren Flug nach Deutschland gebucht.
Sie hören: *Jennifer hat ihren Flug nach Deutschland gebucht.*

Fangen wir an!

1. Maria hat ihren Hausaufgaben
2. ____________
3. ____________
4. ____________
5. ____________
6. ____________
7. ____________
8. ____________
9. ____________

6-4 Weil ... Answer the questions you hear in the perfect tense.

BEISPIEL: Sie hören: *Warum hast du den Hund nicht gefüttert?*
Sie sehen: Weil / ihr / kein Hundefutter / kaufen
Sie sagen: Weil ihr kein Hundefutter gekauft habt.
Sie hören: *Weil ihr kein Hundefutter gekauft habt.*

Fangen wir an!

1. Weil / wir / die Fenster / putzen
   Weil wir die Fenster geputzt haben
2. Weil / sie / den ganzen Tag / arbeiten
   Weil sie den ganzen Tag gearbeitet hat.
3. Weil / ich / meine Hausaufgaben / machen
   Weil ich meine Hausaufgaben gemacht habe
4. Weil / du / den Rasenmäher / nicht / reparieren
   Weil du den Rasenmäher nich repariert hast
5. Weil / ich / meine Vokabeln / lernen
   Weil ich meine Vokabeln gelernt habe
6. Weil / ich / stundenlang / mit Julia / telefonieren
   Weil ich stundenlang mit Julia telefoniert habe.

6-5 Das Perfekt.

Convert the sentences you hear into the perfect tense.

BEISPIEL: Sie hören: *Oma Ziegler bäckt einen Kuchen.*
Sie sagen: Oma Ziegler hat einen Kuchen gebacken.
Sie hören: *Oma Ziegler hat einen Kuchen gebacken.*

Fangen wir an!

1. ____________ 5. ____________

2. ____________ 6. ____________

3. ____________ 7. ____________

4. ____________ 8. ____________

6-6 *Haben* oder *sein*?

Supply the perfect tense of the infinitives you hear.

BEISPIEL: Sie hören: *gehen*
Sie sagen: ist gegangen
Sie hören: *ist gegangen*

ist = motion
hat = no motion

Fangen wir an!

1. ist gereist 6. ____________

2. bin gefahren 7. Ich habe gemacht.

3. habe gegossen 8. ist geblieben

4. ____________ 9. ____________

5. Ich habe genommen 10. ____________

6-7 Annas Tag. Answer the questions you hear with the help of the cues.

BEISPIEL: Sie hören: *Was für eine Klausur hatte Anna am Montagmorgen?*
Sie sehen: eine Klausur in Biologie
Sie sagen: Sie hatte eine Klausur in Biologie.
Sie hören: *Sie hatte eine Klausur in Biologie.*

Fangen wir an!

1. um sieben Uhr

____

2. mit dem Bus

____

3. ihre Notizen

____

4. um halb elf

____

5. ein Stück Kuchen

____

6. ein tolles Kleid

____

7. die Verkäuferin

____

8. ihre Freundin

____

9. ins Kino

____

6-8 Daten. Finish the sentences you hear with the dates you see.

BEISPIEL: Sie sehen: 12. 12.
Sie hören: *Heute ist der ...*
Sie sagen: Heute ist der zwölfte Zwölfte.
Sie hören: *Heute ist der zwölfte Zwölfte.*

Sie sehen: 29. 3.
Sie hören: *Heute haben wir den ...*
Sie sagen: Heute haben wir den neunundzwanzigsten Dritten.
Sie hören: *Heute haben wir den neunundzwanzigsten Dritten.*

Fangen wir an!

1. 25. 9.

____

2. 6. 8.

____

3. 31. 10.

____

4. 24. 12.

____

5. 1. 1.

____

8. 3. 2.

____

6. 8. 7.

____

9. 27. 6.

____

7. 23. 5.

____

6-9 Ein toller Ferienjob. Using the cues, answer the questions in the perfect tense.

BEISPIEL:	Sie hören:	*Wie haben Sie den Job gefunden?*
	Sie sehen:	finden / den Job / durch einen Freund
	Sie sagen:	Ich habe den Job durch einen Freund gefunden.
	Sie hören:	*Ich habe den Job durch einen Freund gefunden.*

Fangen wir an!

1. arbeiten / als Gärtner

____

2. arbeiten / für / eine sehr reiche Familie

____

3. mähen / den Rasen / und / schneiden / die Hecke

____

4. anfangen / morgens / um acht

____

5. gehen / um sechzehn Uhr / nach Hause

____

6. nein / bekommen / dort / auch / ein gutes Mittagessen

____

7. bekommen / zehn Euro / die Stunde

____

8. reisen / im März / durch / ganz Italien und Griechenland

____

NAME: ______________________ DATE ______________

6-10 Ein Blick zurück. Read along as you listen to the narrative. You will hear it twice.

Mein Name ist Richard Brubacher und ich lebe in Harrisburg, Pennsylvania. Hören Sie bitte gut zu, wenn Sie wissen möchten, woher der Name Brubacher kommt.

Mein Urgroßvater war Mennonit, hat in Süddeutschland gelebt und sollte dort als junger Mann in die Armee. Weil er das aber als Mennonit nicht wollte und nicht durfte, ist er nach Amerika ausgewandert. In Amerika ist er nach Pennsylvania gegangen, weil dort schon viele Mennoniten waren. Er hat ein paar Jahre für einen mennonitischen Farmer gearbeitet und hat dann selbst eine Farm gekauft. Dann hat er meine Urgroßmutter kennen gelernt. Sie war auch Mennonitin und sie haben geheiratet und hatten viele Kinder. Mein Großvater und sein Bruder sind dann nach Harrisburg gegangen und dort leben heute noch viele Brubachers. In Süddeutschland gibt es den Namen Brubacher heute auch noch und ich habe dort bestimmt noch Verwandte. Aber es ist alles so weit zurück, dass ich dort leider niemand mehr kenne und dass wir nichts mehr voneinander wissen.

Now listen to the statements and answer with **richtig** or **falsch.** The speaker will verify your answer. If the statement is **falsch** you will hear a question to help you correct the statement.

1. ______________
2. ______________
3. ______________
4. ______________
5. ______________
6. ______________
7. ______________
8. ______________
9. ______________

6-11 Zur Aussprache. German l

Sprechen Sie nach!

Onkel Ludwig liebt Italien.

____

Italien ist Onkel Ludwigs Lieblingsland.

____

Onkel Ludwig liebt leckere italienische Lasagne.

____

Onkel Ludwigs italienische Sonnenbrille ist echt cool.

____

KAPITEL 7

7-1 Mein Berlin. Read along as you listen to the narrative. You will hear it twice.

das Porzellan	*china*
die Porzellanmanufaktur	*china factory*
der Flohmarkt	*flea market*
die U-Bahn	*subway*

Ich heiße Anke und ich komme aus Berlin. Berlin ist eine tolle Stadt. Es gibt hier viel zu sehen und zu tun. Magst du Porzellan? Wir haben eine Porzellanmanufaktur. Aber das Porzellan ist sehr teuer. Hörst du gern Musik? Die Philharmonie gibt klassische und moderne Konzerte und wir haben auch jedes Jahr ein großes Jazz-Festival und viele Kneipen mit Live Bands. Museen und Theater haben wir auch sehr viele. Ja, und dann gibt es viele Geschäfte, Boutiquen und Flohmärkte. Auf Flohmärkten finde ich immer tolle Geschenke für meine Freunde. Meiner Freundin Inge habe ich zum Geburtstag antike Ohrringe aus Silber gekauft und meinem Freund Paul ein altes Radio von 1958. Es ist kaputt, aber ich kenne Paul, er kann es bestimmt reparieren. Wenn du Berlin kennen lernen willst, fährst du viel mit der U-Bahn und du musst viel zu Fuß gehen. Und das KaDeWe darfst du auch nicht vergessen. Viel Spaß!

Now listen to the statements and answer with **richtig** or **falsch.** The speaker will verify your answer. If the statement is **falsch** you will hear a question to help you correct the statement.

1. ____________________   5. ____________________

2. ____________________   6. ____________________

3. ____________________   7. ____________________

4. ____________________   8. ____________________

7-2 Was schenkst du wem? Answer the questions with the help of the cues.

BEISPIEL:	Sie hören:	*Was schenkst du deinem Vater?*
	Sie sehen:	eine Kaffeemaschine
	Sie sagen:	Ich schenke meinem Vater eine Kaffeemaschine.
	Sie hören:	*Ich schenke meinem Vater eine Kaffeemaschine.*

Fangen wir an!

1. einen tollen Heimtrainer

   ____

2. ein Paar weiße Joggingschuhe

   ____

3. neue Fahrräder

   ____

4. eine schicke Sonnenbrille

   ____

5. einen grünen Rucksack

____

7. ein Paar Joggingshorts

____

6. einen neuen Fahrradhelm

____

7-3 Wer, was, wen, wem? Listen to the sentences and respond to the question word you see.

BEISPIEL: Sie hören: *Mein Bruder kauft seiner Freundin eine CD.*
Sie sehen: Wer?
Sie sagen: Mein Bruder.
Sie hören: *Mein Bruder.*

Fangen wir an!

1. Wem?

____

5. Wer?

____

2. Was?

____

6. Wem?

____

3. Wer?

____

7. Was?

____

4. Wem?

____

7-4 Nomen und Pronomen. Repeat the statements you hear, but replace the direct and indirect objects with pronouns.

BEISPIEL:	Sie hören:	*Peter leiht seiner Freundin sein Biologiebuch.*
	Sie sehen:	seiner Freundin / sein Biologiebuch
	Sie sagen:	Peter leiht es ihr.
	Sie hören:	*Peter leiht es ihr.*

Fangen wir an!

1. ihrer Mutter / gelbe Rosen

   ____

2. seinem Mitbewohner / die deutsche Grammatik

   ____

3. Tom / das Deutschbuch

   ____

4. seinem Freund / die Stadt

   ____

5. seiner Tochter / einen Computer

   ____

6. ihrer Freundin / ihr neues Fahrrad

   ____

7. ihrem Bruder / hundert Euro

   ____

7-5 Wie gefällt dir ...? Answer the questions with the help of the cues. Change all nouns to pronouns.

BEISPIEL:

Sie hören:	*Wie gefällt dir Marias neuer Freund?*
Sie sehen:	sehr gut
Sie sagen:	Er gefällt mir sehr gut.
Sie hören:	*Er gefällt mir sehr gut.*

Fangen wir an!

1. nicht so sehr

   ____

2. gar nicht

   ____

3. gut

   ____

4. besonders gut

   ____

5. eigentlich sehr gut

   ____

6. gar nicht

   ____

7. ausgezeichnet

   ____

8. nicht so gut

   ____

NAME: ______________________________ **DATE** ______________

7-6 Aus, außer, bei, mit, nach, seit, von, zu. Choose either a. or b. to answer the questions appropriately. Answer in complete sentences.

BEISPIEL: Sie hören: *Woher kommt Sabine?*
Sie sehen: a. aus Österreich b. nach Österreich
Sie sagen: Sie kommt aus Österreich.
Sie hören: *Sie kommt aus Österreich.*

Fangen wir an!

1. a. mit IBM b. bei IBM

   ____

2. a. zum Bus b. mit dem Bus

   ____

3. a. seit einem Jahr b. für ein Jahr

   ____

4. a. nach Hause b. zu Hause

   ____

5. a. nach Hause b. zu Hause

   ____

6. a. nach Berlin b. zu Berlin

   ____

7. a. mit ihrer Tante b. bei ihrer Tante

   ____

8. a. alle zu Dieter b. alle außer Dieter

   ____

9. a. für ein Jahr b. seit einem Jahr

   ____

10. a. zu seinen Eltern b. nach seinen Eltern

   ____

7-7 Beim, vom, zum, zur. Make sentences from the components you see. Use contractions wherever possible.

BEISPIEL:	Sie sehen:	Meine Mutter / gehen / zu / die Bäckerei
	Sie sagen:	Meine Mutter geht zur Bäckerei.
	Sie hören:	*Meine Mutter geht zur Bäckerei.*
	Sie sehen:	Mein Vater / kommen / von / die Bank
	Sie sagen:	Mein Vater kommt von der Bank.
	Sie hören:	*Mein Vater kommt von der Bank.*

Fangen wir an!

1. Maria / sein / bei / der Zahnarzt

   ____

2. Ich / kommen / von / die Post

   ____

3. Peter / rennen / zu / die Bibliothek

   ____

4. Laura / kommen / von / das Mittagessen

   ____

5. Lisa / laufen / zu / der Bus

   ____

6. Martin / kommen / von / der Bahnhof

   ____

7. Anna und Bettina / sein / bei / der Friseur

   ____

8. das Sweatshirt / passen / gut / zu / die Jeans

   ____

NAME: ______________________ DATE ______________

7-8 Was machen diese Leute? Repeat the sentences you see, inserting the adjectives you hear before the nouns in boldface. Don't forget to add dative endings to the adjectives.

BEISPIEL:	Sie sehen:	Frau Merz kauft ihrer **Tochter** ein Dreirad.
	Sie hören:	*klein*
	Sie sagen:	Frau Merz kauft ihrer kleinen Tochter ein Dreirad.
	Sie hören:	*Frau Merz kauft ihrer kleinen Tochter ein Dreirad.*

Fangen wir an!

1. Anna zeigt ihrer **Mitbewohnerin** die Stadt.

   ____

2. Paul hilft seinem **Großvater** im Garten.

   ____

3. Laura spielt mit ihrem **Bruder.**

   ____

4. Sabine hat dieses Armband von ihrer **Freundin** bekommen.

   ____

5. Maria schickt ihren **Großeltern** viele E-Mails.

   ____

6. Günter geht mit seiner **Freundin** spazieren.

   ____

7. Lisa hat bei einer **Familie** gewohnt.

   ____

8. Florian lebt seit einem **Jahr** in Berlin.

   ____

9. Außer der **Professorin** waren gestern alle hier.

   ____

10. Nach diesem **Essen** sind wir tanzen gegangen.

    ____

7-9 Essen und Trinken. Respond to the questions, using the cues you see. Supply the correct adjective endings.

BEISPIEL: Sie hören: *Was trinkst du denn da?*
Sie sehen: Cola mit kubanisch_____ Rum (m)
Sie sagen: Ich trinke Cola mit kubanischem Rum.
Sie hören: *Ich trinke Cola mit kubanischem Rum.*

Fangen wir an!

1. Weißbrot mit italienisch_____ Salami (f)
2. Pommes frites aus frisch_____ Kartoffeln (pl)
3. Obst mit italienisch_____ Eis (n)
4. Champagner mit kalifornisch_____ Orangensaft (m)
5. Bücher von amerikanisch_____ Autoren (pl)

7-10 Liebe Tante Luise. Listen to the Silvia's letter. You will hear it twice.

Now answer the questions you hear with the help of the cues.

1. Sie hat das alles ____________________ bekommen.
2. Den Fernseher haben ____________________ ihr geschenkt.
3. ____________________ hat ihr eine CD geschenkt.
4. ____________________ hat ihr nichts geschenkt.
5. Er hat ____________________ vergessen.

NAME: ______________________________ DATE ______________

7-11 Zur Aussprache. German **r**

Sprechen Sie nach!

Richard fährt im Regen Fahrrad.

____

Richard wird sehr krank.

____

Richard braucht mehr Aspirin.

____

Armer Richard!

____

Rita hat Geburtstag.

____

Robert schickt ihr rote Rosen.

____

Rote Rosen von Robert?

____

Was für eine Überraschung!

____

KAPITEL 8

8-1 Wie wohnst du? Listen to the telephone conversation. You will hear the text twice.

Now listen to the statements and answer with **richtig** or **falsch.** The speaker will verify your answer. If the statement is **falsch** you will hear a question to help you correct the statement.

1. ____________________ 5. ____________________

2. ____________________ 6. ____________________

3. ____________________ 7. ____________________

4. ____________________

8-2 Wohin? Wo? Answer the questions you hear by choosing a. or b.

BEISPIEL: Sie hören: *Wohin gehst du?*
Sie sehen: a. im Kino b. ins Kino
Sie sagen: Ins Kino.
Sie hören: *Ins Kino.*

Fangen wir an!

1. a. in einem Privathaus b. in ein Privathaus

   ____

2. a. unter dem Fenster b. unter das Fenster

   ____

3. a. an die Wand b. an der Wand

   ____

4. a. unter die Couch b. unter der Couch

   ____

5. a. zwischen den beiden Fenstern b. zwischen die beiden Fenster

   ____

6. a. vor der Couch b. vor die Couch

   ____

7. a. an der Wand b. an die Wand

   ____

8. a. unter dem Schreibtisch b. unter den Schreibtisch

____

9. a. neben der Küchentür b. neben die Küchentür

____

8-3 Kontraktion? Make sentences from the components you see. Use contractions wherever possible.

BEISPIEL:

Sie sehen: ich / gehen / in / das Konzert
Sie sagen: Ich gehe ins Konzert.
Sie hören: *Ich gehe ins Konzert.*

Sie sehen: wir / gehen / in / die Oper
Sie sagen: Wir gehen in die Oper.
Sie hören: *Wir gehen in die Oper.*

Fangen wir an!

1. ich / stellen / den Sessel / an / das Fenster

____

2. Professor Weber / reisen / heute Abend / in / die Schweiz

____

3. Anna / sitzen / in / das Restaurant

____

4. Maria und Florian / trinken / in / die / Kneipe / eine Bacardi-Cola

____

5. wir / gehen / heute Abend / in / das Gasthaus

____

6. Silvia / hängen / das Poster / an / die Tür

____

7. ich / stehen / an / das Fenster

____

8. Herr Ziegler / gehen / auf / das Rathaus

____

9. wir / gehen / auf / die Bank

____

NAME: ______________________________ DATE ____________

8-4 *Stellen* oder *stehen, legen* oder *liegen?*

Complete the questions by choosing a. or b. Then answer the questions, using the cues you see.

BEISPIEL:	Sie sehen:	Wo ... der Schaukelstuhl?
	Sie hören:	*a. steht b. stellt*
	Sie sagen:	Wo steht der Schaukelstuhl?
	Sie hören:	*Wo steht der Schaukelstuhl?*
	Sie sehen:	in / die Ecke
	Sie sagen:	In der Ecke.
	Sie hören:	*In der Ecke.*

Fangen wir an!

1. Wo ... der Papierkorb?

   ______________________________?

   unter / der Schreibtisch

   ______________________________.

2. Wohin soll ich den Fernseher ...?

   ______________________________?

   auf / das Regal

   ______________________________.

3. Wo ... der Teppich?

   ______________________________?

   vor / die Couch

   ______________________________.

4. Wohin soll ich das Buch ...?

   ______________________________?

   auf / der Tisch

   ______________________________.

5. Wo ... die Zimmerpflanze?

   ______________________________?

   zwischen / die beiden Fenster

   ______________________________.

6. Wohin soll ich die Mäntel ...?

   ______________________________?

   auf / der Sessel

   ______________________________.

7. Wohin soll ich den Schaukelstuhl ...?

   ______________________________?

   neben / der Schreibtisch

   ______________________________.

8-5 *Da*-Formen. Complete the responses to the questions you hear, using **da**-compounds of the prepositions provided.

BEISPIEL: Sie hören: *Soll ich die Stehlampe neben den Sessel stellen?*
Sie sehen: Nein, stell sie lieber ______________. (hinter)
Sie sagen: Nein, stell sie lieber dahinter.
Sie hören: *Nein, stell sie lieber dahinter.*

Fangen wir an!

1. Weil die Leute im Haus ________________ so viele Hunde haben. (neben)
2. Weil in der Wohnung ________________ ein Trompeter wohnt. (über)
3. Nein, jetzt liegt sie ________________ .(unter)
4. Ja, legt sie nur ________________ .(auf)
5. Nein, stell ihn lieber ________________ .(vor)
6. Weil eine alte Frau mit zehn Katzen ________________ gewohnt hat. (in)

8-6 Wann? Listen to the questions and answer with the help of the cues you see.

BEISPIEL: Sie hören: *Wann fliegen Sie nach Deutschland?*
Sie sehen: A_____ 16. 1.
Sie sagen: Am sechzehnten Ersten.
Sie hören: *Am sechzehnten Ersten.*

Fangen wir an!

1. A_____ 17. 1.
2. Nach mein_____Vorlesung.
3. A_____ Wochenende.
4. Vor d_____Vorlesung.
5. In d_____ Sommerferien
6. Vor ein_____Jahr.
7. Zwischen d_____ 1. und d_____ 15. Februar.
8. An ihr_____ Geburtstag.

8-7 *Zu*-Infinitive. Using the cues you hear, complete the sentences you see.

BEISPIEL:	Sie hören:	*meine Hausaufgaben heute machen*
	Sie sehen:	Ich habe vor, ...
	Sie sagen:	Ich habe vor, meine Hausaufgaben heute zu machen.
	Sie hören:	*Ich habe vor, meine Hausaufgaben heute zu machen.*

Fangen wir an!

1. Ich habe vor, ...
   ____
2. Es macht mir Spaß, ...
   ____
3. Es ist schön, ...
   ____
4. Hast du Lust, ...?
   ____
5. Wir haben vor, ...
   ____
6. Sie hat geplant, ...
   ____
7. Es ist echt toll, ...
   ____
8. Hast du Lust, ...?
   ____

8-8 Wessen Sachen sind das? Answer the questions you hear, using the cues you see.

BEISPIEL:	Sie hören:	*Wessen Fahrrad ist das?*
	Sie sehen:	mein Bruder
	Sie sagen:	Das ist das Fahrrad meines Bruders.
	Sie hören:	*Das ist das Fahrrad meines Bruders.*

Fangen wir an!

1. mein Freund
   ____
2. Claudia
   ____
3. meine Mitbewohnerin
   ____
4. mein Großvater
   ____
5. unsere Nachbarn
   ____
6. Frau Ziegler
   ____
7. mein Mitbewohner
   ____
8. ein Millionär
   ____

8-9 Ich bin Modedesignerin. Listen to what Ariane, a fashion designer, has to say about her life and work. You will hear the text twice.

Using the appropriate cue, answer the questions you hear in complete sentences.

1. a. 27 b. 37

   ____

2. a. Architektin b. Modedesignerin

   ____

3. a. Krefeld b. Paris

   ____

4. a. für junge Leute b. für das Establishment

   ____

5. a. Frankreich b. Deutschland

   ____

6. a. Design b. Skulptur

   ____

7. a. in der Firma ihrer Eltern b. in der Firma ihres Onkels

   ____

8. a. um mehr Geld zu verdienen b. um ihren eigenen Stil zu finden

   ____

9. a. ihre Eltern b. ihr Onkel

   ____

8-10 Zur Aussprache. Choose a. or b. to match the **st-** or **sp-**sound of the word you hear. Say your choice out loud.

1.	a. Wurst	b. Stadt	4.	a. Spanien	b. Aspartam
	____________			____________	
2.	a. warst	b. stellen	5.	a. spielen	b. Wespe
	____________			____________	
3.	a. Lust	b. Studium	6.	a. sprechen	b. Kaspar
	____________			____________	

KAPITEL 9

9-1 Stefan bekommt Besuch. Listen to the conversation. You will hear it twice.

Now answer the questions you hear with the help of the cues.

1. Am Sonntagnachmittag besuchen ihn seine ______________ und sein ______________.
2. Stefan hat einen ______________ gebacken.
3. Nach dem Kaffeetrinken wollen sie ein bisschen ______________.
4. Stefans Eltern kommen erst am ______________.
5. Er kann nicht ______________.
6. Nein, er hat das Brot beim ______________ und die Wurst beim ______________ gekauft.
7. Den Kartoffelsalat bringt Stefans ______________ mit.
8. Nach dem Abendessen wollen sie Stefans ______________ anschauen.

9-2 Berufe. Complete each sentence by adding the appropriate relative pronoun.

BEISPIEL:	Sie sehen:	Ein Tierarzt ist ein Mann, d_____ kranke Tiere wieder gesund macht.
	Sie sagen:	Ein Tierarzt ist ein Mann, der kranke Tiere wieder gesund macht.
	Sie hören:	*Ein Tierarzt ist ein Mann, der kranke Tiere wieder gesund macht.*

Fangen wir an!

1. Eine Architektin ist eine Frau, d_____ Häuser baut.
2. Ein Apotheker ist ein Mann, d_____ Medikamente verkauft.
3. Ein Briefträger ist ein Mann, d_____ die Post austrägt.
4. Eine Autorin ist eine Frau, d_____ Bücher schreibt.
5. Eine Zahnärztin ist eine Frau, d_____ kaputte Zähne repariert.
6. Ein Hausmann ist ein Mann, d_____ den Haushalt macht.
7. Ein Automechaniker ist ein Mann, d_____ kaputte Autos repariert.
8. Eine Journalistin ist eine Frau, d_____ Zeitungsartikel schreibt.

9-3 In Garmisch-Partenkirchen. Complete each sentence of the narrative by adding the appropriate relative pronoun.

BEISPIEL: Sie sehen: Martin und Peter, d_____ übers Wochenende in die Alpen gefahren sind, sitzen jetzt im Restaurant.
Sie sagen: Martin und Peter, die übers Wochenende in die Alpen gefahren sind, sitzen jetzt im Restaurant.
Sie hören: *Martin und Peter, die übers Wochenende in die Alpen gefahren sind, sitzen jetzt im Restaurant.*

Fangen wir an!

1. Der Ober, d_____ zum Tisch kommt, gibt ihnen die Speisekarte.
2. Sie bestellen beide das Kassler, d_____ sehr gut ist.
3. Die Kartoffeln, d_____ sie bekommen, sind nicht ganz gar.
4. Die Knödel, d_____ der Ober ihnen bringen will, nehmen die Studenten nicht.
5. Peter, d_____ Garmisch-Partenkirchen ganz toll findet, muss leider zurück nach München.
6. Peter will Stephanies Referat, d_____ morgen fertig sein muss, durchlesen.
7. Der Ober, d_____ die Rechnung bringt, sagt: „Vierundzwanzig Euro vierzig, bitte."
8. Martin, d_____ für beide bezahlt, rundet auf fünfundzwanzig Euro auf.

9-4 Im Gasthaus. Using the information in the sentences you hear, complete the questions you see with the appropriate relative pronouns.

BEISPIEL:	Sie hören:	*Der Mann kommt gerade zur Tür herein.*
	Sie sehen:	Wer ist denn der Mann, d________ gerade zur Tür hereinkommt?
	Sie sagen:	Wer ist denn der Mann, der gerade zur Tür hereinkommt?
	Sie hören:	*Wer ist denn der Mann, der gerade zur Tür hereinkommt?*

Fangen wir an!

1. Wer ist denn der Mann, d________ ein Bier nach dem anderen trinkt?
2. Wer ist denn der Mann, d________ der Kellner gerade bedient?
3. Wer ist denn der Mann, d________ die Kellnerin gerade das Schnitzel serviert?
4. Wer ist denn die Frau, d________ eine Zigarette nach der anderen raucht?
5. Wer ist denn die Frau, d________ der Kellner so lange nicht bedient hat?
6. Wer ist denn die Frau, d________ die Kellnerin gerade den fantastischen Nachtisch bringt?
7. Wer ist denn das junge Paar, d________ so schick angezogen ist?
8. Wer ist denn das junge Paar, d________ der Kellner fotografieren musste?
9. Wer ist denn das junge Paar, d________ der Kellner schon die zweite Flasche Wein bringt?
10. Wer sind denn die beiden alten Leute, d________ kein Wort miteinander sprechen?
11. Wer sind denn die beiden alten Leute, d________ der Kellner so besonders freundlich bedient?
12. Wer sind denn die beiden alten Leuten, d________ der große Hund dort gehört?

9-5 Wer sind diese Leute? Using the information in the statements you hear, complete the sentences you see with relative pronouns in the accusative or dative.

BEISPIEL:	Sie hören:	*Ich habe ihn gestern Abend in der Disco kennen gelernt.*
	Sie sehen:	Benedikt ist der Student, d________ ich gestern Abend in der Disco kennen gelernt habe.
	Sie sagen:	Benedikt ist der Student, den ich gestern Abend in der Disco kennen gelernt habe.
	Sie hören:	*Benedikt ist der Student, den ich gestern Abend in der Disco kennen gelernt habe.*

Fangen wir an!

1. Till ist der Student, d________ ich gestern Abend nach Hause gefahren habe.
2. Herr Merz ist der Mann, d________ ich meinen Wagen verkauft habe.
3. Renate ist die Studentin, d________ ich bei ihrem Referat geholfen habe.
4. Gisela ist die Frau, d________ ich beim Chatten kennen gelernt habe.
5. Sarah ist das Baby, d________ ich gestern mit meiner neuen Digitalkamera fotografiert habe.
6. Paul ist das Baby, d________ ich die hübsche Rassel geschenkt habe.
7. Bergers sind die alten Leute, d________ ich letzten Sommer im Garten geholfen habe.
8. Zeuners sind die Leute, d________ ich am Samstag auf dem Flohmarkt getroffen habe.

9-6 *N*-Nouns. Answer the questions you see, using the cues you hear.

BEISPIEL:

BEISPIEL:	Sie sehen:	Wem zeigt die Studentin die Stadt?
	Sie hören:	*der Tourist*
	Sie sagen:	Dem Touristen zeigt die Studentin die Stadt.
	Sie hören:	*Dem Touristen zeigt die Studentin die Stadt.*

Fangen wir an!

1. Wer steht dort an der Ecke?

   ____

2. Mit wem spricht Eva?

   ____

3. Wer ist im Kaufhaus König?

   ____

4. Wen sieht man oft Fußball spielen?

   ____

5. Wer wohnt neben uns?

   ____

6. Wen findet Laura toll?

   ____

7. Für wen kauft das Mädchen die Karotten?

   ____

NAME: ______________________ DATE ______________

9-7 Reflexivpronomen.

Create sentences with the help of the cues you hear and see.

BEISPIEL:	Sie hören:	*sich duschen*
	Sie sehen:	ich / jeden Morgen
	Sie sagen:	Ich dusche mich jeden Morgen.
	Sie hören:	*Ich dusche mich jeden Morgen.*

Fangen wir an!

1. Moritz / heute / nicht

   ____

2. Eva / oft / stundenlang

   ____

3. wir / die Haare

   ____

4. ich / morgens und abends

   ____

5. ich / erst / nach dem Frühstück

   ____

6. ich / noch schnell / die Hände

   ____

9-8 Reflexive Verben.

Create questions with the help of the cues you hear and see.

BEISPIEL:	Sie hören:	*sich aufregen*
	Sie sehen:	warum / du / denn so
	Sie sagen:	Warum regst du dich denn so auf?
	Sie hören:	*Warum regst du dich denn so auf?*

Fangen wir an!

1. warum / du / denn nicht / ein bisschen / ?

   ____

2. warum / du / denn immer / so schlecht / ?

   ____

3. warum / Sie / denn nicht / ?

   ____

4. warum / du / denn so oft / ?

   ____

5. warum / Sie / denn nicht / ?

   ____

6. warum / Sie / denn jeden Morgen / ?

   ____

7. warum / ich / denn heute / gar nicht / ?

   ____

9-9 Beeil dich, du kommst zu spät. Listen to the dialogue. You will hear the text twice.

Now answer the questions you hear with the help of the cues you see.

1. Sie ist noch zu ________________.
2. Sie will um ________________ im Büro sein.
3. Jetzt ist es schon ________________.
4. Sie muss sich ________________ und sich die ________________.
5. ________________ macht das Frühstück.
6. Zum Frühstück gibt es ________________ und ________________ mit Marmelade.

9-10 Zur Aussprache. German **s**-sounds

Sprechen Sie nach!

Seit Sonntag scheint die Sonne,

____

sie scheint sogar sehr heiß.

____

Jetzt reisen Heinz und Susanne,

____

sie reisen in die Schweiz.

____

Sie gehen zusammen zelten

____

bei Sissach in der Schweiz.

____

KAPITEL 10

10-1 Ein neues Märchen. Listen to the conversation between Achim and his mother. You will hear it twice.

Now listen to and read the statements and answer with **richtig** or **falsch.** The speaker will verify your answer. If the statement is **falsch** you will hear a question to help you correct the statement.

1. Achim trank ein Bier und aß ein Schnitzel.

   ____

2. Achim konnte für das Bier und das Schnitzel bezahlen.

   ____

3. Der Mann wollte alles bezahlen, wenn Achim mit ihm ein Bier trank.

   ____

4. Der Mann fuhr Achim im Taxi zu seiner WG.

   ____

5. Achim fuhr am nächsten Tag mit dem Zug zu seiner Mutter.

   ____

6. Der Mann war Sabines Vater.

   ____

7. Achim muss den BMW in einem Jahr zurückbringen.

   ____

10-2 Verbformen. Change the infinitives you hear to the 3rd person singular of the simple past tense.

BEISPIEL:	Sie hören:	*kommen*
	Sie sagen:	kam
	Sie hören:	*kam*

Fangen wir an!

1. ____________________ 6. ____________________

2. ____________________ 7. ____________________

3. ____________________ 8. ____________________

4. ____________________ 9. ____________________

5. ____________________ 10. ____________________

10-3 Wer machte was? Restate the statements you hear in the simple past tense.

BEISPIEL:	Sie hören:	*Der Student kommt durch das Dorf.*
	Sie sagen:	Der Student kam durch das Dorf.
	Sie hören:	*Der Student kam durch das Dorf.*

Fangen wir an!

1. ____________________ 6. ____________________

2. ____________________ 7. ____________________

3. ____________________ 8. ____________________

4. ____________________ 9. ____________________

5. ____________________

NAME: ______________________ DATE ______________

10-4 Erzählen Sie! Tell a story by constructing sentences in the simple past tense, using the cues.

BEISPIEL: Sie sehen: Es / sein / einmal / ein armer Mann
Sie sagen: Es war einmal ein armer Mann.
Sie hören: *Es war einmal ein armer Mann.*

Fangen wir an!

1. Der arme Mann / haben / keine Kleider

   ____

2. Der reiche Mann / geben / ihm / Kleider und Geld

   ____

3. Jetzt / müssen / der arme Mann / nicht / mehr / frieren

   ____

4. Der arme Mann / sagen / es / allen armen Leuten

   ____

5. Da / wollen / alle / Geld / von dem reichen Mann

   ____

6. Der reiche Mann / sein / bald / auch / arm

   ____

7. Nun / arbeiten / der Mann / sehr schwer

   ____

8. Bald / sein / er / wieder reich

   ____

9. Jetzt / geben / er / den armen Leuten / Arbeit

   ____

10-5 Der Geist aus der Flasche. Listen to the vocabulary and the story. You will hear the story twice.

das Netz	*the net*
die Wolke	*the cloud*
der böse Geist	*the evil spirit*
töten	*to kill*

Now listen to the statements and answer with **richtig** or **falsch.** The speaker will verify your answers.

1. ____________________
2. ____________________
3. ____________________
4. ____________________
5. ____________________
6. ____________________
7. ____________________
8. ____________________
9. ____________________

10-6 *Als* oder *wenn?* Answer the questions you hear with the help of the cues you see.

BEISPIEL:

Sie hören:	*Wann hast du tanzen gelernt?*
Sie sehen:	Ich war achtzehn Jahre alt.
Sie sagen:	Als ich achtzehn Jahre alt war.
Sie hören:	*Als ich achtzehn Jahre alt war.*
Sie hören:	*Wann fährst du nach Europa?*
Sie sehen:	Ich habe Geld.
Sie sagen:	Wenn ich Geld habe.
Sie hören:	*Wenn ich Geld habe.*

Fangen wir an!

1. Ich war acht Jahre alt.

   ____

2. Ich brauchte ein Auto.

   ____

3. Das Semester ist zu Ende.

   ____

4. Ich komme nach Hause.

   ____

5. Ich fing mit dem Studium an.

   ____

6. Meine Eltern kauften dort ein Haus.

   ____

7. Ich kam ins Wohnzimmer.

   ____

8. Mein Referat ist fertig.

   ____

9. Du besuchst mich nächste Woche.

   ____

NAME: ______________________________ DATE ______________

10-7 Kennst du diese Leute? Using the information in the statements you hear, complete the questions you see with the appropriate prepositions and relative pronouns.

BEISPIEL: Sie hören: *Monika hat ist mit dem Mann ausgegangen.*
Sie sehen: Kennst du den Mann, ____________ d________ Monika ausgegangen ist?
Sie sagen: Kennst du den Mann, mit dem Monika ausgegangen ist?
Sie hören: *Kennst du den Mann, mit dem Monika ausgegangen ist?*

Fangen wir an!

1. Kennst du die Frau, ____________ d________ Florian die Karten bekommen hat?
2. Kennst du den Verkäufer, ____________ d________ Stefan den Scannner gekauft hat?
3. Kennst du die amerikanische Studentin, ____________ d________ Peter Rosen gekauft hat?
4. Kennst du den Typ, ____________ d________ Helga immer Briefe bekommt?
5. Kennst du die Leute, ____________ d________ Anna wohnt?
6. Kennst du die Zahnärztin, ____________ d________ Claudia geht?

10-8 Definitionen I. Using the information in the statements you hear, complete the definitions you see.

BEISPIEL: Sie hören: *In dem Gebäude sieht man Filme.*
Sie sehen: Ein Kino ist ein Gebäude, ______________________.
Sie sagen: Ein Kino ist ein Gebäude, in dem man Filme sieht.
Sie hören: *Ein Kino ist ein Gebäude, in dem man Filme sieht.*

Fangen wir an!

1. Eine Bibliothek ist ein Gebäude, ______________________.
2. Eine Bank ist ein Gebäude, ______________________.
3. Eine Disco ist ein Gebäude, ______________________.
4. Die Post ist ein Gebäude, ______________________.

10-9 Definitionen II. Using the information in the statements you hear, complete the definitions you see.

BEISPIEL:	Sie hören:	*Mit dem Gerät macht man Dosen auf.*
	Sie sehen:	Ein Dosenöffner ist ein Gerät, ____________________.
	Sie sagen:	Ein Dosenöffner ist ein Gerät, mit dem man Dosen aufmacht.
	Sie hören:	*Ein Dosenöffner ist ein Gerät, mit dem man Dosen aufmacht.*

Fangen wir an!

1. Eine Mikrowelle ist ein Gerät, ____________________.
2. Ein Videorekorder ist ein Gerät, ____________________.
3. Eine Videokamera ist ein Gerät, ____________________.
4. Ein Staubsauger ist ein Gerät, ____________________.

10-10 Der Hase und der Igel. Say the sentences you see, adding the adjectives you hear. Use appropriate adjective endings.

BEISPIEL:	Sie sehen:	Die __________ Sonne schien vom __________ Himmel.
	Sie hören:	*warm / blau*
	Sie sagen:	Die warme Sonne schien vom blauen Himmel.
	Sie hören:	*Die warme Sonne schien vom blauen Himmel.*

Fangen wir an!

1. Der __________ Igel stand vor der Haustür.
2. Er schaute in den __________ Morgen hinaus.
3. Die Frau des __________ Igels zog die __________ Kinder an.
4. Der Igel sagte zu dem __________ Hasen: „Guten Morgen!"
5. Aber der __________ Hase grüßte nicht zurück.
6. Der __________ Igel machte mit dem __________ Hasen einen Wettlauf.
7. Der Igel dachte: „Der Hase hat die __________ Beine, aber ich habe den __________ Kopf."
8. Der Igel saß am __________ Ende des __________ Feldes.
9. Seine Frau saß am __________ Ende des __________ Feldes.
10. Der Igel und seine Frau gewannen das __________ Goldstück und die __________ Flasche Schnaps.

NAME: ______________________ DATE ______________

10-11 Was möchten Sie? Answer the questions you hear with the help of the cues you see. Add appropriate adjective endings.

BEISPIEL: Sie hören: *Was für einen Film möchten Sie sehen?*
Sie sehen: einen / lustig / Film
Sie sagen: Ich möchte einen lustigen Film sehen.
Sie hören: *Ich möchte einen lustigen Film sehen.*

Fangen wir an!

1. ein / klassisch / Konzert

   ____

2. eine / italienisch / Pizza

   ____

3. ein / bayerisch / Bier

   ____

4. mit einem / schnell / Zug

   ____

5. ein / italienisch / Fahrrad

   ____

6. einen / neu / Audi A4

   ____

10-12 Internationaler Geschmack. Answer the questions you see, using the adjectives you hear. Add appropriate endings.

BEISPIEL: Sie sehen: Was für Bier (n) ist das?
Sie hören: *deutsch*
Sie sagen: Das ist deutsches Bier.
Sie hören: *Das ist deutsches Bier.*

Fangen wir an!

1. Was für Käse (m) ist das?

   ____

2. Was für Wurst (f) ist das?

   ____

3. Was für Oliven (pl) sind das?

   ____

4. Was für Brot (n) ist das?

   ____

5. Was für Wein (m) ist das?

   ____

6. Was für Salami (f) ist das?

   ____

7. Was für Spaghetti (pl) sind das?

   ____

10-13 Zur Aussprache. German **f, v** and **w**

Sprechen Sie nach!

waren fahren

Welt Feld

wir vier

Wort fort

wund Fund

In vier Wochen sind die Vorlesungen vorbei.

In vier Wochen haben wir haben Ferien.

Wir vier fahren mit dem Fahrrad nach Finnland:

Veronika, Verena, Volker und Volkmar.

In Finnland wollen wir viele Feste feiern.

KAPITEL 11

11-1 Die Berliner Luftbrücke. Read and listen to the report. You will hear the text twice.

Nach dem Zweiten Weltkrieg wurden Deutschland und auch Berlin von den Alliierten in vier Zonen geteilt, in eine amerikanische, eine britische, eine französische und eine sowjetische. Weil Berlin aber tief in der sowjetischen Zone lag, wollten die Sowjets diese Stadt allein kontrollieren. Am 24. Juni 1948 begannen sie deshalb, alle Straßen und alle Wasserwege, die von den drei westlichen Zonen nach Berlin gingen, zu blockieren. Aber schon zwei Tage später, am 26. Juni 1948, begannen die westlichen Alliierten das größte Lufttransportprojekt der Geschichte, die Luftbrücke. Aus der ganzen Welt holten sie Transportflugzeuge nach Deutschland. Diese Flugzeuge flogen von westdeutschen Flughäfen über die sowjetische Zone nach Berlin und brachten den Berlinern alle Lebensmittel, alle Kohle und alle Medikamente, die sie brauchten. In mehr als 200 000 Flügen flogen die westlichen Alliierten über 1,7 Millionen Tonnen Güter nach Berlin. Erst nach elf Monaten, im Mai 1949, verstanden die Sowjets, dass sie Westberlin nicht aushungern konnten. Sie öffneten die Straßen und die Wasserwege, und die Amerikaner, die Briten und die Franzosen blieben in Berlin.

Now choose and say the correct answers to the questions you hear. The speaker will then repeat the correct answer.

1. a. Nach der sowjetischen Blockade. b. Nach dem Zweiten Weltkrieg.

   ____

2. a. Von den Alliierten. b. Von den Sowjets.

   ____

3. a. Die Sowjets. b. Die Franzosen.

   ____

4. a. Am 24. Juni 1948. b. Am 26. Juni 1948.

   ____

5. a. Von ostdeutschen Flughäfen. b. Von westdeutschen Flughäfen.

   ____

6. a. In über 1,7 Millionen Flügen. b. In über 200 000 Flügen.

   ____

7. a. Nach elf Monaten. b. Nach elf Jahren.

   ____

11-2 Fragen und Antworten. Respond to the questions you hear by completing the sentences you see. Use the verb given in parentheses in the present tense of the passive voice.

BEISPIEL: Sie hören: *Warum bist du denn mit dem Bus zur Uni gekommen?*
Sie sehen: Weil mein Wagen ______________ ______________. (reparieren)
Sie sagen: Weil mein Wagen repariert wird.
Sie hören: *Weil mein Wagen repariert wird.*

Fangen wir an!

1. Weil ich gleich ______________ ______________. (abholen)
2. Weil dort ein neuer Teppich ______________ ______________. (legen)
3. Weil ich dort gut ______________ ______________. (bezahlen)
4. Weil ihre Wohnung ______________ ______________. (renovieren)
5. Weil immer mehr Fabriken ______________ ______________. (automatisieren)
6. Weil die Geschäfte erst um halb zehn______________ ______________. (öffnen)
7. Weil so viele Geschenke ______________ ______________. (umtauschen)
8. Weil dann die Preise ______________ ______________. (reduzieren)

11-3 Fragen und Antworten. Respond to the questions you hear by completing the sentences you see. Use the verb given in parentheses in the simple past tense of the passive voice.

BEISPIEL: Sie hören: *Warum warst du nicht auf Lauras Fete?*
Sie sehen: Weil ich nicht ______________ ______________. (einladen)
Sie sagen: Weil ich nicht eingeladen wurde.
Sie hören: *Weil ich nicht eingeladen wurde.*

Fangen wir an!

1. Weil er dort so schlecht ______________ ______________. (bezahlen)
2. Weil er ______________ ______________. (operieren)
3. Weil unsere Klausur auf nächste Woche ______________ ______________. (verschieben)
4. Weil der Wagen kaum ______________ ______________. (benutzen)
5. Weil sie total ______________ ______________. (renovieren)
6. Weil mir der Weg nicht richtig ______________ ______________. (beschreiben)
7. Weil ich nicht rechtzeitig ______________ ______________. (wecken)
8. Weil sie alle ins Deutsche ______________ ______________. (übersetzen)

NAME: ______________________________ DATE ________________

11-4 Gute Vorsätze! Using the verbs in the sentences you hear, complete the following resolutions in the passive voice.

BEISPIEL: Sie hören: *Ich esse zu viel Schokolade.*
Sie sehen: Von morgen ab ____________ weniger Schokolade ____________.
Sie sagen: Von morgen ab wird weniger Schokolade gegessen.
Sie hören: *Von morgen ab wird weniger Schokolade gegessen.*

Fangen wir an!

1. Von morgen ab ____________ viel mehr Obst und Gemüse ____________.
2. Von morgen ab ____________ überhaupt kein Bier mehr ____________.
3. Von morgen ab ____________ viel mehr Wasser ____________.
4. Von morgen ab ____________ täglich ein bisschen Sport ____________.
5. Von morgen ab ____________ jeden Tag eine Stunde lang Deutsch ____________.
6. Von morgen ab ____________ mein Zimmer einmal in der Woche ____________.

11-5 Von wem wurde das gemacht? Complete the sentences you see with the information provided in parentheses.

BEISPIEL: Sie sehen: Müllers Pudel wurde ____________ überfahren. (ein riesiger Lastwagen)
Sie sagen: Müllers Pudel wurde von einem riesigen Lastwagen überfahren.
Sie hören: *Müllers Pudel wurde von einem riesigen Lastwagen überfahren.*

Fangen wir an!

1. Frau Mercks Kanarienvogel wurde ____________ gefressen. (eine hungrige Katze)
2. Frau Maiers Mercedes wurde ____________ gestohlen. (ein vierzehnjähriger Schüler)
3. Ich wurde heute früh ____________ fotografiert. (ein verstecktes Radargerät)
4. Dieser brutale Film wurde mir ____________ empfohlen. (meine beste Freundin)
5. In dem Film wurde ein Diplomat ____________ ermordet. (zwei maskierte Terroristen)
6. Die beiden Mörder wurden ____________ fotografiert. (eine versteckte Videokamera)

11-6 Was passt wo? Complete the sentences you see by choosing the appropriate past participle from the two you hear. Don't forget to add the required adjective ending.

BEISPIEL:	Sie sehen:	Ich sehe eine elegant ______________ Dame.
	Sie hören:	*a. gekleidet b. gesattelt*
	Sie sagen:	Ich sehe eine elegant gekleidete Dame.
	Sie hören:	*Ich sehe eine elegant gekleidete Dame.*

Fangen wir an!

1. Ich sehe eine ______________ Jacke.
2. Ich sehe einen gut ______________ Mann.
3. Ich sehe ein ______________ Pferd.
4. Ich sehe ein frisch ______________ Hemd.

11-7 Mit den Fahrrädern auf Rügen. Listen to the dialogue. You will hear the text twice.

Stephanie, Claudia, Peter, and Martin are sitting in the cafeteria planning their bike trip to Rügen, an island in the Baltic Sea not far from Stralsund.

die Fähre	*ferry*
der Damm	*causeway*
die Liste	*list*
die Felsen	*cliffs*

Now read and listen to the statements and answer with **richtig** or **falsch.** The speaker will verify your answer. If the statement is **falsch** you will hear a question to help you correct the statement.

1. Stephanie möchte eine Radtour auf der Insel Rügen machen.

   ____

2. Sie fahren mit der Fähre von Stralsund nach Rügen.

   ____

3. Stephanie hat schon eine Karte von Rügen.

   ____

4. Die Liste von den Campingplätzen hat sie auch schon.

   ____

5. In Stralsund gibt es ein Museum für Fische und Meerestiere.

   ____

6. Am Strand gibt es viele Wasservögel.

   ____

7. Im Nationalpark Jasmund gibt es rote Felsen.

   ____

NAME: ______________________________ **DATE:** ______________

11-8 Verben mit Präpositionen. Answer the questions you hear, using the cues you see.

BEISPIEL: Sie hören: *Über wen ärgerst du dich?*
Sie sehen: über / mein Bruder
Sie sagen: Über meinen Bruder.
Sie hören: *Über meinen Bruder.*

Sie hören: *Woran denkst du?*
Sie sehen: an / mein Referat
Sie sagen: An mein Referat.
Sie hören: *An mein Referat.*

Fangen wir an!

1. auf / meine Ferien

   ____

2. an / mein Referat

   ____

3. an / mein Opa

   ____

4. für / Fotografie

   ____

5. über / meine schlechten Zensuren

   ____

6. auf / meine Freunde

   ____

7. vor / die Examen

   ____

8. von / meine Schwester

   ____

9. über / die Blumen

   ____

10. von / mein Vater

    ____

11-9 *Wo*-Formen? Construct questions from the statements you hear, using the cues you see.

BEISPIEL:

Sie hören:	*Ich freue mich über das Paket.*
Sie sehen:	sich freuen über
Sie sagen:	Worüber freust du dich?
Sie hören:	*Worüber freust du dich?*
Sie hören:	*Ich denke an meine Mutter.*
Sie sehen:	denken an
Sie sagen:	An wen denkst du?
Sie hören:	*An wen denkst du?*

Fangen wir an!

1. Angst haben vor

   ____________________________?

2. sich freuen über

   ____________________________?

3. sich ärgern über

   ____________________________?

4. sich freuen auf

   ____________________________?

5. arbeiten an

   ____________________________?

6. denken an

   ____________________________?

7. erzählen von

   ____________________________?

8. wissen von

   ____________________________?

9. sich verlieben in

   ____________________________?

10. warten auf

    ____________________________?

11. sich aufregen über

    ____________________________?

12. sich interessieren für

    ____________________________?

NAME: ______________________________ DATE: ______________

11-10 Zur Aussprache. The consonant clusters **pf** and **kn**

Sprechen Sie nach!

Knackwurst mit Knäckebrot,

____

Knödel mit Knoblauch.

____

Was für eine Kneipe!

____

Herr Knopf pflückt Äpfel,

____

Herr Knopf pflückt Pflaumen,

____

und Wasser tropft auf seinen Kopf.

____

Ach, Herr Knopf, Sie armer Tropf!

____

KAPITEL 12

12-1 Hausarbeit, Beruf und Familie, das ist schwer. Listen to Silke's report. You will hear the text twice.

Now choose and say the correct answers to the questions you hear. The speaker will then repeat the correct answer.

1. a. Seit sechs Jahren. b. Seit einem halben Jahr.

   ____

2. a. Sie ist Architektin. b. Sie ist Bibliothekarin.

   ____

3. a. Sie hat drei Kinder. b. Sie hat zwei Kinder.

   ____

4. a. Seit zwei Jahren. b. Seit einem halben Jahr.

   ____

5. a. Sie sind im Kindergarten. b. Sie sind in der Schule.

   ____

6. a. Dann holt Jürgen sie ab. b. Dann holt Frau Jenninger sie ab.

   ____

7. a. Weil Frau Jenninger mehr Zeit für ihre Kinder hat. b. Weil Frau Jenninger mehr Kinder hat.

   ____

12-2 Wünsche. Make hypothetical statements based on the factual statements you hear.

BEISPIEL: Sie hören: *Ich habe kein Fahrrad.*
Sie sagen: Ich hätte gern ein Fahrrad.
Sie hören: *Ich hätte gern ein Fahrrad.*

Sie hören: *Ich bin nicht reich.*
Sie sagen: Ich wäre gern reich.
Sie hören: *Ich wäre gern reich.*

Fangen wir an!

1. ______________________ 5. ______________________

2. ______________________ 6. ______________________

3. ______________________ 7. ______________________

4. ______________________ 8. ______________________

12-3 Wenn wir viel Geld hätten, ... Use the information you hear to complete the sentences you see.

BEISPIEL: Sie hören: *Wir könnten einen Porsche kaufen.*
Sie sehen: Wenn wir viel Geld hätten, ______________________.
Sie sagen: Wenn wir viel Geld hätten, könnten wir einen Porsche kaufen.
Sie hören: *Wenn wir viel Geld hätten, könnten wir einen Porsche kaufen.*

Fangen wir an!

1. Wenn wir länger schlafen dürften, ______________________.
2. Wenn wir ein Handy hätten, ______________________.
3. Wenn wir nicht krank wären, ______________________.
4. Wenn wir nicht in die Vorlesung müssten, ______________________.
5. Wenn wir eine Katze hätten, ______________________.
6. Wenn wir ein Auto hätten, ______________________.
7. Wenn wir keine Kinder hätten, ______________________.
8. Wenn wir bessere Zensuren hätten, ______________________.

NAME: ______________________ DATE: ____________

12-4 Was würdest du tun? Answer the questions you hear with the help of the cues you see.

BEISPIEL: Sie hören: *Was würdest du tun, wenn du müde wärst?*
Sie sehen: früh ins Bett gehen
Sie sagen: Ich würde früh ins Bett gehen.
Sie hören: *Ich würde früh ins Bett gehen.*

Fangen wir an!

1. ein gutes Buch lesen
   ____
2. weniger Kaffee trinken
   ____
3. meine Eltern anrufen
   ____
4. damit zur Uni fahren
   ____
5. zu Fuß gehen
   ____
6. ins Kino gehen
   ____
7. lernen
   ____
8. ein Aspirin nehmen
   ____

12-5 Wir sind höflich! Restate the sentences you hear in a more polite way.

BEISPIEL: Sie hören: *Kannst du mir zehn Euro leihen?*
Sie sagen: Könntest du mir zehn Euro leihen?
Sie hören: *Könntest du mir zehn Euro leihen?*

Fangen wir an!

1. ______________________
2. ______________________
3. ______________________
4. ______________________
5. ______________________
6. ______________________

12-6 Pauls Traumberuf. Listen to the story. You will hear it twice.

die Musikhochschule	*conservatory*
die Konkurrenz	*competition*

Now listen to the statements and answer with **richtig** or **falsch.** The speaker will verify your answer. If the statement is **falsch** you will hear a question to help you correct the statement.

1. ____________________ 5. ____________________

2. ____________________ 6. ____________________

3. ____________________ 7. ____________________

4. ____________________ 8. ____________________

12-7 Wenn ich das nur nicht getan hätte! Convert the statements you hear into wishes in past-time subjunctive.

BEISPIEL:		
	Sie hören:	*Ich habe geraucht.*
	Sie sehen:	Wenn ich nur nicht ____________________!
	Sie sagen:	Wenn ich nur nicht geraucht hätte!
	Sie hören:	*Wenn ich nur nicht geraucht hätte!*
	Sie hören:	*Ich bin nicht in die Bibliothek gegangen.*
	Sie sehen:	Wenn ich nur ____________________!
	Sie sagen:	Wenn ich nur in die Bibliothek gegangen wäre!
	Sie hören:	*Wenn ich nur in die Bibliothek gegangen wäre!*

Fangen wir an!

1. Wenn ich nur ____________________!
2. Wenn ich nur nicht ____________________!
3. Wenn ich nur nicht ____________________!
4. Wenn ich nur ____________________!
5. Wenn ich nur ____________________!
6. Wenn ich nur nicht ____________________!
7. Wenn ich nur nicht ____________________!
8. Wenn ich nur nicht ____________________!

NAME: ______________________________ DATE: ____________________

12-8 Genitivpräpositionen. Answer the questions you hear by completing the sentences you see with the cues in parentheses.

BEISPIEL: Sie hören: *Warum kommst du nicht zu unserer Fete?*
Sie sehen: Weil ich __________ __________________ die ganze Nacht lernen muss. (wegen / eine wichtige Klausur)
Sie sagen: Weil ich wegen einer wichtigen Klausur die ganze Nacht lernen muss.
Sie hören: *Weil ich wegen einer wichtigen Klausur die ganze Nacht lernen muss.*

Fangen wir an!

1. Weil ich __________ __________________ das Fenster offen gelassen habe. (trotz / die große Kälte)
2. Weil ich __________ __________________ lieber einen Teller heiße Suppe esse. (statt / der gemischte Salat)
3. Weil sie __________ __________________ nie zu Hause war. (während / die ganze Woche)
4. Weil sie __________ __________________ abends lieber zu Hause bleiben. (wegen / ihr kleines Baby)

12-9 Relativpronomen im Genitiv. Complete the sentences you see with the appropriate relative pronoun.

BEISPIEL: Sie sehen: Das ist der Mann, d________ Tochter ich heiraten möchte.
Sie sagen: Das ist der Mann, dessen Tochter ich heiraten möchte.
Sie hören: *Das ist der Mann, dessen Tochter ich heiraten möchte.*

Fangen wir an!

1. Das ist die Frau, d________ Bild gestern in der Zeitung war.
2. Das ist das Fußballteam (n), d________ Trainer so berühmt ist.
3. Das ist die Studentin, d________ Referat so interessant war.
4. Das sind die Studenten, d________ Zensuren nicht gut genug waren.
5. Das ist der Professor, d________ Vorlesungen ich so toll finde.

12-10 Zur Aussprache. The glottal stop

Sprechen Sie nach!

__Am __achten __August fliegt __Anna nach __Australien.

____

Frau __Erdmanns __einzige __Enkelin heißt __Elke __Elisabeth.

____

__Irene findet __im __Internet __immer __ihre besten __Ideen.

____

__Osman fährt __oft zu __Onkel __Oskar nach __Oldenburg.

____

__Um wie viel __Uhr fahren __Ulrich __und __Ulrike zur __Uni?

____